FENLAND PUMPING ENGINES

K. S. G. Hinde

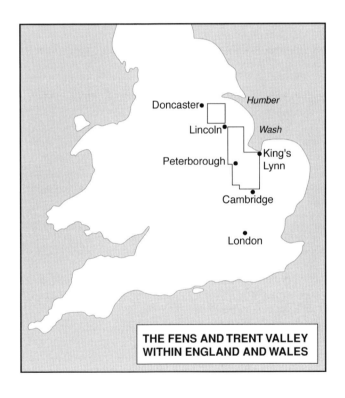

THE FENS AND TRENT VALLEY
WITHIN ENGLAND AND WALES

LANDMARK COLLECTOR'S LIBRARY

FENLAND PUMPING ENGINES

K. S. G. Hinde

Landmark Publishing

Published by

Landmark Publishing Ltd
Ashbourne Hall, Cokayne Ave, Ashbourne, Derbyshire DE6 1EJ England
Tel: (01335) 347349 Fax: (01335) 347303
e-mail: landmark@clara.net
web site: www.landmarkpublishing.co.uk

ISBN 1 84306 188 0

Print: Cromwell Press Ltd, Trowbridge

Design: Mark Titterton

Cover: James Allsopp

Front cover: Hundred Foot (S14B) Mirrlees engine house c. 1927 (COC)

Title page (opposite): Lakenheath (S13) engine house c. 1920 (Cambs. Coll.)

Back cover: Middle Fen, Overfall (S17B) engine house c. 1930 (Cambs. Coll.)

CONTENTS

Preface   6

Acknowledgements   7

Abbreviations   8

Sources   9

Notes on Illustrations   10

Introduction   11

Maps   16

1. Pumps   29
2. Organisation, Staff and Buildings   33
3. Middle Level   37
4. Marshland north of Middle Level   94
5. North Level   103
6. South Level   107
7. South Lincolnshire – Nene to Glen   162
8. The Witham Districts   168
9. Black Sluice Districts   182
10. Upper Witham   190
11. Trent Valley   191

Appendices   207
1. Conversion tables   207
2. Makers of engines and pumps   207
3. Particulars of engine and pump makers   210
4. Examples of engine running records   213
5. Boiler longevity   214
6. Ruston diesel engine types and cylinder sizes   215
7. Some long service engine drivers   216
8. Bibliography   216
9. Index of names of pumping stations   217

PREFACE

This is not a history of fen drainage as such, but of the steam and diesel engines which powered the pumps providing that drainage. It is intended to assist historians, local and national, by providing details of most of such plant; and to serve as a companion volume to the works of Richard Hills and George Watkins by supplementing the information given by them. It should also serve as a gazetteer to enable those travelling by road or water to identify the surviving structures on the ground. Many of these have been altered or truncated, and several have been converted into houses.

Listing is by Internal Drainage Boards within main areas in alphabetical order. A few not strictly within a particular area have been included for want of any other appropriate category. This particularly applies to the large secondary stations serving main river outfalls.

The glossary and maps are provided to elucidate as many as possible of the problems of the diverse nomenclature used in the various sources. Map references are stated throughout, not least because so many sources, such as Wheeler, Clark and Watkins, do not identify exact positions.

The extent of the work has precluded reproduction of all available photographs. In particular, those contained in books still in print, such as Hills (2003) and Watkins SSE, have been avoided. These adequately cover the early steam-powered stations and enable the illustrations in this work to concentrate on later plant and buildings.

This work began as an attempt to record all steam-powered pumping stations in the Fens. It has been extended to include as many diesel-powered units as possible to illustrate the progression in the source of power, but cannot pretend to record all of the latter. Electrically-powered plant has only been noted to place previous plant in context.

All particulars have to be treated with caution. There are conflicting statements given by various authors, and some statistics are suspect. Every effort has been made to identify discrepancies and the extensive notes are designed to justify the facts stated. The particulars given in my booklet *Steam Pumping Stations in the Fens* (5 editions, 1974 – 2001), as partly set out in Hills (2003) Appendix II have required correction and expansion. The extent of available information about individual stations varies so greatly that attempts to present the material on a *pro forma* basis have had to be abandoned.

Appendix 9 is provided because some stations have been known by a variety of names taken from the place, district, nearest village or farm, or even the name of the owner. Acts of Parliament constituting the drainage districts have been cited because they often indicate the earliest date when plant could have been constructed, except where private plant was taken over; and identify the extent of districts. The confusion of districts in the Middle Level has been such that the Clerk recommended that the only sure method of identifying some was by the date of the Act. In recent years, the records of many districts have become available in Record Offices, but these can often be tantalisingly vague. Others seem to have been totally lost. Therefore no adequate account of some stations can be given.

ACKNOWLEDGEMENTS

This work is not really the product of one person, but of many. Without the most extensive help from a large number of people over a long period of time, it would not have been comprehensive enough to merit publication. Errors and inadequacies must be attributed to the author, and certainly not to those who have given so much documentary and verbal information.

Tributes must be paid to C.O. Clarke, Superintendent of Waterbeach Level 1943 – 1974, for much initial tutelage, information and documents; Peter Filby, who has provided a vast amount of data from his research into windpumps; Henry Gunston, formerly of the Institute of Hydrology; A. Batson, formerly of Allens and Dereck Lambe, formerly of Perkins. Brian Hillsdon supplied notes of the Watkins Collection, to which Colin Bowden added guidance. The Revd. Dr. R.L. Hills and the late K.A. Knell also provided much material, as has Ray Hooley, formerly of Rustons.

In the early days of my research, Chris Hodrien, Martin Salzer and Chris Hereward, together with several other members of the Cambridge Society for Industrial Archaeology, gave much assistance, as did Chris Taylor of the Royal Commission on Historic Monuments. The late Professor Sir Clifford Darby provided skilful guidance in his gentle way.

Michael Farrar and Dr. Philip Saunders of the Cambridge and Huntingdon Record Offices, and Michael Petty and Chris Jakes of the Cambridge Library, have been unstinting in giving help. Iain Smith, Clerk to the Middle Level Commissioners, generously gave full access to the records in his care. The staff of Norfolk Record Office have also been most helpful. Pothecary & Barratt, the firm in which I was formerly a partner, have been most generous in the provision of office facilities.

Finally, this task would never have been possible without the continuous and devoted support and assistance of my wife. Besides much else, she has visited almost all of the stations with me. My son, Edward Hinde, B.Eng., A.M.I.Mech.E., has produced much of the material relating to diesel engines and has been my mainstay in producing the work on computer. Both the text and production would have been quite inadequate without the extensive help of Tony Woolrich, Consulting Editor to Landmark Publishing.

The accounts of stations in Norfolk are substantially taken from the papers by the author published in three parts in the Journal NIAS, Vol. 7, nos. 2, 3 and 4 (2002-2004). The author is most grateful to the Society for permission to reproduce these, albeit slightly amended and up-dated. The Clerk to Welland & Deepings IDB kindly consented to reproduction of Fig. 128

It remains to apologise to all of those correspondents and contacts over the years who have not been specifically named.

ABBREVIATIONS

INSTITUTIONS, etc.

ADA	Association of Drainage Authorities
CAS	Cambridge Antiquarian Society
CRO	Cambridge Record Office
HRO	Huntingdon Record Office
IDB	Internal Drainage Board
IME	Institution of Mechanical Engineers
LRO	Lincolnshire Record Office
MAF	Ministry of Agriculture, Fisheries and Food
MLO	Middle Level Office
NIAS	Norfolk Industrial Archaeology Society
NMR	National Monuments Record, Swindon
NRO	Norfolk Record Office
OS	Ordnance Survey
RCHME	Royal Commission on the Historical Monuments of England
RSA	Royal Society of Arts
RASE	Royal Agricultural Society

TECHNICAL (D)

This indicates provision of a diesel engine on a site where no steam engine had previously existed

Bhp	brake horse power
Hp	nominal horse power according to the Watt notation. This is given in the text as stated in the various sources. Bourne, J. (1879) *Handbook of the Steam Engine,* Longmans Green p. 303 contains a table for calculating the nominal horse power of low pressure engines. Although some stated in the text accord with this table, others show a wide variation. For beam engines stated as below 60 hp, the figures given should be treated with caution.
ihp	indicated horse power per indicator diagrams
psi	pounds per square inch
rpm	revolutions per minute
tpm	tons per minute

SERIAL NUMBERS

The serial numbers have been applied to districts and, where more than one station existed or exists within a district, they are indicated by a capital letter after the serial number.
  The divisions are as follows:

M	Middle Level
NM	Marshland north of Middle Level
N	North Level
S	South Level
L	South Lincolnshire
T	Trent Valley

SOURCES – Abbreviations applied throughout footnotes

Allen — Allen, R.W. (1913) "Modern Pumping Machinery for Drainage of the Fens", *Minutes of the Proceedings of Institution of Mechanical Engineers*, 1913, Part 3, 787 – 804

CC — *Cambridge Chronicle*

Charnley — Charnley, P.R. (1996) *Old Dykes I have known – A History of The North Level*, Barney Books

CIP — *Cambridge Independent Press*

Clark — Clark, R.H. (1936/38), "Early Engines of the Eastern Counties" published in a series of articles in almost every issue of *English Mechanics* from January 1936 to January 1937, and "Engines of the Trent Valley", published in three parts in the issues of the same journal of 24 and 31 December 1937 and 7 January 1938

Clarke JA — Clarke, J.A., "On the Great Level of the Fens" *Journal of the Royal Agricultural Society* viii, 1848, 80 – 133

Cory — Cory, V. (1985), *Hatfield and Axholme*, Providence Press

Crocker — Crocker, E.G. "The Drainage of the River Great Ouse Basin", *Minutes of the Proceedings of the Institution of Mechanical Engineers*, 1913, Part 3, pp. 805 – 829

CWN — *Cambridge Weekly News*

Darby (1936) — Darby, H.C. "The Middle Level of the Fens and its Reclamation", *Victoria County History of Huntingdon*, Vol. III, 1936

Darby (1983) — Darby, H.C. (1983), *The Changing Fenland*, Cambridge University Press

Davey — Davey, H. (1905), *The Principles, Construction, and Application of Pumping Machinery*, second edition, Charles Griffin & Co., London, 304 – 306

Dempsey — Dempsey, G.D. (1887), *Drainage of Lands, Towns and Buildings*, revised edition, Crosby Lockwood & Co.

Doran — Doran, W.E. (1945), "Drainage during the War (2)", *Water & Water Engineering*, April 1945, 163 – 174

Filby — Filby, P. personal communications

Gibbs — Gibbs, L., "Pumping Machinery in the Fenland and by Trentside", *Minutes of the Proceedings of the Institution of Civil Engineers*, xciv, 1888, 264 – 283

Gibbs's Map — Map accompanying Gibbs

Glynn — Glynn, J., "Draining Land by Steam Power", *Transactions RSA*, li, 1838, 3 – 24

Grantham — Grantham, R.F., " The Drainage of the Fens", *Minutes of the Proceedings of Institution of Mechanical Engineers*, 1913, Part 3, 777 – 785

Gwynnes — This firm produced a series of trade brochures or booklets between 1899 and c. 1953, not all of which are dated. Those of 1943 and c. 1953 contain a map of all stations containing their pumps with a number allocated to each. In addition, Mr. A. Batson has supplied an unpublished Allen-Gwynnes list of all plant supplied up to 1977. The dates of the relevant publications and lists are cited in the footnotes. Between 1868 and 1904 there were two firms named Gwynne: Gwynne & Co. and J. & H. Gwynne. Where applicable, the latter has been separately identified. It also produced the brochures dated 1899 and 1901.

Heathcote — Heathcote, J.M. (1877), *Scoop Wheel and Centrifugal Pump*, Longmans Green

Hills (1967) — Hills, R.L. (1967) *Machines, Mills and Uncountable Costly Necessities*, Goose & Son, Norwich

Hills (2003) — Hills, R.L. (2003), *The Drainage of the Fens*, Landmark Publishing

Howling — Howling, B. (1996), *A History of Marshland Smeeth & Fen*, Marshland Smeeth & Fen IDB

Hutchinson — Hutchinson, J.N. "The Record of Peat Wastage in the East Anglian Fenlands at Holme Post 1848 – 1878", *Journal of Ecology*, 68, March 1980, 229 – 249

Ince — Ince, L. (2000), "The Soho Engine Works 1796 – 1895", *Journal of the International Stationary Steam Engine Society* No. 16

Korthals-Altes — Korthals-Altes, J. (1925), *Sir Cornelius Vermuyden*, Williams & Norgate

Lambe	Lambe, D.H. of Fenstanton – personal communications
Leafe	Leafe, F.E. (1985) *Black Sluice Internal Drainage Board.*
Lenny's Map	Lenny, J.G. (1833) *Map accompanying Particulars of the Bedford Level subject to the Eau Brink Tax.* The book was not published until 1844.
McLeod	McLeod, G., "Recent Land Drainage Pumping Stations", *Journal of the Institute of Water Engineers,* Vol. IV, no. 6, October 1950, 469 - 480
Marshall	Marshall, S. (1967), *Fenland Chronicle,* Cambridge University Press
Pattison	Pattison, W.F., "Formation and Reorganisation of Internal Drainage Districts", *Journal of Municipal and City Engineers,* lxii, 1936, 1517 – 1522
RCHME (NEC)	RCHME, *North East Cambridgeshire,* 1972
Reaney	Reaney, P.H. (1943), *The Place Names of Cambridgeshire and the Isle of Ely,* Cambridge University Press
Rigby	Rigby, W. (c. 1963) *Land Drainage Pumping Stations in England,* Gwynnes
Sly	Sly, R. (2003), *From Punt to Plough – A History of the Fens,* Sutton Publishing
Wells	Wells, S. (1828 & 1830) *The History of the Great Level of The Fens called the Bedford Level,* 2 vols.
Wheeler (1868)	Wheeler, W.H. (1868), *History of the Fens of South Lincolnshire,* first edition, J.M. Newcomb, Boston
Wheeler DF	Wheeler, W.H. (1888), *The Drainage of Fens and Low Grounds by Gravitation and Steam Power,* E.& F. Spon, London
Wheeler SL	Wheeler, W.H. (1896) *A History of the Fens of South Lincolnshire,* Second edition, J.M. Newcomb, Boston
Watkins's Notes	Watkins, G. Notes in NMR, Swindon, transcribed by Brian Hillsdon.
Watkins's SEI	Watkins, G. (1978) *The Steam Engine in Industry Part 1.* Moorland Publishing
Watkins's SSE	Watkins, G. (2000 – 2005): *Stationary Steam Engines of Great Britain,* 10 vols., Landmark Publishing

All sources quoted more than once are defined in the abbreviations. The remainder are quoted in the footnotes. The bibliography (Appendix 8) is restricted to general works not quoted in the text.

NOTES TO ILLUSTRATIONS

Except where otherwise stated, all photographs were taken by the author or by members of his family, some of whom are now deceased. The Cambridgeshire Collection of Cambridge Central Library has kindly consented to reproduction of some of the photographs held there. These are marked "Cambs. Coll.". The author donated the negatives of some of his earliest photographs to the Cambridgeshire Collection, and these are acknowledged as "Cambs. Coll. – KH." Those marked COC were provided many years ago by C.O. Clarke, and mostly came from E. Stevens, engineer at Hundred Foot Station 1911 – 1927, and Superintendent of Waterbeach Level 1931 – 1943. Both Ray Hooley, Curator of the Ruston Archives, and the Middle Level Office have kindly provided photographs from their collections, and these are acknowledged as RH and MLO respectively. Welland & Deepings IDB have kindly consented to the reproduction of figure 128, and R.C. Hodrien to figures 53 and 54. Some of the photographs are of poor quality, but are the only ones available of plant since demolished.

INTRODUCTION

This survey covers some 220 pumping stations in the lowlands of the Eastern Counties between Cambridge in the south and the Humber in the north. This area is mostly contained within the counties of Cambridgeshire, Norfolk and Lincolnshire, but also impinges upon the neighbouring counties of Northampton, Suffolk, Nottingham and Yorkshire. It is some 130 miles from north to south and has a maximum width of some 36 miles, covering over 1300 square miles. The Trent Valley drains into the Humber, and the remainder into the Wash. The actual area drained through the Fens is far greater than this in that vast areas of neighbouring upland can only discharge their surplus water through the Fens. These form a basin into which the upland water flows and, without a drainage system, would become trapped. The description of this area as the sink of thirteen counties is probably an understatement. For instance, the water from over 3000 square miles is discharged into the Wash at King's Lynn, but only 600 square miles of this comes from the actual fenland.

The soil of the Fens was formed following the end of the last Ice Age. This caused a major rise in sea level which inundated the land, to be followed by a series of mild periods and inundations. This created alternate layers of peat and silt, or only silt where inland rivers overflowed. Extensive areas of peat soil arose in the Bedford Level and in the Isle of Axholme and Hatfield Chase to the west of the Trent Valley. Silt soils predominated around the Wash and in South Lincolnshire. The effect of drainage upon peat is profound. It is like a sponge. When first drained, it shrinks rapidly as it dries out. Thereafter bacterial action causes further wastage. High winds blow away the top soil, and this can also catch fire. Thus intensive drainage has led to extensive falls in land levels, so that many parts are now well below mean sea level. Silt does not shrink as does peat, but gradually compacts and wastes so that pumping becomes necessary.

The Romans were responsible for the creation of an extensive network of drains and canals, some of which have survived to this day. In the third century A.D. the climate changed from temperate to harsh and there was a major incursion of the sea which led to the gradual desertion of the Roman settlements. It also caused the formation of lakes or meres where water was trapped in depressions in the ground, and some of these survived until the nineteenth century. These eventually caused drainage problems for those areas – see Waterbeach Level (S28A), Willingham West Fen (S29) and Whittlesey Mere (M33A).

During Anglo-Saxon times, a few monastic houses were established on islands in the Fens. These suffered severe attacks and even destruction at the hands of the Danes, and little drainage work can have been achieved until stability returned. Resuscitation of these houses from the tenth century onwards seems to have led to their undertaking some local drainage work. Except for the construction of Morton's Leam by Bishop Morton between 1478 and 1490, few general drainage works seem to have been accomplished during the Middle Ages. Any attempt to secure drainage on a systematic, if local, basis seems to have awaited a great flood of 1253/4, whereafter the Crown appointed Commissions of Sewers, which identified works required in particular districts, specified those to be responsible, and appointed overseers to secure performance. These Commissions were the precursors of the internal drainage boards which have been responsible for local drainage in most parts of the fens for the past 250 years or more. Some of these Commissions survived into the twentieth century.

The first major work of drainage was carried out in the early seventeenth century in Hatfield Chase, west of the River Trent, containing some 60,000 acres. Cornelius Vermuyden contracted with Charles I to render it dry ground. His efforts did not prove effective, and were met by riots and sabotage before, during and after the Civil War. Although some major works were carried out in the late eighteenth and early nineteenth centuries, and the Hatfield Chase Corporation was formed in 1862, these lands were not properly drained until powered pumping machinery was introduced in the nineteenth century; and no overall system for administration of the drainage existed until after the passing of the Land Drainage Act in 1930.

Meanwhile Vermuyden had turned his attention to the Bedford Level where, under the patronage of Charles I and the Earl of Bedford, he designed and built a general drainage system between 1637 and 1653. This relied on gravity to discharge the water into the rivers and eventually to the sea.

To maintain the banks of the rivers and watercourses upon which this system depended, the Bedford Level Corporation was created. This was intended to be responsible for all main drainage works within the Level, with power to levy rates to pay for its operations. Lack of income, coupled with the flooding which resulted from wastage of the soil, soon led to its being incapable of performing this function satisfactorily.

Even before Vermuyden had commenced his operations, one district, that of Waldersea, had obtained an Act of Parliament in 1607 to create a separate drainage district. This bore some resemblance to a Commission of Sewers, but with more permanence and power.

By the early eighteenth century, the inadequacy of the Corporation and frequent flooding persuaded individual districts to obtain Acts to constitute permanent Commissions to achieve drainage of their respective areas, with power to levy rates and borrow money to meet the cost. The formation of these districts was not systematic. They evolved according to the ownership of land, the extent of agreement between neighbours, and in some cases parish and county boundaries. Thus they varied in extent from 250 to 30,000 acres. Many arose as a result of enclosure.

Haddenham was the first district to obtain such an Act after the Bedford Level Corporation was formed. This was enacted in 1727. Others followed rapidly, until most of the Fenland was covered by such districts, now called Internal Drainage Boards; but some areas remained drained privately by their owners until well into the twentieth century. Glassmoor in Whittlesey, Wood Hall Estate in Hilgay and Stonea Grange in Wimblington are examples of these.

Vermuyden had divided the Bedford Level into three parts: the North, Middle and South Levels. As the inadequacy of the Bedford Level Corporation to provide proper overall drainage became increasingly apparent, these sections sought to carry out their own works. In 1763 the North Level obtained an Act to procure independence. This created five districts within it. After some attempt to become a separate entity in 1810, the Middle Level achieved complete independence in 1844.

South Lincolnshire was not slow to follow the precedent. The land on either side of the River Witham was first drained under an Act of 1762, which divided the area into six districts. The Black Sluice Act followed in 1765, comprising the land east and west of the South Forty Foot Drain from Gutheram Gote on the River Glen to the Black Sluice on the Witham. This also contained part of the areas within the Second and Sixth Witham Districts.

The first Act relating to Deeping Fen was passed in 1664, although this fen had first been drained in the 1630s, independently of the Bedford Level but in similar manner.

Within these three main districts, namely the Witham, Black Sluice and Deeping Fen, numerous internal drainage districts arose, often as a result of enclosure. Thus a two-tier system emerged, with the principal districts maintaining the main river banks and watercourses, and the internal districts maintaining their own ditches and drains, and procuring discharge of their water into the main rivers and drains.

The general drainage enterprises of the seventeenth and eighteenth centuries expected to rely on gravity to discharge the waters into the sea. Wastage of the soil soon led to this method being inadequate in many areas. Thus windpumps were applied to lift the water from the land into the rivers. These proliferated, particularly towards the end of the eighteenth century, but were useless when there was no wind, a common occurrence after a flood. They were also prone to catching fire and to being blown over. In addition, they were expensive to maintain and costly in manpower.

This is an account of the machinery which replaced the windpumps: powered at first by steam, then internal combustion engines, and now predominantly by electric power. It has to be appreciated that, without continual pumping, the Fens would rapidly reurn to their former water-logged state.

The Age of Steam

In Holland a steam engine had been applied to land drainage as early as 1785, and one was suggested for Middle Fen in 1789. The first steam engine known to have been used in the Fens was a 6 hp Boulton & Watt and was applied to pumping water out of the foundations of the new Hobhole Sluice, laid to serve the East, West and Wildmore Fens in Witham Fourth District in 1804. This plant survived until after 1814. It was not until 1817 that a permanent steam-powered pumping plant was installed. This was at Sutton St. Edmund in South Holland, Lincolnshire. It was followed by that at Borough Fen in the North Level. Both became redundant when the North Level Main Drain was dug in 1834.

In 1820 Littleport & Downham District erected a 30 hp engine at Ten Mile Bank, followed by Swaffham & Bottisham District in 1821. Thus by that date there were four engines at work in the Fens. They were all single-cylinder condensing double-acting beam engines driving scoop wheels, and set a style for such plant almost entirely adopted for over thirty years. By that time all four of the early engines had been removed, the latter two being found to have insufficient power. In the 1820s, the Butterley Company of Derby entered the scene, employing Joseph Glynn as their engineer. He proposed the rough rule that 10 hp was required for each thousand acres to be drained. The first plant to be installed by him was an 80 hp unit at Pode Hole, Lincolnshire, in 1824, with another firm supplying an additional 60 hp engine. These worked successfully for a hundred years. Another station was established near March in 1825, and others at Misterton and Heckdyke in the Trent Valley in 1828; and Littleport & Downham installed an 80 hp engine at Hundred Foot in 1830. Yet by that date there were only 13 engines at work.

These engines were relatively prodigious in their consumption of coal. Almost all of this was sea-borne and thus attracted the tax on this source of supply. The abolition of this tax in 1831 must have provided an incentive to instal steam engines. The major drainage works carried out in the Middle Level during the mid-1840s led to a material increase in the number of stations in that area alone.

J.A. Clarke was quite correct in stating that over fifty such installations were at work in the Fens by 1848. In fact, 65 have been traced, of which 11 were in the Trent Valley. These varied greatly in size. Only four of 80 hp were erected: at Pode Hole, Hundred Foot, Ten Mile Bank and Sutton & Mepal. There were three of 70 hp, being those at Waldersea and Marton, both Cornish engines, and Swaffham & Bottisham (not erected until 1850). Stretham is one of seven of 60 hp, two of which were side-lever engines of the marine type used when the sub-soil was considered too soft to support an ordinary beam engine. Of the remainder by this date, 15 were 40 hp or over, 11 between 20 and 30 hp, and 17 under 20 hp.

The death-knell for the installation of beam engines and scoop wheels was sounded in 1851 when Appold's centrifugal pump was exhibited at the Great Exhibition. First applied in the Fens to the drainage of Whittlesey Mere in that year, this pump soon proved its superiority over the scoop wheel, being more capable of handling the varying lifts. Initially the Mere pump was driven by a beam engine, but engine development soon provided much faster and less cumbersome power units. Eastons supplied many of the early engines to drive the Appold pumps, including the largest plant erected in the Fens during the nineteenth century – that at Lade Bank installed to drain the eastern part of Witham Fourth District.

Heathcote's plea in 1877 for the centrifugal pump to be preferred to the scoop wheel fell on deaf ears in some places and not least in his own Middle Level. Perhaps most surprising was the installation in 1893 of a wheel at Black Ham, Whittlesey, in the very area where the pump had been pioneered. Others were used at Jenny Hurn and Dirtness in the Trent Valley in 1867, Upwell South in 1877, Chatteris Dock in 1900, and Bourne South in 1912. Nevertheless most districts were attracted to the application of high pressure steam engines driving centrifugal pumps during the latter part of the century. This was accompanied by the increasing use of portable or semi-portable engines to drive existing scoop wheels in windpumps, particularly in the Middle Level.

Steam power survived for many years, and Kirk Bramwith was installed only just before the Second World War; but by 1947 only 15 were in operation. Eight of these were in the Bedford Level, four in South Lincolnshire and three in the Trent Valley. The last to survive in the Bedford Level were Wype and Ironsides in Whittlesey, not being replaced until 1955. Dowsby and Bicker Fen in South Lincolnshire seem to have survived until the 1960s. In the Trent Valley, Owston Ferry resorted to diesel in 1952 and Kirk Bramwith in 1958.

In total at least 150 stations were powered by steam at some time. Of these, only four have survived, being those at Stretham (S28A), Pinchbeck (L3), Dogdyke (L21) and Owston Ferry T8D. The first three of these are open to the public.

The use of drainage plant is intermittent and depends primarily upon the weather. Excessive rainfall will require an engine to be worked for long periods, but dry seasons will require little use. Normally the pumps are only used between October and April, with summer running restricted to occasional evacuation of water for drainwork. The variations in usage are illustrated by the examples in Appendix 4. Because of this varying use, the boilers of the steam drainage engines in the Fens often lasted much longer than such engines employed for industrial use. Appendix 5 shows that the boilers in the Fens could last for long periods of time.

The Internal Combustion Engine

The first use of an internal combustion engine for fen drainage was in 1895 at Burwell. At first this was geared to the existing scoop wheel, but this soon proved unsatisfactory and never seems to have been tried at any other station.

Initially, only small districts tried oil engines. Burwell in 1895, Denver Parts in 1897, Willingham (West Fen) in 1901, Botany Bay (March Third) in 1908 and Washingborough & Heighington in 1910 seem to have been the earliest. March Third (Burrowmoor Fen) may have invested in one in 1901, but this has not been verified. These were all hot-bulb paraffin engines, but it will be noted that Bourne South purchased a Tangye gas engine in 1912. By that time a few larger districts were showing interest in such plant, although others were still buying steam engines. Methwold & Feltwell placed a 90 bhp crude oil engine in their new Decoy Bridge station in April 1913, believed to be the first crude oil engine installed in the Fens. It was followed shortly afterwards at Burwell, and then at Pode Hole in 1914. These set the trend for the future. Replacement of plant was necessarily curtailed during the First World War. During that time, the only examples traced are Cottenham (Smithey Fen), Feltwell New Fen (Southery), South Kyme, Ewerby and Bourne North.

Gradual relinquishment of steam engines took place in the 1920s, with marine air-blast diesel engines being favoured by some of the larger boards. The depression led to much old machinery being kept in operation until the mid-1930s, when Government grants encouraged replacement. This process accelerated during the War when food production became of paramount importance. A by-product of this was the provision of concrete roads across the

Fens where only muddy droves, almost impassable in winter, had existed. This greatly improved access to many pumping stations, and enabled others to be sited on low-lying land in previously inaccessible places. The continuation of Government grants for some years after the War led to even more stations arising.

The oil engine offered many advantages over those powered by steam. The latter required substantial buildings to house the boiler or boilers and coal, as well as the engine and, when used, the scoop wheel. Coal is a fuel of bulk and required much labour in transporting, unloading and stacking, as well as stoking. Oil was much cheaper than coal, and could be much more easily delivered and stored. The oil engines, running at relatively high speeds, were well-suited to drive the horizontal centrifugal pumps which became the preferred option as being best in handling the increasing lifts consequent upon the continuing wastage of the soil. At the larger stations, labour costs were reduced because no stoker was needed. There was less saving in this respect at the smaller stations where the engine driver was expected to stoke as well as drive.

The early suppliers of oil engines were Hornsby, Allen, Ruston, Mirrlees, Campbell, Blackstone, Vickers Petter and Crossley as shown in Appendix 3. Ruston engines were much favoured throughout the entire area, and a good number have been preserved. They were simple, economical and required little maintenance. After producing at least three pumps during the First World War, Rustons then recommended Gwynnes pumps for connection to their engines. The predominance of these pumps is shown by the Gwynnes brochure of 1953, which lists a total of 168 stations equipped with them.

Allens normally supplied their own pumps. A very few early pumps originally driven by steam were later driven by oil engines. One 1874 Tuxford and two Easton pumps of 1870 and 1895 followed this path. Other early suppliers of pumps were Clayton & Shuttleworth, Smithdale, and Dodmans. It was not uncommon for existing pumps to be retained when engines were replaced. Later pump makers included Hathorn-Davey, Worthington, Mirrlees-Watson and Sulzer.

The predominance of the oil engine did not last quite as long as that of steam, but made a significant improvement to the effectiveness of land drainage, and proved invaluable during the Second World War and the years immediately succeeding it.

Electric Power

The first pumping station in the Eastern Counties to be powered by electricity seems to have been Dirtness in 1928, followed by Torksey in 1934 and Kirkstead possibly before 1936. Diesel engines were still generally preferred until the 1950s and 1960s. Then provision of the National Grid throughout most of the country radically changed the position. Some idea of the progression can be derived from Gwynnes maps, although these were not fully up-dated and relate only to stations provided with Gwynnes pumps. In 1943, the map records 122 stations, of which seven were steam-powered, four electric and the remainder oil. Of the 168 stations shown in 1953, two are marked as steam, although by then one was not, 37 electric and the rest oil.

From the 1960s most Boards were replacing plant with automatic electrically-driven pumps. These require minimal infrastructure and no manning, thus offering economy in capital outlay and maintenance costs. Only small buildings were required, and in some cases the whole installation could be sunken. This saved the cost of a building and was also much more proof against the vandalism which has afflicted drainage plant for many years. Only the high cost of electricity has persuaded a few districts to resort to automatic diesel engines in recent years. These require no labour, but are not as durable as the manned diesels.

Some of the most prudent Boards have retained old oil engines for use in emergency both to supplement the electric motors in times of flood and for use if the power supply fails. A very small number, such as Welch's Dam and Bottisham Lode, still rely solely on diesel engines.

MAPS

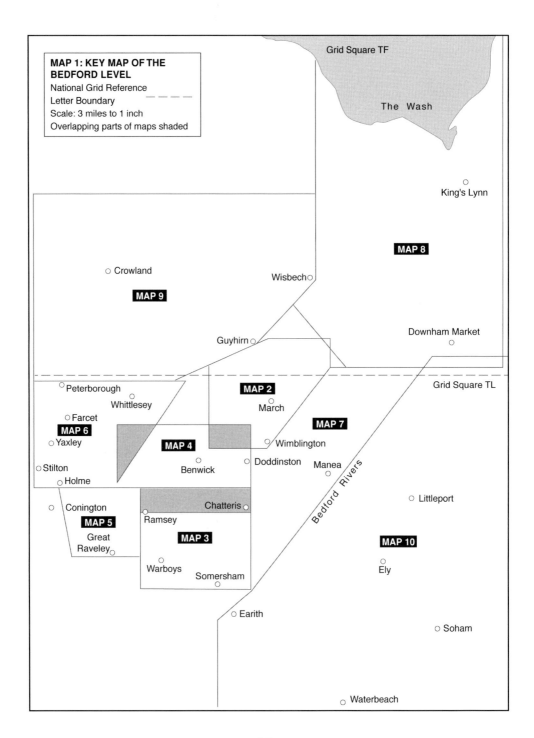

MAP 1: KEY MAP OF THE BEDFORD LEVEL
National Grid Reference
Letter Boundary — — — —
Scale: 3 miles to 1 inch
Overlapping parts of maps shaded

Grid Square TF

The Wash

○ King's Lynn

MAP 8

○ Crowland

Wisbech ○

MAP 9

Guyhirn ○

Downham Market ○

Grid Square TL

○ Peterborough

MAP 2

○ Whittlesey

March ○

○ Farcet

MAP 7

MAP 6

○ Yaxley

MAP 4

○ Wimblington

○ Doddinston

Manea ○

○ Stilton

Benwick

○ Holme

Littleport ○

○ Conington

Chatteris ○

MAP 5

Ramsey ○

Great
Raveley ○

MAP 3

MAP 10

○ Warboys

Somersham ○

Ely ○

○ Earith

○ Soham

○ Waterbeach

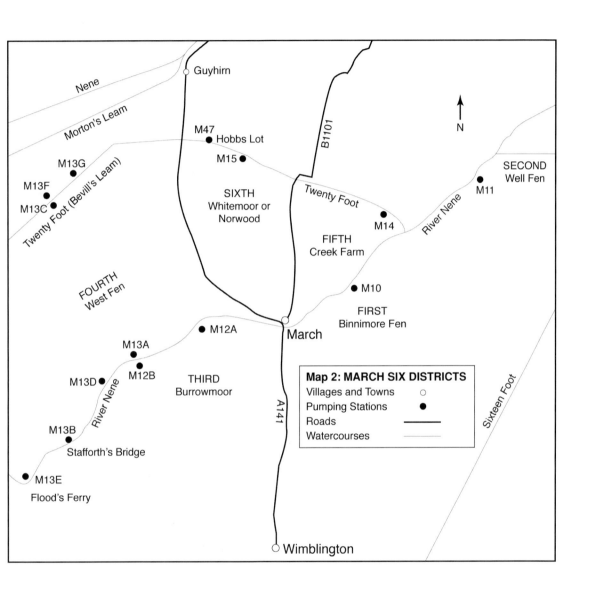

Map 2: MARCH SIX DISTRICTS

Villages and Towns	○
Pumping Stations	●
Roads	
Watercourses	

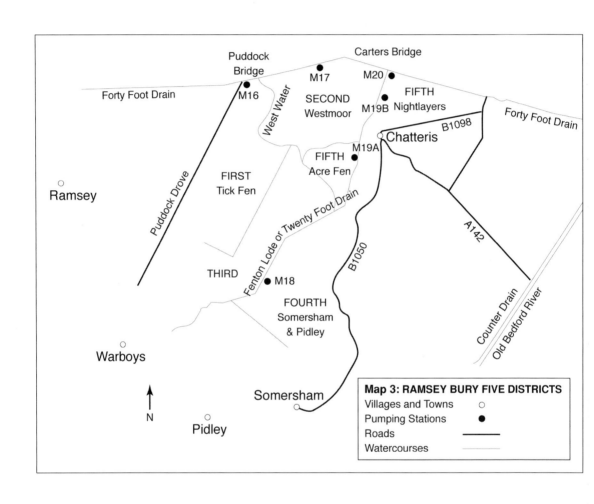

Map 3: RAMSEY BURY FIVE DISTRICTS

Villages and Towns	○
Pumping Stations	●
Roads	▬▬▬
Watercourses	___

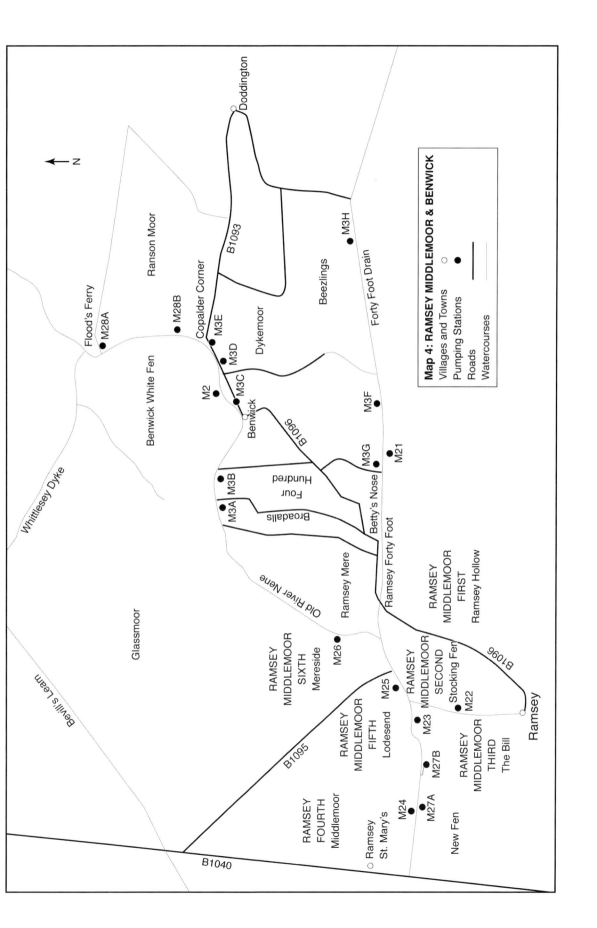

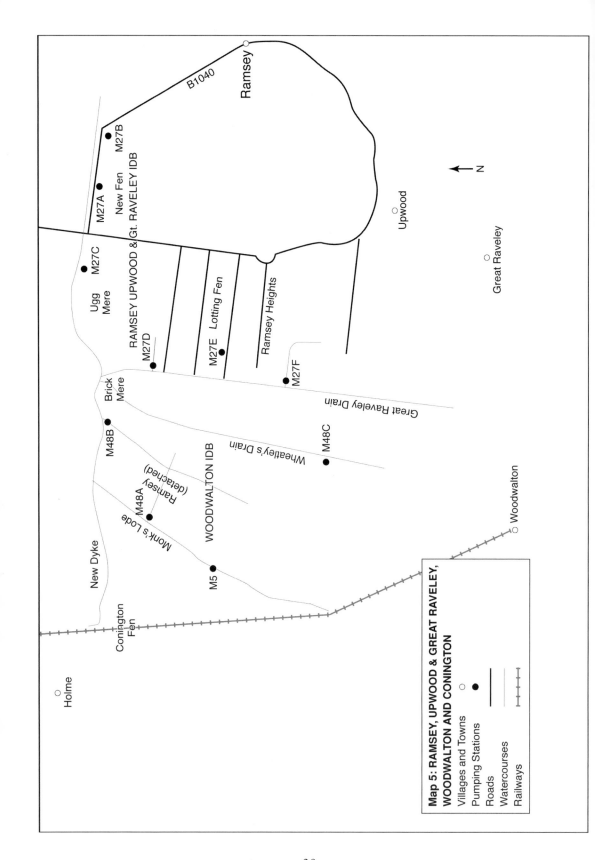

Map 5: RAMSEY, UPWOOD & GREAT RAVELEY, WOODWALTON AND CONINGTON

Villages and Towns ○
Pumping Stations ●
Roads
Watercourses
Railways

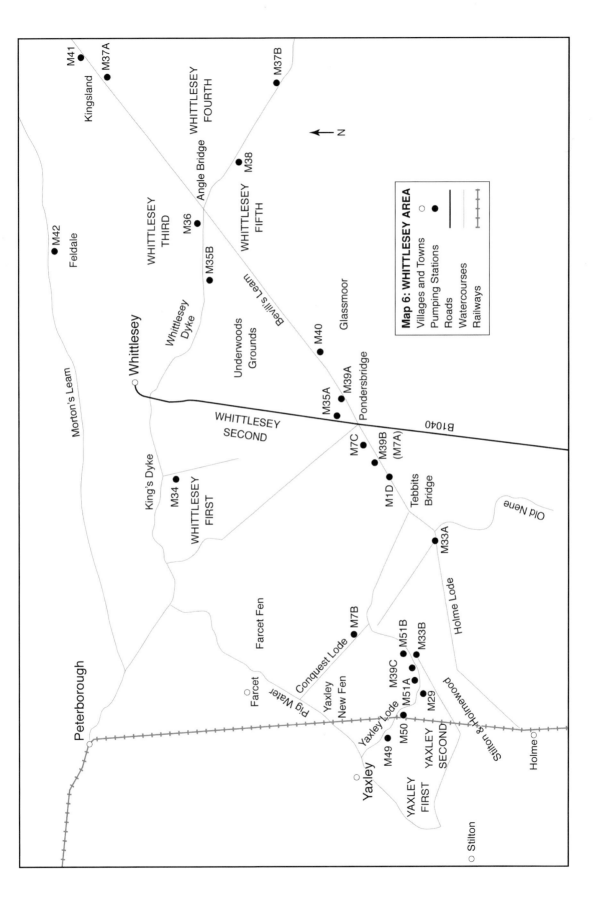

Map 6: WHITTLESEY AREA

Villages and Towns ○
Pumping Stations ●
Roads
Watercourses
Railways

← N

M41
M37A
Kingsland
M37B
WHITTLESEY FOURTH
Angle Bridge
M38
M42
Feldale
WHITTLESEY THIRD
M36
WHITTLESEY FIFTH
M35B
Whittlesey Dyke
Bevill's Leam
Glassmoor
Underwoods Grounds
M40
Whittlesey
Morton's Leam
M35A
M39A
Pondersbridge
WHITTLESEY SECOND
B1040
M7C
M39B (M7A)
King's Dyke
M34
M1D
Tebbits Bridge
WHITTLESEY FIRST
M33A
Old Nene
Holme Lode
Farcet Fen
Conquest Lode
M7B
M51B
M33B
Yaxley New Fen
M39C
M51A
Pig Water
Farcet
Stilton & Holmewood
M29
Yaxley Lode
M50
YAXLEY SECOND
Peterborough
M49
YAXLEY FIRST
Yaxley
Holme
Stilton

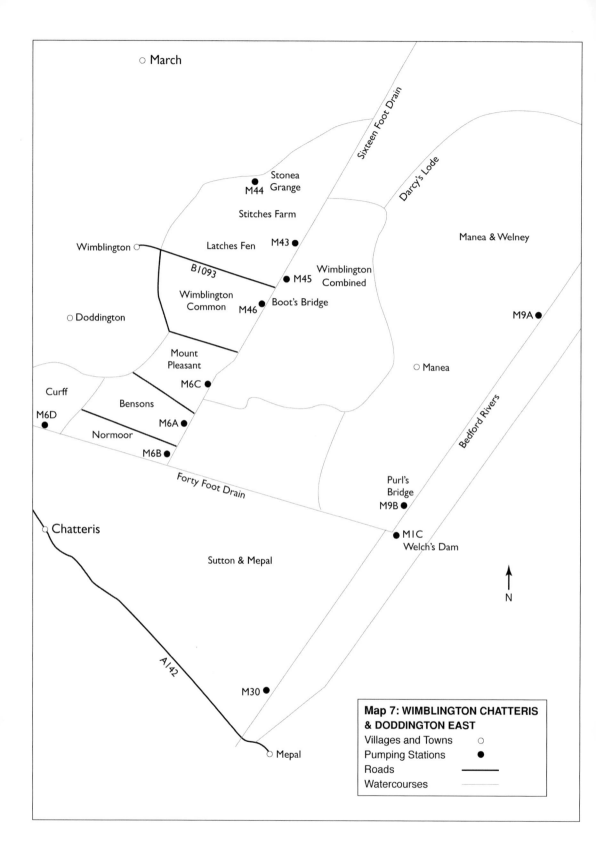

○ March

Sixteen Foot Drain

Darcy's Lode

Stonea
Grange
● M44

Stitches Farm

Manea & Welney

Latches Fen ● M43

Wimblington ○

B1093

Wimblington
Combined

● M45

Wimblington
Common
M46 ● Boot's Bridge

○ Doddington

M9A ●

Mount
Pleasant

○ Manea

Curff

M6C ●

Bensons

M6D
●

M6A ●

Normoor

M6B ●

Bedford Rivers

Forty Foot Drain

Purl's
Bridge
M9B ●

Chatteris ○

● M1C
Welch's Dam

Sutton & Mepal

N

A142

M30 ●

○ Mepal

**Map 7: WIMBLINGTON CHATTERIS
& DODDINGTON EAST**
Villages and Towns   ○
Pumping Stations   ●
Roads   ▬▬▬▬
Watercourses

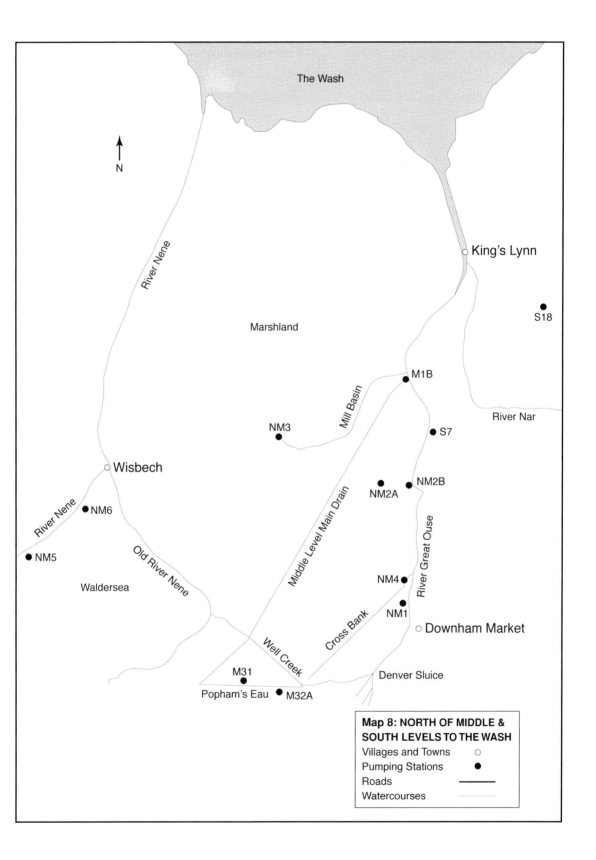

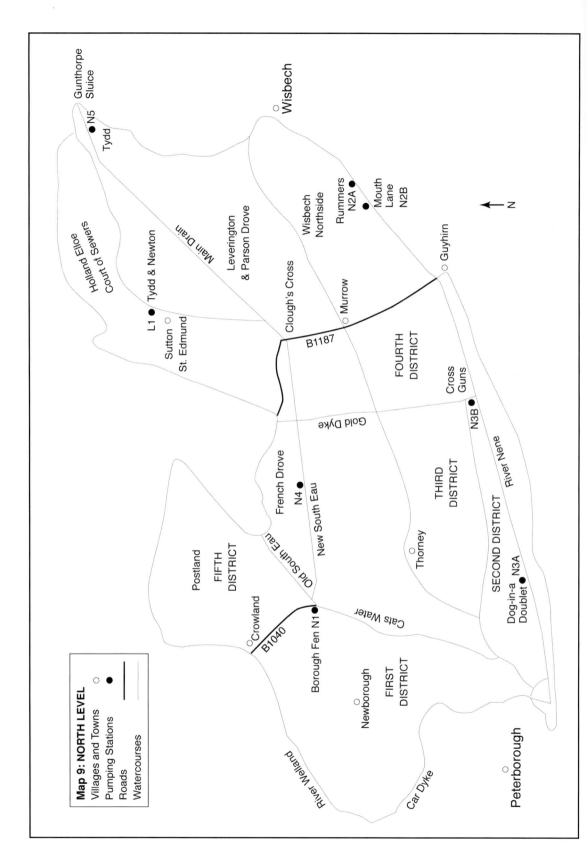

Map 9: NORTH LEVEL

Villages and Towns ○
Pumping Stations ●
Roads
Watercourses

N ←

Gunthorpe Sluice

N5 ● Tydd

Wisbech ○

Holland Elloe Court of Sewers

Main Drain

Leverington & Parson Drove

Wisbech Northside

Rummers N2A ●

Mouth Lane N2B ●

L1 ● Tydd & Newton

Sutton ○

St. Edmund

Clough's Cross

B1187

Murrow ○

Guyhirn ○

FOURTH DISTRICT

Gold Dyke

Cross Guns

N3B ●

French Drove

N4 ●

New South Eau

THIRD DISTRICT

River Nene

Thorney ○

SECOND DISTRICT

Postland

FIFTH DISTRICT

Old South Eau

Dog-in-a Doublet N3A ●

Crowland ○

B1040

Borough Fen N1 ●

Cats Water

Newborough ○

FIRST DISTRICT

River Welland

Car Dyke

Peterborough ○

24

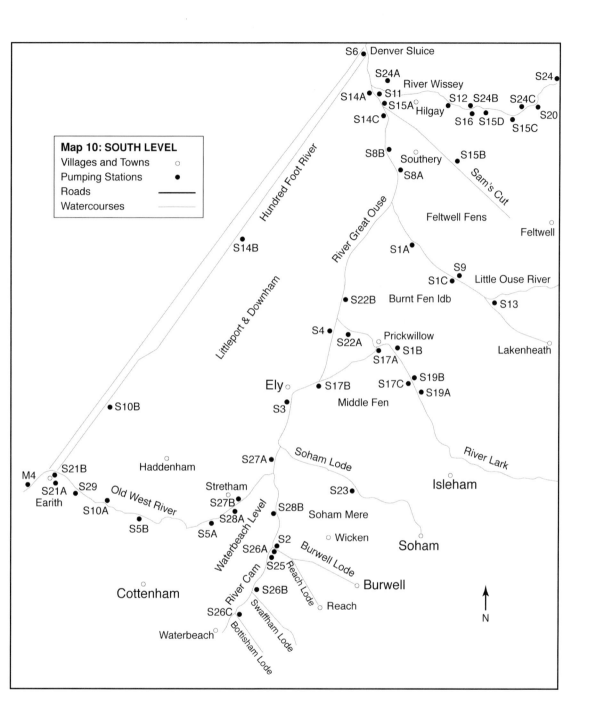

Map 10: SOUTH LEVEL

Villages and Towns	○
Pumping Stations	●
Roads	▬▬▬
Watercourses	▬▬

S6 ● Denver Sluice

S24A

River Wissey

S24

S14A ● S11

S15A ○

Hilgay

S12 S24B

S24C

S16 S15D

S20

S15C

S14C

S8B ●

Southery

S15B

S8A

Sam's Cut

Feltwell Fens

Feltwell ○

S14B ●

Hundred Foot River

River Great Ouse

S1A ●

S9

S1C ●

Little Ouse River

S22B ●

Burnt Fen Idb

S13

Littleport & Downham

S4 ●

S22A ●

Prickwillow ○

S1B ●

S17A

Lakenheath ○

Ely ○

S17B ●

S17C ●

S19B

S19A

S3 ●

Middle Fen

S10B ●

Soham Lode

River Lark

S27A ●

Haddenham ○

Isleham ○

M4 ●

S21B ●

S29 ●

S23 ●

Stretham ○

S21A ○

Earith

Old West River

S10A ●

S27B ●

S28B ●

Soham Mere

S5B ●

S5A ●

S28A ●

Waterbeach Level

S2 ●

Burwell Lode

Wicken ○

Soham

Cottenham ○

S26A ●

S25 ●

Reach Lode

Burwell

River Cam

S26B ●

Reach ○

S26C ●

Swaffham Lode

N

Waterbeach ○

Bottisham Lode

25

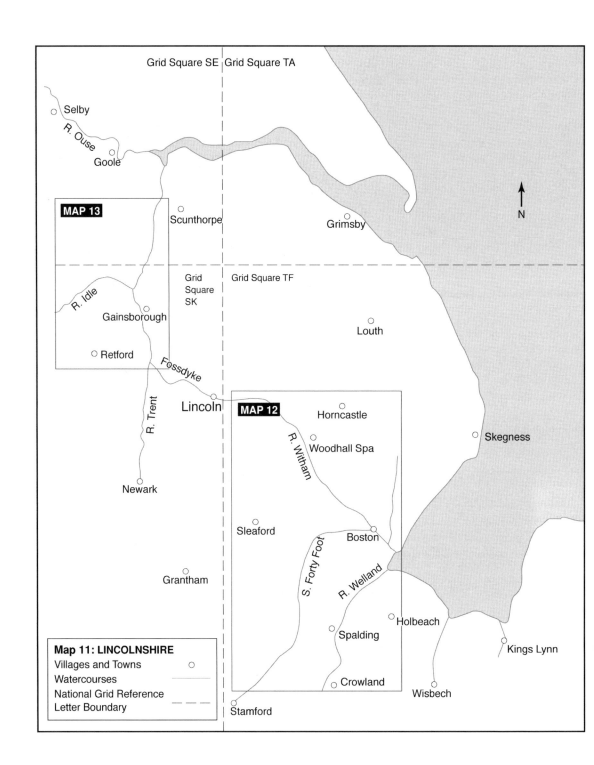

Grid Square SE | Grid Square TA

Selby

R. Ouse

Goole

MAP 13

Scunthorpe

Grimsby

Grid Square SK

Grid Square TF

R. Idle

Gainsborough

Louth

Retford

Fossdyke

R. Trent

Lincoln

MAP 12

Horncastle

R. Witham

Woodhall Spa

Skegness

Newark

Sleaford

S. Forty Foot

Boston

Grantham

R. Welland

Holbeach

Kings Lynn

Spalding

Map 11: LINCOLNSHIRE
Villages and Towns   ○
Watercourses
National Grid Reference
Letter Boundary

Crowland

Wisbech

Stamford

N

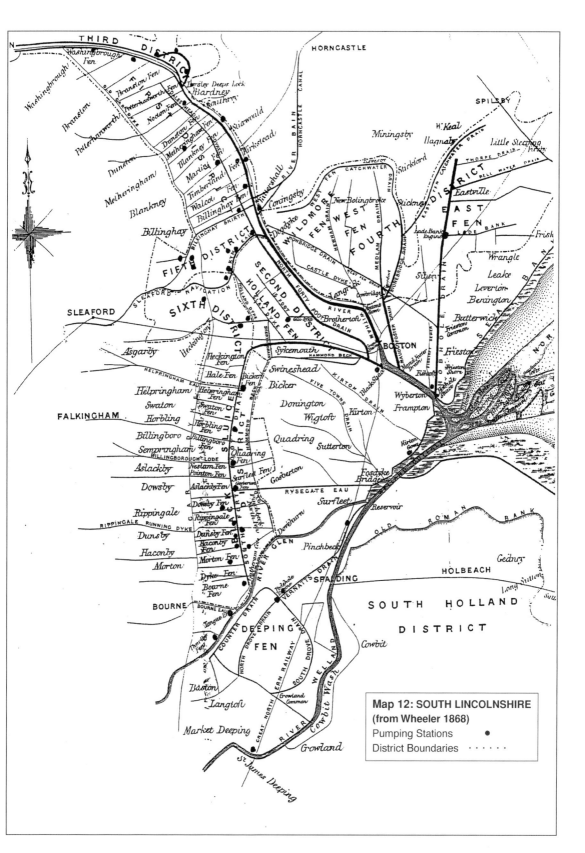

Map 12: SOUTH LINCOLNSHIRE
(from Wheeler 1868)
Pumping Stations ●
District Boundaries · · · · · ·

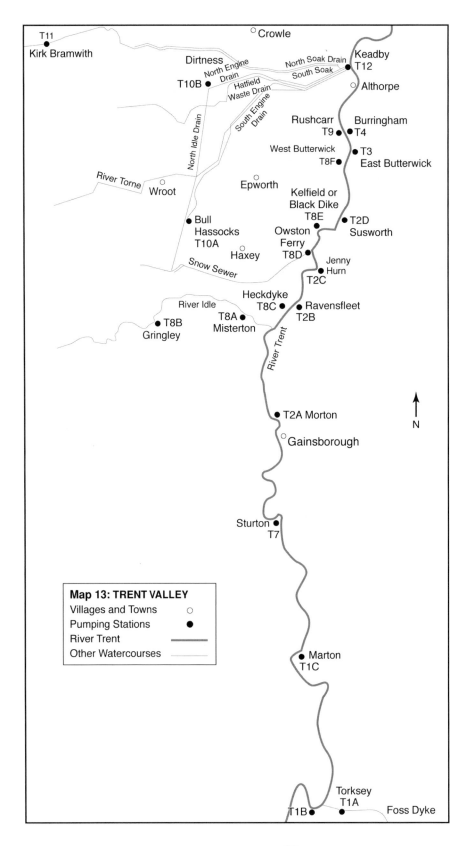

1
PUMPS

The Scoop Wheel

Scoop wheels were adopted for pumping by windmills by at least the mid-seventeenth century [1], and remained almost the sole type of pump used in the Fens until the Appold pump was introduced to drain Whittlesey Mere in 1852. The exceptions were the bucket pumps installed at Waldersea and Marton. At least 100 of the stations listed were equipped with scoop wheels at some time.

The scoop wheel resembles a breast-water wheel with reverse action. In its simplest form it consists of an axle upon which is fastened a spoked wheel having sockets into which are fastened arms. The latter are variously called starts, start posts or strakers. On to these are fixed boards, variously called scoops, ladles, floats or paddles. Throughout this work they are called scoops, following Wheeler's practice. These actually lifted and pushed the water. Wheels of narrow width, such as that at Middleton, Norfolk, had only one start post and the scoops were placed lengthways parallel with the start post. The wider wheels had two or more start posts and the scoops were placed on them widthways. This arrangement can be seen at Stretham. The starts were inserted at an angle of between 25 and 55 degrees, but generally 40 [2].

The wheel was driven by a gear wheel from the main shaft of the flywheel of the engine engaging usually on the inside rim of the cast iron centre of the scoop wheel. The scoop wheel was geared down from the engine at 3 or 4 to 1, making about 4 rpm.

The width of the wheel was most relevant to the volume of water discharged, and the diameter to the lift. The narrowest scoops traced, of 5½in., are at Middleton, which also has the least diameter, of 16ft., except for Over and Bourne North, both of 15ft. The latter clearly handled a small lift because it was 51in. wide. The largest diameter wheel was the later one at Hundred Foot, being 50ft. The widest, of 72in., was at Dirtness in the Trent Valley.

Of such as are recorded, the number of scoops (excepting the iron wheel at Upwell) varied from 30 (Bourne North) to 60 (Hundred Foot), the most common being 40 or 48.

At a later stage, and in three instances, curved iron scoops were adopted as being more effective, particularly if supplied with a shuttle to adjust the flow of water from the intake [3]. They could be run at a greater speed than the ordinary scoop wheel, and Wheeler states that they could be made of less diameter; but the examples in the Fens, namely Ravensfleet (35ft.), Upwell South (24ft.) and Sturton (26½ft.) suggest that this was not implemented.

Various devices were applied to scoop wheels to increase their efficiency. At Hundred Foot Engine, which pumped into tidal water, two gears were originally fitted so that the wheel could be driven at slow speed when pumping against a high tide. It was not used extensively and by 1862 a rising breast had been fitted on the outlet side so that high water could be held back from the river [4]. This was operated with rack and pinion by a handle in the engine room. A similar device had been fitted at Burnt Fen Little Ouse station in 1860, and was later fitted at several other stations, such as Stretham, Southery and Ten Mile Bank. At Metheringham, slats or sections seem to have been placed in front of the wheel as a simple alternative, probably only for use in times of flood [5].

Shuttles behind the wheel, to control the volume of water entering the wheel race, were also installed at a few stations, such as Pode Hole and Hundred Foot [6]. At Haddenham and Burwell, an assistant wheel was eventually installed behind the wheel to assist the lift. This device does not seem to have been applied at any other station.

Unlike the later centrifugal pumps, scoop wheels could handle fairly heavy debris drawn from the drain, and the bars of weed racks could be much wider apart than for the later pumps. At some stations, there was a continual loss of the boards forming the scoops. The log book of Metheringham records regular replacements of these, and it is a problem encountered in working both the Dogdyke and Stretham engines at the present time.

The Centrifugal Pump

Appold exhibited a model of a centrifugal pump at a British Association meeting in Birmingham in 1849, and followed this with display of an actual pump at the Great Exhibition of 1851 [7]. This pump consisted of a vertical spindle driving a fan immersed in water at the bottom of a well. The fan propelled the water upwards in a pipe or channel until it reached a discharge outlet which was its only means of escape. Discharge was greatest when the engine drain was full. It depended upon an engine running at relatively high speed and, although a beam engine was at first used to drive it, faster engines were much more suitable. These pumps did not require charging or vacuumising [8].

Although applied successfully to the drainage of Whittlesey Mere in 1852, the Appold pump was not used widely in the Fens, and none have survived there. The largest example was at Lade Bank, and others were installed at Whittlesey Glassmoor, Whittlesey Kingsland and Ramsey Middlemoor Fourth. A fine example remains preserved at Westonzoyland in the Somerset Levels, where such pumps were almost entirely used. Several were installed on the Norfolk Broads [9]. The Smithdale turbine pump was probably similar. The rare Clayton & Shuttleworth pump at Willingham is believed to be a vertical-spindle of similar type, but it has not yet been possible to prove this.

Although introduced later, the horizontal pump had its origins in a patent for a multi-stage centrifugal pump taken out by John Gwynne in 1851. A further patent in 1868 established the general design of the horizontal spindle pump which became common throughout the Fens from the 1890s. In appearance the visible part of the pump resembled a snail. These pumps required charging, or vacuumising, before starting, and an auxiliary engine was required to achieve this. They are more effective for higher lifts than the Appold pump [10]. Vertical spindle pumps were not wholly discarded, and one such was installed at Black Sluice Pumping Station, Boston, in 1946 [11].

Discharge

Although the volume of water discharged by pumps was obviously of prime concern to districts, information regarding the performance of scoop wheels is relatively slight. There are good reasons for this. Most plant was situated in inaccessible places with limited staff, who rarely possessed the skill to take the required measurements. Whilst the lack of shrinkage of the siltlands provided reasonably consistent delivery, in the peat fens the steady fall in ground levels progressively diminished performance until the wheel was either lowered or removed [12]. Those wheels discharging into tidal waters inevitably produced much variation in capacity, which was also generally affected by the level of lift at particular times and places. Therefore all information about the performance of scoop wheels must be taken with reservation.

The most reliable assessments of discharge are those available for Pode Hole in Lincolnshire, draining silt land, and Littleport and Downham District in the Bedford Level dealing with peat soil. In the latter district, Joseph Glynn estimated that the 80 hp Hundred Foot wheel originally discharged 98 tpm in low gear and 146 tpm in high gear. The major renovations in 1881 led Wheeler to state that the new wheel provided a maximum discharge of 197 tpm, but an average of 122 tpm with a lift of 13.8ft [13]. At the same time he estimated the 80 hp Ten Mile Bank Station as having a maximum delivery of 213 tpm, but an average of 128.55 tpm with a lift of 11.16ft. He stated that the estimated capacity of the two wheels at maximum dip was 410 tpm, which was equal to a discharge of water due to a continuous daily fall of 0.17in. of rain. This should be compared with the modern practice of providing pumping capacity for at least 0.25in. of rainfall per day on the area drained, and more commonly for 0.375in. [14]. The lift and maximum head at these stations was considerable.

At Pode Hole, the combined discharge of the 60 and 80 hp engines was estimated at 563 tpm. The difference between this performance and that of the two similar stations in Littleport & Downham District amply illustrates the much greater output achievable in the silt land than in peat fen.

Other statements of discharge give some useful comparative material. R.H. Clark stated that the 80 hp Sutton & Mepal plant, similar to that at Hundred Foot, delivered 120 tpm. His statement that the small Fordham engine delivered 100 tpm must be taken as excessive unless the lift was slight. Gibbs gives the discharge of the 60 hp Middle Fen wheel as 73 tpm with a 9ft. 10in. lift, and that of the 1880 pump at the same station as 82 tpm with a 10ft. lift, or 69 tpm with a 12ft. 5½in. lift.

The 60 hp Cornish engine at Waldersea drove a bucket pump claimed to raise 63 tpm against a head of tidal water varying between 10 and 24ft. The wheel driven by the 30 hp engine at March First District, which was 21in. wide, was expected to discharge 70 tpm, but this was almost certainly an over-statement. The same rate claimed for the 40 hp March West Fen wheel, 33in. wide, is more likely to be accurate. That for the wheel 18 in. wide driven by a 25 hp engine at Ramsey Hollow, given as 40 tpm against a 5 ft. head, is probably correct. This also applies to the 4ft. wide wheel driven by the 40 hp Upwell South engine, said to deliver 120 tpm, because the head and dip only normally totalled 8ft. 6in. The performance of the Haddenham wheel, 33in. wide, driven by a 60 hp engine, is given as 100 tpm; and the same power at Stretham delivered similarly. In Lincolnshire, the 16 hp engine at Tattershall drove a wheel 15½in. wide delivering 25 tpm, but the lift was not great.

Such relatively slight information does enable the performance of other similar plant to be estimated. Joseph Glynn worked on a rough rule of providing 10 hp of engine size per thousand acres drained, except for Soham Mere where the lift required a 40 hp engine to drain 1600 acres. This guideline can only be applied in conjunction with other data such as width of wheel, lift, discharge into tidal water and run-off from land outside the district. The introduction of centrifugal pumps provided a more accurate measure of discharge because they were less affected by soil shrinkage and varying levels of head. In estimating the delivery of scoop wheels, it can be safely assumed that any replacement plant was designed to provide a greater capacity than its predecessor.

Wheeler [15] provides the following table for discharge by centrifugal pumps handling low lifts in ordinary use:

Diameter of suction and discharge pipes in inches	Discharge in tpm
15	22.32
18	31.25
24	49.10
30	80.35
36	89.28
42	120.53
48	178.57
54	312.50
60	446.43

NOTES

1. Darby, H.C. (1983), 107-108.
2. Wheeler DF, 70-87. This contains a full account of these wheels.
3. Wheeler DF Plate 6, Figure 12.
4. Notebook of James Stevens, engine driver, in the author's possession, Wheeler DF, 114, and Hills, R.L. "Joseph Glynn and fen drainage", *Journal of the Royal Society of Arts*, Vol. CXLIV, No. 5468, April 1996, 67-69.
5. Log Book of E. Stevens, engine driver, in the author's possession: "5 January 1901 – Test of coal burning. No. of breast plates in – 5", and "27 June 1900 – Grooves cut for breast."
6. Wheeler DF, 108. This device does not seem to have worked well at Hundred Foot. The log book (CRO) records that in October 1880 the engine was found to throw more water without the shuttle, making 13 rpm with it and 17 rpm without it, and used less fuel. The head and dip were very high at that time.
7. Wheeler DF, 92
8. Wheeler DF, 93-94 and 98-101.
9. Ward, A.J. (2003), *Smoke drifting over the Reeds*, NIAS
10. Wheeler DF, 95-96
11. McLeod, 473-474
12. For instance, the log book of the Hundred Foot engine records the dip of the scoop wheel at starting. Taking rough averages, these show the extent of wastage of the soil and the diminishing effectiveness of the wheel:

1833	5ft. 9in.
1841	5ft. 4in.
1844	4ft. 8in. maximum
1844	Wheel lowered – then 6 ft. Maximum
1861	5ft.
1872	4ft.
1880	3ft.
1881	New wheel
1883	4ft. 5in.

    By comparison, the dip at Metheringham, on silt land, did not vary materially from 1896 to 1911.
13. Wheeler, W. H., "The Drainage of Fens and Low Lands by Steam Power", *The Engineer*, No. XI, 2 September 1887.
14. McLeod, 469-470 states that "ten or fifteen years ago, it was standard practice in many areas to design pumps with a capacity equivalent to $1/4$ in. of rainfall per day on the area drained…. In recent years it has become quite common to adopt a figure equivalent to $3/8$ in. of rainfall…. This is equivalent to 15.75 cusecs (26.3 tpm) per 1000 acres."

2
ORGANISATION, STAFF AND BUILDINGS

Organisation

The Acts which created drainage districts constituted Boards of Commissioners charged with their administration. As drainage was primarily required for agricultural purposes, the Commissioners were mainly landowners within the district. Each Act prescribed the qualification required to serve as such, and some entitled owners to nominate others to represent them. The Acts often appointed named individuals to be the initial Commissioners, and some gave a power of appointment to office-holders such as the Bishop of Ely, the Dean and Chapter, Rectors and Vicars and Lords of the Manor, as well as corporate bodies such as Cambridge Colleges. It can be assumed that these all owned land within the district. Besides these, those owning land of a prescribed acreage were usually entitled to serve. The acreage was not strictly related to the area of the district. For instance, in March it was 40 acres for districts varying in size from 700 to 2500 acres. The qualification usually varied from ownership of between 8 and 100 acres and sometimes possession of rights of common. In other districts, the owners of from 5 to 20 acres were given power to elect one or more Commissioners.

Staff

The Commissioners appointed officers to carry out the management of the district. A Collector of Taxes performed an essential function; and a Clerk was required to deal with all administrative affairs. These posts were often, although not always, combined. It was customary for the larger districts to employ a local attorney or solicitor as Clerk, but in recent years these have been replaced by full-time Clerks operating from offices separately provided. Literate, but unqualified, Clerks were employed by some of the smaller districts. Supervision of work on the ground was carried out by an officer variously called District Officer, superintendent or surveyor. The smaller districts often employed a part-time superintendent [1], or none at all [2]; and in others he was also the engine driver. The large Littleport & Downham District had two officers, one for the upper part and the other for the lower, both part-time; and the engine driver at each of the two pumping stations had to act as foreman and pay the wages. Thus the organisation varied greatly between districts.

The wages of engine drivers varied considerably, not necessarily being related to the size of the district or engine. Some drivers also acted as superintendent, not always being paid for the additional responsibility. Most wages remained static until 1914.

The salary of £80 paid to Housely of Waterbeach Level [3] was far higher than most, but he also acted as Collector of Taxes. By the mid-nineteenth century, a wage of 18/- a week, with house and coal provided, seems to have been the most common rate for engine drivers [4], but they were often paid extra for night work, since it was unusual for them to be provided with any relief unless also stoking. Some districts, even when small, paid more [5], whilst in others the driver or superintendent might also practise a trade [6].

Many of the smaller districts only employed part-time engine drivers at salaries varying from £15 to £25 p.a. (7). Private engines must commonly have been driven by farm workers from the estate on hourly rates, as was the case on the Heathcote Estate at Conington.

At the larger stations, a permanent stoker was employed, often being supplied with a house and coal. He was generally paid the same as the men working on the district [8], and was expected to work on the district during the summer. The drivers of the smaller engines had to stoke the boilers themselves, but were often allowed an assistant (called a nightman), when working at night, and often casual staff to clean the boiler or boilers [9].

Despite the relatively low pay, the post of engine driver was clearly attractive to many, as numerous Minutes evidence from the number of applicants for any vacancy. Although the smaller engines normally attracted only farm workers, the larger were staffed by a variety of tradesmen. Amongst these were fitters, blacksmiths, millwrights and carpenters. These posts offered regular and quite secure employment and the benefit of a free house and coal in most districts. Long service was common (see Appendix 5). Three generations of the Stevens family drove eight different engines over a period of more than 100 years, in several cases son succeeding father [10].

Driving was not the only duty involved in running a steam engine. The early engines were not necessarily fitted with metallic piston rings, and therefore had to be packed with hemp. The engine driver was responsible for this. At Hundred Foot this was undertaken after about each 1000 hours of running. Most of these engines seem to have been fitted with metallic rings at a later date.

Boiler cleaning was a frequent and unpleasant task. It was usually the task of the stoker, but would be carried out by any other district employee or casual hand if necessary.

About once a year, the flues had to be cleaned out. This involved removal of bricks from the outside of the chimney. At Hundred Foot in the 1860s, a contractor was employed for this task at a cost of 6/- [11].

Coal was delivered by barge to most engines. It then had to be barrowed over the river bank to the coal yard, usually by porters, often called "nippers". At Hundred Foot in the 1860s, three men were usually engaged for this task, at between 6d and 7d a ton, shared between them. Later a gangmaster or firm was contracted for the task. Each delivery was commonly about 70 tons. At Swaffham Engine in 1912 the porterage was 10d a ton. The larger stations were often provided with a weighbridge so that the weight of coal delivered could be checked. The engine driver usually, but not always, manned this. Either the stoker or the driver stacked the coal in the yard.

Buildings

The architecture of fenland pumping stations has been so diverse over time that it almost merits a separate study. The beam engine and scoop wheel required a tripartite building to contain the engine, boiler or boilers, and scoop wheel. Relatively small plant of this type could be contained in a single building with the roof pitched in the centre to provide the height for the engine. Examples of these can be seen at Fordham, Dogdyke and Timberland. Others, such as West Dereham and Willingham, had the roof pitched laterally. At some of the smallest, such as Willingham, the scoop wheel was separated from the engine room only by a wooden partition, and these engines were merely provided with ladders and trestles for access to the beam loft, as can be seen at Dogdyke and Pinchbeck Marsh.

The larger stations required a different type of building, in three parts, with roofs built only to the height needed for each section. The Butterley Co. specified the design for their stations and evolved a standard form [12]. This type of structure is exemplified by Misterton

Kate and Stretham, both of which have survived unaltered. Others lacking chimneys exist at Mepal and Hundred Foot. The design was even applied to smaller Butterley stations such as March West Fen and March Binnimore Fen. Except for Misterton, this style was rarely used in Lincolnshire, where Butterley seem to have had no great following, and some quite ornate buildings were erected. The engine houses of these larger engines had three floors, with stone stairways giving access to the cylinder landing and beam loft.

The first building at Upware of 1821 sensibly provided space for a second boiler [13], but it was not appreciated that the largest engines would require three boilers to enable one to be cleaned when two were required to operate in times of flood. Thus the boiler houses at Hundred Foot and Stretham had to be extended in 1843 and 1846 respectively to provide for a third boiler. At Hundred Foot all three boilers had to be fired on occasion to cope with high water [14].

Although at first the scoop wheel at Upware was not covered, this seems to have been an exception to the invariable practice of housing the wheel. The larger engine houses contained a separate structure for the wheel, with the roof pitched at right angles to that of the engine house. At Hundred Foot, the installation of the new 50ft. wheel in 1881 required the roof of the wheel house to be raised so that it was higher than that of the engine house. Martin's Farm had a separate wheelhouse much higher than the engine house, although the latter may have been lowered by the time that it was photographed.

The chimneys varied in height from about 50ft. to 100ft. Stretham is 75ft and the Upware 1850 chimney was 100ft. The only instance of a chimney being lowered whilst the plant was operational is at Downham West Fen. Many of the chimneys of redundant plant were felled during the Second World War following Government advice. In December 1939 Nene Catchment Board wrote to all IDBs advising demolition of chimneys at any pumping station where they were redundant as they were considered dangerous landmarks in the event of any air raids [15], and other River Boards followed in giving this advice. Despite this, several chimneys have survived. Some, such as Glassmoor, Wisbech Northside and Misterton, have even remained on buildings converted into dwelling houses. Only two of the four surviving steam plants, Stretham and Owston Ferry, have retained their chimneys.

Provision of a coal yard was essential. These were usually walled in brick against the main building, although at Upware a separate corrugated iron shed existed by at least 1900. Some of these yards were covered, probably as a deterrent against theft rather than for the convenience of the stoker.

The Cornish engines and bucket pumps installed at Waldersea, Torksey and Marton did not demand a tripartite building, and the side-lever engines at Prickwillow and both Burnt Fen stations allowed for a lower engine house.

Although the first application of an Appold pump, at Whittlesey Mere, needed a high building to house its beam engine, it did afford the opportunity to alter the standard design in that no wheel house was needed. As at Westonzoyland in Somerset, living quarters for the engine driver were incorporated in the building. This unusual arrangement was also provided at Ramsey Middlemoor.

The adoption of horizontal and grasshopper engines enabled much lower and simpler buildings to be provided. At Haddenham and Ten Mile Bank the engine house was lowered so as to be level with the boiler house when new machinery was installed in 1897 and 1912 respectively; and this practice was followed extensively elsewhere in later years. The expense of laying new foundations on usually unstable soil led to the adaptation of many old engine houses. An account of the works required to achieve this is given for Cottenham Smithey Fen (S5B).

Diesel engines did not require large buildings, and a variety of patterns for these emerged.

The depression of the inter-war years demanded economies which produced corrugated asbestos or iron houses, such as those at Lakenheath, Feltwell Second, Manea & Welney, Burnt Fen Little Ouse and Green Dyke Bank; and even wooden sheds as at Purl's Bridge and Boot's Bridge, Wimblington. The latter were used where the ground conditions were not thought to be capable of sustaining brick.

At the same time, some substantial brick or concrete houses were constructed, such as those at Stretham, Hundred Foot, Southery, Overfall and Sutton Gault.

Generous Government grants for drainage plant became available from 1937 onwards, and new diesel-powered plant then proliferated. Rectangular brick buildings of uniform design then became common.

Pumps powered by electric motors generally require very small buildings or none at all. Many of these are uncovered, and some totally buried, although a few are contained within old buildings.

Many examples of all types of engine houses have survived, but their number is diminishing. Often sited in remote places, they have served as targets for vandalism for many years. Windows have had to be bricked up or shuttered. There is no incentive for IDBs to retain redundant plant and demolition then becomes the best option. The engines can usually be sold, although there is no significant market for old pumps. A new use for such structures is becoming increasingly popular by conversion into dwellinghouses.

NOTES

1. E.g. at Willingham in 1847 the posts of Collector of Taxes and Superintendent were combined for a total salary of £5 p.a.; and at Whittlesey Third (Wype) the District Officer was paid £6 p.a. in 1898.
2. At Marshland, no superintendent was thought necessary from 1863 to 1882, when the driver was given the additional responsibility.
3. Hills (2003), 162
4. E.g. Hundred Foot, Marshland and Ramsey Middlemoor
5. E.g. Digby in 1873, £52; Pinchbeck Marsh in 1899, £60; and Hunt's Sluice in 1883, £57
6. E.g. William Stevens practised as a blacksmith from the Swaffham Engine at Upware
7. E.g. Willingham, March Sixth and Whittlesey Kingsland
8. This was invariably slightly more than the wages paid to a farm worker
9. The log books of Marshland and Metheringham record when such were employed
10. These were Hundred Foot (59 years), Ten Mile Bank (53 years), Marshland (50 years), Swaffham (50 years), Haddenham (23 years), Metheringham (14 years), Stretham (12 years) and Pinchbeck Marsh (10 years)
11. Notebook of James Stevens in the author's possession
12. Hills (2003), 119-121, showing designs for the Hundred Foot building; and 90-96 for a full description of this type of building
13. Hills (2003), 107
14. Log Book in author's possession
15. Whittlesey & Farcet IDB Minutes, 11 December 1939 (CRO ref. 99/100)

3
MIDDLE LEVEL

DISTRICTS

Serial No.	Name	Serial No.	Name
M1	Middle Level – General	M27	Ramsey Upwood & Great Raveley
M2	Benwick White Fen	M28	Ransonmoor
M3	Benwick IDB	M29	Stilton
M4	Bluntisham*	M30	Sutton & Mepal*
M5	Conington	M31	Upwell North
M6	Curff & Normoor	M32	Upwell South
M7	Farcet	M33	Whittlesey Mere
M8	Laddus Fen	M34	Whittlesey First
M9	Manea & Welney*	M35	Whittlesey Second
M10	March First	M36	Whittlesey Third
M11	March Second	M37	Whittlesey Fourth
M12	March Third	M38	Whittlesey Fifth
M13	March Fourth	M39	Whittlesey & Farcet
M14	March Fifth	M40	Whittlesey - Glassmoor
M15	March Sixth	M41	Whittlesey - Kingsland
M16	Ramsey Bury First and Third	M42	Whittlesey - Feldale
M17	Ramsey Bury Second	M43	Wimblington – Stitches Farm
M18	Ramsey Bury Fourth	M44	Wimblington – Stonea Grange
M19	Ramsey Bury Fifth	M45	Wimblington Combined
M20	Ramsey Bury Lower	M46	Wimblington Common
M21	Ramsey Middlemoor First	M47	Wisbech St. Peter – Hobbs Lot
M22	Ramsey Middlemoor Second	M48	Woodwalton
M23	Ramsey Middlemoor Third	M49	Yaxley First
M24	Ramsey Middlemoor Fourth	M50	Yaxley Second
M25	Ramsey Middlemoor Fifth	M51	Yaxley New Fen
M26	Ramsey Middlemoor Sixth	*	Not strictly within Middle Level

This level contains some 170,000 acres. Its northern boundary runs along Moreton's Leam from Peterborough to Guyhirn, and then along the Twenty Foot River from whence it meanders east of Waldersea District until it joins the Well Creek at Outwell. The eastern boundary follows the River Delph and then the boundaries of the Manea and Welney and the Sutton and Mepal Districts. The southern boundary passes south of Ramsey and Warboys.

The works of Vermuyden in the seventeenth century created a system of drainage almost entirely to the Old Bedford River and the River Great Ouse. The Whittlesey area drained to the old course of the River Nene through March and thence to Well Creek, which discharged into the Ouse at Salter's Lode. The Ramsey area drained into the Forty Foot and thence to Welches Dam on the Old Bedford, and the Chatteris area to Well Creek via the Sixteen Foot Drain. Tongs Drain (or the Marshland Cut) was built outside the Level from Well Creek at Nordelph to the Ouse below Downham Bridge to serve as a relief channel when there was great pressure at Salters Lode. The Bedford Level Corporation was responsible for maintenance of all of these main drains until 1810, when the Middle Level Commission was created to carry out these functions independently of the Corporation [1].

Extensive floods in 1841-2 submerged a great part of this Level, and led to the passage of the Middle Level Act of 1844 [2]. This enabled the Middle Level Main Drain to be constructed, eleven miles in length, from the north end of the Sixteen Foot Drain (near Popham's Eau) to the River Great Ouse at Wiggenhall St. Germans. From Upwell to St. Germans this passed through the Marshland area, and not the Middle Level itself. This work was completed in 1848, with a sluice at St. Germans [3]. The districts of Manea and Welney and Sutton and Mepal declined to join the Middle Level under the Act because the rate burden of so doing would have been much greater than the cost of operating their existing pumps; but they have been included in this chapter, with the later plant at Welches Dam, for want of any more suitable category. Bluntisham, also not within this Level, has been included for the same reason.

This Level spawned a large number of internal districts as well as private pumping stations. The constitutions of some of these districts and sub-districts produced a wide variety of names given to each, particularly in the Whittlesey and Ramsey areas. Subsequent amalgamations have not assisted identification of these. It has been necessary to elucidate these in order to ascertain the position and names of pumping plant. The index is provided to assist in this task.

It is also served by two major pumping stations at St. Germans (map 8, p.23) and Welches Dam, which discharge water already lifted by IDB plant. The former belongs to the Middle Level Commission, although it is not within that Level; and the latter to the Environment Agency.

M1 MIDDLE LEVEL – General

M1A St. Germans Syphon Sluice (TF 585138)

On 4 May 1862, the sluice at St. Germans gave way, and some nine square miles of the Level were inundated. Sir John Hawkshaw was retained to remedy the situation. He decided that only a cofferdam would resist the highest tides. This was constructed in a new channel about 150ft. south-west of the old sluice. Two rows of sheet piling, 25ft. apart, were driven across the slopes at the side of the drain. The intermediate portion, across the bottom and the lower parts of the sides, consisted of pairs of whole timbers driven down, 7½ft. apart from centre to centre, and the intervening spaces were occupied by panels 7in. thick. The dam was filled with clay, sacks of gravel, and in the centre, clunch (Figs. 1 and 2).

Sixteen large bent tubes, each 150ft. long and 3ft. 6in. in diameter were placed on the dam at an inclination of 2 to 1 at each side. The ends were laid 18in. clear below the level of low water at spring tides. The top of the syphon was 20ft. above the same level. An air pump was attached to the syphons and was used to exhaust the air from the tubes. This had three 15in.

Fig 1: St. German's syphon sluice (M1A) under construction in 1862
Illustrated London News, 25 October 1862

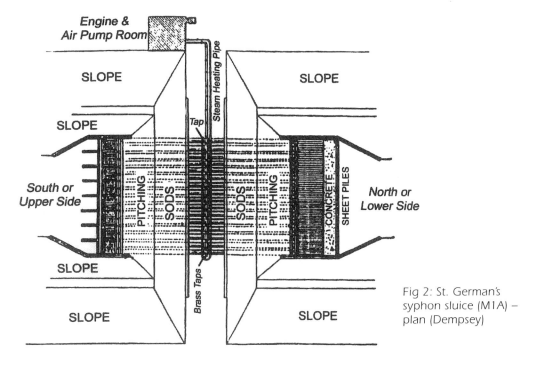

Fig 2: St. German's
syphon sluice (M1A) –
plan (Dempsey)

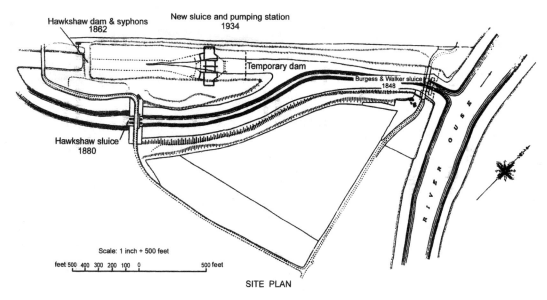

Fig 3: St. German's sluices (M1) – plan (Clark, R.G., Ch. 4, note 5)

cylinders worked together by means of a three-throw crankshaft with a stroke of 18in. It was driven by a steam engine of 12 nhp, having a cylinder 12in. in diameter and a stroke of 20in. No further details of this engine have been traced, but if Appold designed the pumps, the engine was probably made by Easton & Amos.

The total weight of the metalwork in one syphon, exclusive of the pipes etc., was 36 tons, and that of the sixteen syphons together, with all connections, 610 tons [4].

This structure was the only one of its kind to be applied to a sluice in the Fens. Although ingenious, it proved incapable of discharging sufficient water at the highest tides.

In 1880, Hawkshaw was again retained and prescribed an ordinary sluice placed in a new channel by-passing the syphon sluice, which was abandoned. The 1880 sluice discharged solely by gravity. Initially effective, it was eventually rendered inadequate by the continued shrinkage of the soil, and by silting on the tidal side of the sluice gates.

M1B St. Germans Pumping Station (D) (TF 589142)

By the 1920s, the difficulty in discharging flood water persuaded the Middle Level Commission to adopt a completely new system designed by their engineer, Major R.G. Clark. This involved the construction of a new larger sluice slightly north-east of the old syphon sluice, supplemented by pumping machinery for use in time of flood. The syphon sluice was demolished and the 1880 channel abandoned (Fig. 3).

Two pumping stations were constructed on either side of the new sluice, one to the north and the other to the south. Two sets of plant were installed in the north house, and one in the south, with space provided for a fourth. The new buildings (Fig. 4) housed pumping plant (Fig. 5) consisting of three Crossley Premier Gas Engine Co. type NO8 horizontal eight-cylinder 1000 bhp diesel engines coupled through David Brown gear boxes to Gwynnes pumps, each 8ft. 6in. in diameter and designed to discharge 840 tpm against a head of 10ft [5]. In 1951 a fourth plant was installed in the south engine house. This was an eight-cylinder Crossley Premier horizontal type 00S8 (no. 126534) diesel engine having a bore of $18^1/_2$in. and stroke

Fig. 4: St. German's pumping station (M1B) – exterior in 2004

Fig. 5: St. German's pumping station (M1B) – interior in 2004

of 28in., and is rated at 1200 bhp. In 1970 the two pumps in the north engine house were re-built with modified impellers and the diesel engines were scrapped, to be replaced by two 1500 bhp electric motors.

In 1981 the original engine in the south engine house was replaced by an Allen eight cylinder vertical diesel type S12-F (no. D5/56571) turbo intercooled, and rated at 1550 bhp. [6]

M1C Welches Dam (D) (TL 471859)

Parallel to the Old Bedford River runs the Counter Drain from just north of Earith to Welches Dam. It then continues northwards as the Old Bedford River up to the tidal Ouse. This drain takes the discharge from both the Sutton and Mepal and the Manea and Welney engines, each discharging 300 tpm, as well as highland water. The floods of 1937 and 1939 produced water levels in the tidal river so high that the water from the Old Bedford could not be discharged and the Drain became so full that the water began to spill over its bank, and the two engines had to be stopped. The cost of raising the 20 mile long bank would have been so high that it was deemed preferable to instal a pumping station to pump water from the Drain into the washland between the two Bedford Rivers to relieve the pressure in times of flood. Welches Dam was chosen for the site of this as being midway between the two engines (map 7, p.22). Alternatively it could have been placed at the northern end, but would then have had to be capable of discharging the whole flow of the Drain, some 750 tpm, against high tidal heads.

Construction commenced in 1945, but was not completed until 1948. The plant consisted of two 500 bhp six-cylinder Allen four-stroke type S37C diesel engines, each driving an Allen Conqueror pump delivering 375 tpm [7].

This massive plant was over-prescribed, and only one pump has ever been used at one time. It is only used in flood conditions. Both engines failed in January 2003 and eight portable engines and pumps had to be placed on the bank by the Mepal bridge over the A142 road to evacuate the water.

M1D Bevill's Leam (D) (TL 914249)

A further station was established in the 1970s at Tebbit's Bridge on Bevill's Leam to cope with the evacuation of water from the very low-lying land in the south-west of the Level. This was constructed by the Middle Level Commission.

This station was installed between 1977 and 1981 to serve some 25,000 acres of fenland drained by IDB pumps and a further 20,000 acres of highland. This fenland was then too low for its water to reach St. Germans from the pumped outlets by gravity. The plant consists of three Dorman 8 cylinder 274 bhp diesel engines and three Lawrence Scott 168 kw electric motors, each driving an Allen 1000 mm. Diameter vertical axial flow pump. Each of these pumps can discharge 180 tpm. Thus the total capacity of the plant is 1080 tpm. It stands across the Leam.

M2 BENWICK WHITE FEN, Cambs. (TL 348911)

This district was created by Act of 1767 [8], and contained 2400 acres.

In 1847 a Butterley A-frame beam engine (Figs. 6, 7 and 8) was installed on the north bank of the Old River Nene to replace a windpump burnt down in the previous year. The date on the engine house was 9 August 1847. The cylinder was 30in. by 36in. with beam centres 9ft. 6in. The flywheel was 15ft. in diameter. The D slide valve survived throughout its existence [9]. Steam was provided at 7 psi by a single boiler, replaced by Butterley in 1869 at a cost of £180, and again in 1897 by a Lancashire boiler at a cost of £286. The engine ran at 36 rpm

Fig. 6: Benwick White Fen (M2) –
scoop wheel (COC)

Fig. 7: Benwick White Fen (M2) –
beam engine cylinder (COC)

Fig. 8: Benwick White
Fen (M2) – beam engine
parallel motion (COC)

Fig. 9: Benwick White Fen 1937 (M2) - Blackstone engine (MLO)

and was geared down to the wheel 8:1. The diameter of the scoop wheel was 28ft. 6in. with scoops 5ft. 9in. long and 20in. wide. It was lowered in 1861. The cost of this plant was £1415 for the engine and £970 for the building [10]. Discharge was into the Old River Nene.

This plant was scrapped in 1937 and replaced by a 58 bhp Blackstone diesel engine with four cylinders each 8 by 16ins. driving a 21in. Mirrlees-Watson pump (Fig. 9). This plant cost £1107 and was housed in a new building. Only fragments of the old building remained in 1971, and these have since wholly disappeared.

In 1954 a new plant was built slightly east of the original plant at TL 352910, comprising a Ruston three-cylinder vertical diesel engine driving a submersible pump. Later an electric motor was fitted above this.

This district is now called White Fen IDB, and must not be confused with Benwick IDB.

M3 BENWICK IDB, Cambs. and Hunts. (inc. BENWICK SECOND)

Five districts were created by Act of 1772 [11] for the drainage of 8600 acres in the parishes of Ramsey, Doddington, March, Benwick, Wimblington and Chatteris. They were (map 4, p.19):

1. Broadalls, later called Benwick Second,	530 acres	
2. Benwick Turf Fen,	440 acres	
3. Dykemoore in Doddington and Benwick	770 acres	
4. Beezlings Fen in Doddington and Chatteris,	1080 acres	
5. Ranson Moor	4180 acres	

The acreages are taken from the Act.

The evolution of this district is somewhat complex. It originally comprised the First and Second Districts under the 1772 Act. To these, in course of time, were added the farms called Four Hundred and Betty's Nose and the area of Benwick Mere, otherwise called Ibbersons, after the name of the landowner. By the early twentieth century these had been formed into Broadalls, Four Hundred and Betty's Nose Drainage Board. In 1941 the area of Ramsey Mere (which had become Mereside and Ramsey Mere Drainage Board) and Ramsey

Doddington Third (by 1927 called Benwick Third) and Fourth Districts were added to all of these to create Benwick IDB. It is important to note that Benwick White Fen and Ramsey Doddington Fifth (Ransonmoor) are not within Benwick IDB, and have remained independent.

The eastern part of this district lies in Cambridgeshire and the western part in Huntingdonshire.

Originally this area contained a plethora of windpumps, mostly later provided with portable steam engines. Over time, some of these disappeared completely. This account only records those known as having had engines. Due to the difficulty of obtaining full information, it cannot be regarded as complete or fully accurate.

Ramsey Mere contained a windpump at TL 305895 discharging into the east bank of the old River Nene, possibly provided with an auxiliary engine; but this was demolished in 1937 [12]. It does not seem to have been replaced until an Allen-Gwynnes electric motor driving a 15in. pump was installed in 1969 [13].

M3A Broadalls (TL 322910)

A windpump existed on the south bank of the Old River Nene to drain this area from 1774 until the 1920s [14]. Later a portable engine was hired to drive the scoop wheel [15]. This survived until after 1902, but the entire plant had disappeared by 1926 [16].

M3B Four Hundred (TL 328912)

Another windpump existed on the south bank of the Old River Nene in 1887 [17]. This was near Four Hundred Farm. It remained until after 1930 [18]. By 2002 a diesel engine house existed on the site, probably erected in 1944 to house an Allen engine, but by then containing an electric pump [19].

M3C Lilly Holt (D) (TL 34790

A windpump on this site was replaced at some time before 1930 by a 25 hp Campbell paraffin engine driving a 9in. Allen pump [20]. This was sold in 1946. This area was originally within Ramsey Doddington Second District

M3D Copalder (D) (TL 352910)

In 1954 a 136 hp Ruston vertical engine driving a 30in. Gwynnes submersible pump was erected on a former windpump site [21]. Later an electric motor was fitted above the pump [22].

M3E Copalder (TL 356911)

A windpump on this site burnt down in 1877. In the following year a steam engine was installed[23]. Later an oil engine was installed. This was sold in 1957 [24]. This area was originally in Ramsey Doddington Third District.

M3F Ibbersons or Benwick Mere (TL 349881)

By 1877 a 14 hp high pressure condensing steam engine driving a scoop wheel 28ft. in diameter existed on the north bank of the Forty Foot Drain to serve the areas known as Benwick Mere and Betty's Nose [25]. Ibberson was the principal farmer in the area, and this was probably a private plant. By 1946 this station contained a portable steam engine and Smithdale pump. This was sold in 1946 and the water inlet was sealed off in 1954 [26]. An electric plant now occupies the site, and there are no remains of the old plant. To confuse, this station was also sometimes called Betty's Nose.

M3G Betty's Nose (D) (TL 331880)

In 1944 a two-cylinder Allen type S30 vertical diesel engine was installed to drive an Allen pump discharging 50 tpm against a head of 10ft. The engine was rated at 54.7 bhp and ran at 370 rpm. This plant cost £2700 and the building £3700. By c. 1990 it was frost-damaged, and was removed soon after this date [27].

M3H Beezlings and Westmoor (D) (TL 374885)

Beezlings Fen was formed as the Fourth District under the Ramsey, Doddington Act of 1772 and was originally drained by a windpump rebuilt in 1898. This was scrapped when the district was amalgamated with Ramsey, Bury etc. (1775 Act) Second District (Chatteris and Doddington – Westmoor) in 1904. A channel and culvert was then constructed to take the water from Beezlings Fen southwards to the Westmoor plant [28].

This was replaced in 1920 by a 63 hp Campbell hot-bulb oil engine driving a 24in. Gwynnes Invincible pump [29] placed near Carter's Bridge on the site of the old Beezlings windpump (Fig. 10) [30]. The pump delivered 49 tpm. This plant became redundant around 1945/50 and the machinery was sold in 1990. There are no remains of the original steam plant and a modern Allen-Gwynnes electric now occupies the site.

Fig. 10: Benwick IDB – Beezlings (M3H) engine house in 1990

M4 BLUNTISHAM SEPARATE DISTRICT, Hunts. (TL 369732)

This district was originally managed by Fen Reeves. The drainage board was created by Act of Parliament in 1861.

A steam engine driving a scoop wheel had been installed by 1854 [31] on the west bank of the River Ouse, which is tidal at this point. Later a centrifugal pump was added for use when the water in the river was high. In 1918 a tractor was built into the engine house to replace the steam engine [32].

Between 1941 and 1945 this plant was wholly scrapped. A two-cylinder 75 bhp Allen engine (presumably a vertical type S30B) driving an Allen-Gill 32/26in. axial-flow pump was installed at a cost of £3000 for the plant and £2500 for the building and foundations. This discharged 50 tpm against a head of 12ft. [33]. This plant was surrounded by water and the engine room flooded to a depth of about 2ft. in March 1947.

An Allen-Gwynnes 26in. electric pump was installed before 1977 in the same building (Fig. 11). This district has now become Bluntisham IDB

Fig. 11: Bluntisham (M4) engine house in 1992

Fig. 12: Conington (M5) engine house in 1990

M5 CONINGTON FEN, Hunts. (TL 209857)

This fen, containing about 500 acres, (map 5, p.20) belonged to J.M. Heathcote of Conington Castle, Hunts. He installed a pumping station to drain his estate on the west bank of Monk's Lode in 1868 to replace a windpump. It discharged into Monks Lode.

The Estate Accounts state the cost as £219.10s. for an Easton and Amos pump, £393.5s. for a Clayton & Shuttleworth engine, £153.3s.4d for the pump house and £60 for the engine house. The total cost of the installation, including a new road, was £900 [34]. The engine was a portable [35], rated at 14 hp [36]. The pump was replaced by Easton & Anderson in 1877 at a cost of £827. 18s. The Accounts list payments to an engine driver at 3d an hour, and show that the plant was run during the winter for between 10 and 20 hours a week.

In 1926 a 70 bhp Allen two-stroke hot-bulb oil engine type HFOE driving a 22in. Allen pump was installed [37], and presumably the old plant was scrapped at this time. This Allen engine was removed by persons unknown in 1998. The vandalised building and pump remain (Fig. 12). An Allen-Gwynnes electric pump had been installed by 1977 [38]. This area is now within Conington & Holme IDB.

M6 CURFF AND NORMOOR, Cambs.

An Act of 1791 called Chatteris and Doddington [39] created two districts containing Curff Turf Fen, Normoor, Bensons, Mount Pleasant and Wimblington Common, and enabled the latter to be enclosed. These contained a total of 3000 acres and were sometimes called Curff and Normoor Districts (map 7, p.22). Normoor, Bensons and Mount Pleasant originally each had private pumping stations, but the first two later became separate IDBs before being amalgamated with Curff to form Curff IDB, being the southern part of the area to which the Act related. The northern part became Wimblington Common IDB, and is listed under M46.

M6A Bensons (TL 427882)

This area of about 600 acres was drained under the provisions of a Deed dated 6 August 1850. A steam engine was installed, probably soon after this, on the west bank of the Sixteen Foot Drain, to drive a scoop wheel. This wheel was replaced in 1941 by a Gwynnes centrifugal pump having a diameter of 18in. and suction of 20in., at a cost of £535 together with £100 for dismantling the old wheel and installing the pump. It is not known whether the steam engine drove this pump, but in 1942 the chimney was demolished and the buildings altered to receive a 30 hp Ruston diesel engine type 6XHR driving the Gwynnes pump. An electrically driven pump was installed in 1972 [40]. The building and Ruston engine survived in derelict condition until shortly after 1988 [41].

M6B Normoor (TL 423876)

This was a small private area of about 600 acres next to Benson's Farm. It was drained by a steam engine [42] on the west bank of the Sixteen Foot Drain driving a scoop wheel erected before 1887 [43] and probably about 1850 [44]. The engine was replaced before 1928, when the chimney was demolished , but the scoop wheel survived until 1936 when a Ruston 6XHR was installed to drive a 14in. Dodman's Triton pump. This cost £450. In 1952 subsidence of the engine house was reported and it was agreed to erect a new engine house at a cost of £420. This does not seem to have been done, because the old engine house survived, in heavily vandalised condition in 1988, but had been demolished by 1992. Following discussions in 1972, the three areas of Benson's, Normoor and Mount Pleasant joined together to instal an electrically-driven pump next to the existing pump and the Normoor plant became redundant. Discharge was into the Sixteen Foot Drain.

M6C Mount Pleasant (TL 430889)

This farm, of some 600 acres next to Benson's, was originally drained by a windpump [45]. Between 1867 and 1871 a 12in. Easton Amos & Anderson [46] pump was installed on the west bank of the Sixteen Foot Drain, driven by an unknown engine by belt-drive, probably portable or semi-portable. By about 1940 [47] a permanent engine (possibly a 28 hp Blackstone diesel engine) had been installed in a brick building above and beside the pump (Fig. 13), which was driven by long belt-drive. This plant had broken down by 1972 [48], and in 1979 an electric plant had been installed on Benson's Farm to provide a common drainage system. The old pump remains buried in the ground (Fig. 14). Discharge was into the Sixteen Foot Drain.

Fig. 13: Mount Pleasant (M6C) engine house in 1996

Fig. 14: Mount Pleasant (M6C) - Easton, Amos & Anderson pump in 1996

M6D Curff (TL 392883)

A windpump stood on this site as early as 1780 and survived until the 1920s. [49]. By that time it had been provided with a steam engine and lineshaft. This plant was removed in 1937 [50]. A 47 hp Ruston diesel engine (probably type 8HR) driving an 18in. pump was then installed in a new building. This was removed in about 1989 and an electric pump was provided.

M7 FARCET FEN, Hunts

Farcet Fen was first drained under an Act of 1773 [51] and contained some 2000 acres (map 6, p.21). In 1937 the district was amalgamated with Whittlesey First and Second Districts to form Whittlesey & Farcet IDB [52]. Three pumping stations served this district:

M7A Tebbits Bridge (TL 252918)

A plant existed in 1886 near Tebbit's Bridge. No information has been obtained about this, save that it was described as old before it was scrapped in 1941 [53]. See also M39B.

M7B Frog Hall (TL 214922)

A station existed at a place called Frog Hall in 1887 [54], discharging into Conquest Lode. It was probably that latterly described as Farcet Fen Engine, having a 16 hp portable steam engine driving a Dodmans Triton pump. This plant was scrapped in 1941 [55]. By 1926 this was called Bird's Pumping Station, belonging to Huntingdonshire County Council [56].

M7C Pondersbridge (TL 257920)

A third plant existed in 1900 [57] near Pondersbridge. It is believed to have contained a Clayton & Shuttleworth portable steam engine driving a Dodmans pump. This was also described as old before it was scrapped in 1941 [58].

Both the first and third of these stations discharged into Bevill's Leam. One of these must have been that described in Gwynnes' brochure of c. 1936 as a 25 hp steam engine driving a 16in. Gwynnes pump. The later plant serving Farcet Fen is described under Whittlesey First and Second Districts.

M8 LADDUS FEN, Elm, Cambs. (TL 453993)

This fen lies between Waldersea IDB and the old course of the River Nene, north-east of March. It is almost entirely owned by the Coldham Estate, formerly the property of Lord Overstone [59] and, since before 1916, of the Co-operative Wholesale Society [60].

The windpump on this site (Lord Sandon's mill, otherwise called Coldham White mill), which stood on the north bank of the Old River Nene, was removed in 1860 [61]. In 1877 a 12 hp Armitage & Ruston semi-portable steam engine was installed, probably driving a scoop wheel [62]. This engine is believed to have been replaced in the 1930s. By the 1950s a four-cylinder Ruston vertical engine had been installed. This is almost certainly that described as Coldham Hall, containing a 40 hp Ruston diesel engine (probably type 4VSH) driving a 20in. Gwynnes pump, installed in 1940 (Figs. 15 and 16)[63].

This area is not within Laddus Fen IDB, which does not seem to have had any pumped drainage, and which contains 1400 acres to the east of this fen and was constituted by an Act of 1771 [64].

M9 MANEA & WELNEY, CAMBS.

This district was created by Acts of 1758 and 1799 [65], and contains 8685 acres (map 7, p.22). Although strictly within the Middle Level, the Commissioners declined to join the district created by the Middle Level Act of 1844 because they already had a steam engine. Sutton & Mepal District acted likewise [66].

M9A Manea (TL 511915)

In 1842 [67] a 60 hp Butterley beam engine [68] was erected on the west bank of the Counterdrain next to the Old Bedford River. This drove a scoop wheel 32ft. by 33in., rotating at 3 rpm. Steam was supplied by three Lancashire boilers and consumption at full load was 5 tons per 24 hours [69]. Discharge was into the Counterdrain.

Fig. 15: Laddus Fen (M8) engine house in 2002

Fig. 16: Laddus Fen (M8) - Ruston engine in 2002

This plant was demolished in 1928 [70]. It was replaced by twin 180 hpVickers Petter oil engines driving 36in. Gwynnes pumps each delivering 120 tpm [71].

In 1948 a separate brick building (Fig. 17) was erected to house two horizontal four cylinder Ruston type 9XHRF diesel engines driving 36in. Gwynnes pumps each discharging 120 tpm (Fig. 18) [72]. The large enines were required to overcome a 17ft. head. These were housed in a separate brick building and were scrapped in 1997. The original steam engine building no longer exists. The Vickers-Petter building still existed in 1995, albeit empty (Fig. 19).

Fig. 17: Manea & Welney (M9A) Ruston engine house in 2002

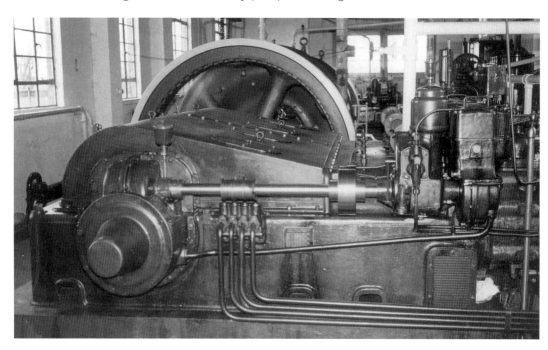

Fig. 18: Manea & Welney (M9A) – Ruston engines

Fig. 19: Manea & Welney (M9A)Vickers Petter engine house in 1995

Fig. 20: Manea & Welney – Purl's Bridge (M9B) engine house

M9B Purl's Bridge (D) (TL 473865)

At some time, probably in the 1920s, a small diesel engine and pump, housed in a curious wooden building (Fig. 20), was installed between Purl's Bridge and Welches Dam. This seems to have replaced a windpump [73]. No information has been obtained about this, but it has long been disused. It was probably operational up to 1975 [74]. An Allen-Gwynnes electric pump has since been erected in a brick building north of Purl's Bridge (TL 489884). Both plants discharged into the Old Bedford River.

MARCH, Cambs.

The fens around March were first drained under an Act of 1754, which divided them into five districts. A sixth was added by Act of 1774 [75]. Parts of these were in the parishes of Wimblington and Upwell.

They were (map 2, p.17):

1. Binnimore Fen	2500 acres (later 3771)
2. Well Fen	1200 acres (later 1368)
3. Burrowmoor Fen	700 acres (later 998)
4. West Fen	6000 acres
5. Creek	800 acres
6. Norwood or Whitemoor	700 acres

M10 MARCH FIRST – Binnimore Fen (TL 433975)

In 1833 a 30 hp Butterley beam engine was erected on the south bank of the Old River Nene to drain this district. The cylinder had a bore of 30in. and a stroke of 72in. This drove a scoop wheel 34ft. in diameter and 21in. wide. A single boiler, 7ft. in diameter and 27ft. in length, was provided [76]. The wheel was expected to deliver 70 tpm [77]. This plant was scrapped in 1932, although the empty engine house, without chimney, remained until about 1980 (Figs. 21 and 22)[78].

In 1932 twin Allen 3-cylinder vertical diesel engines, each driving a 24in. Allen pump, were installed in a separate brick building erected beside the old engine house (Fig. 21). This plant was exactly the same as that at Upwell South (M32A). It was sold in 1999 and the building demolished. Before 1977 the district had been provided with two Allen-Gwynnes electric pumps of 26 and 28 in. diameter [79]. This area is now within March East IDB.

M11 MARCH SECOND – Well Fen (TL 462997)

Between 1848 and 1858 [80] a small beam engine and scoop wheel [81] were installed on the south bank of the Old River Nene, for discharge into that river. The engine was replaced in 1917 by a new 10 hp engine [82], and the scoop wheel was replaced in 1919 by a Dodmans Triton pump at a cost of £350 [83]. The entire plant was replaced in 1935 by an Allen diesel engine at a cost of £730 [84]. This was possibly a two cylinder Allen type S30.

In 1959 this plant was described as disused and consisting of a 38 hp Blackstone single-cylinder horizontal engine driving a 14in. Dodmans Triton pump [85]. This conflicts with the earlier information. It is probable that the Dodmans pump was that installed in 1919.

By that date this district had been amalgamated with the adjoining Euximoor IDB, a district formed before 1947 and containing 1550 acres [86]. The Well Fen plant was then abandoned, and the drainage directed to the Reed Fen Pumping Station at TL 453992, which had been erected in 1958 [87]. This contained twin Allen-Gwynnes electric motors driving 12in. pumps, contained in a small brick building [88].

Euximoor Fen had another pumping station at TL 461998 in 1903 [89] and 1988, of which no details have been obtained.

Fig. 21: March First (M10) engine houses in 1972

Fig. 22: March First (M10) - empty beam loft in 1972

M12 MARCH THIRD – Burrowmoor Fen

A windpump served this district before 1875 [90], and another existed to drain the western part called Botany Bay by 1886 [91].

M12A Burrowmoor (TL 397969)

In 1875 a 12in. pump was provided to assist an existing windpump. It was driven by a steam engine made by Armitage & Ruston of Chatteris [92]. In 1892 the pump was removed and the engine attached to the scoop wheel of the mill [93]. In 1901 the mill was taken down [94] and a 50 hp Campbell oil engine costing £800 [95] installed to drive a 24in. pump, probably an Allen, and probably in a new building (Fig. 23). The old engine was then sold [96]. The Campbell

engine was replaced in 1939 by a 76 hp Blackstone driving the old pump by belt-drive (Fig. 24)[97]. In 1968 two Allen-Gwynnes electric pumps of 18in. diameter were installed. The old plant remained until after 1981 [98], but had been wholly demolished by 1992 [99]. The site of the old plant is now within an industrial estate.

Fig. 23: March Third (M12A) engine house in 1972

Fig. 24: March Third (M12A) - Blackstone engine (MLO)

M12B Botany Bay (TL 381962)

Although a windpump, possibly with an auxiliary engine, existed to drain this area of some 520 acres in 1886 [100], by 1908 the Minutes state that the Botany Bay Estate was drained through March Third by agreement, which was then about to expire. Possibly as a result, it seems that in that year a 25 hp Blackstone oil engine was installed to drive a 12in. Allen pump [101]. In 1960 an electric motor was installed to drive a 14in. Allen-Gwynnes pump [102].

M13 MARCH FOURTH

Besides the main engine M13A, this district contained at least three other small pumping stations, probably all originally private. In 1938 the district amalgamated with Whittlesey Fourth (M39) to become March and Whittlesey IDB [103], although Whittlesey Fourth was not formally disbanded until 1941 [104]. In 1939 two new stations were erected at Stafforths Bridge and Infields Farm, and in 1946 all of the old machinery was discarded. The district is now within Whittlesey IDB.

Fig. 25: March Fourth (M13) engine house in 1972

Fig. 26: March Fourth (M13) after conversion into a dwellinghouse in 1992

M13A March West Fen (TL 381963)

In 1825 [105] a 40 hp Butterley beam engine was installed on the north bank of the River Nene, west of March town. This drove a scoop wheel 28ft. in diameter and 33in. wide, which discharged 70 tpm [106]. Coal consumption was 1 ton 17 cwt. in 12 hours.

This engine was replaced in 1899 by a Marshall twin cylinder compound horizontal engine having cylinders of 10in. and 20in. bore and stroke of 24in. This worked at 100 rpm on 12 psi of steam, and cost £857 [107]. Fosters supplied a boiler of 8ft. 6in. in diameter and 27ft. in length for £370 [108]. This drove a scoop wheel, possibly the original. This plant was supplemented in 1931 by a Parsons paraffin engine driving a 22in. Gwynnes pump housed in a lean-to shed over the drain [109].

The Marshall engine, boiler and scoop wheel were sold in 1940, but the chimney was not then demolished. It had gone by 1972, when the building was in use as a barn (Fig. 25). The Parsons engine had been sold in 1946 [110]. In about 1991 the boiler room was demolished and the engine house was converted into a dwellinghouse (Fig. 26). With the possible exception of such remains as survive at Pode Hole, this is the earliest steam engine house remaining in the Fens.

M13B Stafforths Bridge (TL 369949)

A pumping station existed on this site by 1886. By 1930 a 12 hp Marshall portable (presumably steam) engine existed on this site. It belt-drove an 18in. Amos and Anderson centrifugal pump [111]. If the pump-maker is correctly stated, this pump would have dated from about 1870. It was housed in a boarded and galvanised shed [112]. In 1939 a new station was erected close to the old plant, which was not scrapped until 1946. The new station contained two Ruston type 9XHR diesel engines driving 22in. Gwynnes pumps [113].

M13C Infields Farm (D) (TL 358994)

In 1939 another station, identical to that at Stafforths Bridge [114], was erected on the south bank of the Twenty Foot River. This has survived.

M13D Top Hakes (TL 376961)

This area was originally drained by two windpumps. One was sold in 1852, whilst the other, at TL 376961, survived until after 1887, and probably had an auxiliary steam engine attached. By 1930 a Smithdale pump existed at Top Hakes Farm, on the west bank of the River Nene at TL 375961, housed in a boarded and galvanised shed. By 1942 there was no engine [115], and the plant was abandoned in 1946.

M13E Floods Ferry (D) TL 355941

By 1930 a 6 hp Ruston diesel engine belt-driving a Smithdale pump, and housed in a boarded and galvanised shed, existed on the west bank of the Nene near Flood's Ferry [116]. This seems to have been abandoned in 1946.

M13F and M13G Goosetree (TL 357994 and TF 368003)

The area within March Fourth District which lay north of the Twenty Foot River was called Goosetree. This was isolated from the catchment of the main engine of the district. Two pumping stations, presumably steam-powered, existed within this district in 1886 [117]. They were presumably privately owned.

One of these stations existed in 1849 [118], to drain the Wakelin Estate, but it has not been established which of the two this was. One was at Goosetree Farm (TF 368003), later called Warwick Farm. It existed until after 1924, but there are now no remains. The other was at TL 356994 and existed by 1887[119]. The site is now occupied by a diesel engine house bearing a plaque inscribed "IECC 1936" [120]. Discharge of both of these stations was into the Twenty Foot River, north side. This part of the district was amalgamated with Whittlesey Fourth (M37) in 1940 and is now within Whittlesey IDB.

M14 MARCH FIFTH – Creek Farm (D) (TL 437982)

Although a pumping station is marked on the OS 6in. map of 1886, it was almost certainly a windpump, as shown on Gibbs's map. The district does not seem to have been provided with an engine until 1922, when a diesel engine (possibly an Allen) was procured to drive a Dodmans pump [121]. This plant was replaced in about 1952 by a Ruston diesel engine driving an 18in. Gwynnes pump [122]. Discharge was into the Twenty Foot River, south-west side.

M15 MARCH SIXTH – Norwood or Whitemoor (TL 409006)

A steam engine to drain this district was installed between c. 1900 and 1907 [123] on the Twenty Foot River to replace a windpump [124]. This was possibly a Clayton and Shuttleworth [125], and was clearly very small. The boiler was repaired in 1915. This plant was replaced in 1939 by a 17 hp Ruston diesel engine driving a 14in. Gwynnes pump [126]. This had been replaced by 1977 by an Allen-Gwynnes electric motor driving an 18in. pump [127].

RAMSEY, BURY etc. (1775 Act)

An Act of 1775 [128] provided for the draining of land in Ramsey, Bury, Wistow, Warboys, Somersham, Colne and Pidley with Fenton in Huntingdonshire and Chatteris and Doddington in the Isle of Ely in Cambridgeshire. This area contained 9100 acres.

The Act provided for the drainage of part of the land included in an Act of 1749 which related to Sutton and Mepal [129]. The 1775 Act did not relate to those parishes. The position is further complicated by division of responsibility for the banks into two districts, called the Upper and Lower Districts, and for draining into five districts, all within the overall area.

The drainage districts were as follows (map 3, p.18):

1. Warboys Somersham and Pidley	2000 acres
2. Chatteris and Doddington Westmoor [130]	1050 acres
This district was amalgamated with Ramsey Doddington Fourth Beezlings in 1904.	
3. Warboys	2200 acres
4. Somersham Colne and Pidley – now part of the First District	2700 acres
5. Chatteris (including Acre Fen) – part now forming Nightlayers IDB	2500 acres

The acreages are taken from the Act. The collection of districts under this Act must not be confused with those under Ramsey, Middlemoor etc. (sometimes also called Ramsey, Bury) 1757 Act, or Ramsey, Doddington, etc. 1772 Act. The First, Second, Third and Fourth Districts have now been amalgamated and called Warboys, Somersham and Pidley IDB.

M16 FIRST AND THIRD DISTRICTS – Tick Fen and High Fen (TL 351880)

The First District, Tick Fen, may have been drained by a steam engine before 1887 [131]. The Third District was drained by Crease Mill [132], near the Forty Foot Drain, until 1906 when the two districts were amalgamated to form Warboys United District.

In 1908 a 75 hp Gwynnes steam engine was erected at Puddocks Bridge driving a 36in. Gwynnes pump delivering 72 tpm at a 9ft. lift [133].

This plant was replaced in 1939 by a pair of Ruston type 9HRC diesel engines each driving a 33in. Gwynnes pumps. These engines were scrapped in 1992 and the building demolished, but the pumps remain outside and uncovered. At that time an electric station was installed on part of the old engine room floor slab [134]. Discharge was into the Forty Foot Drain.

M17 SECOND DISTRICT – Chatteris and Doddington –
Westmoor (TL 370883)

This district lay north-west of Chatteris and was bounded on its north by the Forty Foot Drain. It had been provided with a steam engine, possibly made by Armitage & Ruston, and scoop wheel [135] by about 1881 [136]. The engine was replaced by a Ruston & Proctor, installed by Fowell of St. Ives, in 1893 [137]. The windpump was then truncated and the scoop wheel was worked by the engine alone. Discharge was into the Forty Foot Drain.

In 1904 the district was amalgamated with Beezlings Fen, which was Ramsey, Doddington (1772 Act) Fourth District, and the combined area was named Westmoor and Beezlings. The Westmoor plant then took the water from Beezlings until a new plant was built near Carter's Bridge in 1920 (see M3H). The Westmoor plant then became redundant and has been wholly demolished. An electric pump now stands on the site.

M18 FOURTH DISTRICT – Warboys,
Somersham and Pidley (TL 352817)

This district was originally drained by two windpumps. One of these, the Somersham Mill at TL 355821, was built in 1793 and survived until 1920. The other, called Pidley Fen Mill, was built soon after 1775 and rebuilt in 1839. A 12 hp Ruston & Proctor portable steam engine was installed at this mill in 1884 to drive the scoop wheel and the windmill ceased to be used.

This plant, including its buildings, was scrapped in 1918, and the portable engine seems to have been moved to the other mill, but did not survive for long. At Pidley Fen, a 75 hp Gwynnes compound steam engine was installed, having high and low pressure cylinders 9in. and 17in. diameter respectively, with a stroke of 10in. [138]. This drove a 30in. (possibly 36in.) Gwynnes pump having a delivery of 70 tpm [139]. Steam was provided at 150 psi by a single Lancashire boiler 22ft. long and 6ft. in diameter supplied by Meldrum Brothers.

This plant was demolished in 1944, not least because the boiler room had subsided badly. It was replaced by a 102 hp Ruston & Hornsby diesel engine driving a 33in. Hathorn Davey pump in a new building.

This was superseded in 1981 [140] by an electric pump with a new outfall at the side of the old building. This building has been retained, but the old outlet has been filled in. The stump of the old chimney can be seen in the bank to the south of the diesel engine house.

This district was often called Somersham and Pidley Fourth, but is now within Warboys, Somersham and Pidley IDB. The engine was called Somersham.

Discharge is into Fenton Lode, otherwise called Twenty Foot River. It should be noted that to operate at times of high water, this station relied upon the pump at Chatteris Dock (M20) to discharge the water from the Twenty Foot into the Forty Foot Drain.

M19 FIFTH DISTRICT – Chatteris and Doddington

This district was divided into two parts, one south of Chatteris called Acre Fen, and the other north of Chatteris called Nightlayers Fen [141]. Each had its own drainage plant.

M19A Acre Fen (TL 384853)

This fen, sometimes also called Warboys Fifth District, was originally drained by a windpump. This existed before 1872, when the scoop wheel was lowered by 18in., and in 1874 the scoops were lengthened from 12in. to 14in. [142]. A portable steam engine seems to have been installed to work the mill when necessary in about 1885. The fire box of this was repaired in 1924 [143] and the top of the mill was removed in 1926 [144], when a new roof was fitted and the scoop wheel cased, at a cost of £36 [145]. This plant still existed in 1931 [146], but was replaced in about 1936 by a Ruston 6XHR diesel engine (no. 199762) coupled to a 20in. Gwynnes pump. In turn this was removed in about 1990 [147]. Discharge was into Fenton Lode (Twenty Foot Drain). This area is now within Warboys, Somersham and Pidley IDB.

M19B Nightlayers (TL 393873)

This fen was also originally drained by a windpump [148], which existed in 1876 [149]. In 1883 a 12 hp portable steam engine was fitted to the existing wheel [150]. This was sold to Ruston & Proctor for £40 in 1904 when they supplied a new steam engine in a new building at a cost of £475 [151]. This drove a scoop wheel and had one boiler. This plant was replaced in 1920 by a 50 bhp Campbell oil engine costing £895 [152]. This drove a 22in. Gwynnes pump delivering 53 tpm. By 1953 this had been replaced by a 102 hp engine (Possibly a Lister) and Gwynnes pump [153], which has since been removed. Discharge was into Fenton Lode. The district is now called Nightlayers IDB.

M20 CHATTERIS LOWER DISTRICT – Chatteris Dock (TL 395881)

This district was created by the Act of 1775 to be responsible for the embankments within the lower part of the five drainage districts. It covered some 5000 acres, and was also known as Chatteris and Somersham Lower District.

To fulfil its role, it was obliged by the Act to erect mills at the junction of the Twenty Foot Drain with the Forty Foot Drain north of Chatteris, and later to provide a sluice there to allow water back into the Twenty Foot in times of drought. The two mills which were erected were sold in 1850 when the Forty Foot Drain was widened.

The Act also provided that the Fourth District was not to use its mills at any time when the Lower District mills were disabled from working. The Fourth District Minutes evidence that this occurred in 1895 and may have prompted installation of a new engine.

It was in 1862 that a 30 hp steam engine was erected to drive a scoop wheel. This cost a total of £1223 [154]. This plant was known as Chatteris Dock Pumping Station. It must not be confused with that of Nightlayers (M19B) nearby [155].

This was replaced in 1899 by a 40 hp Ruston & Proctor compound steam engine and locomotive boiler driving a scoop wheel 28ft. in diameter and 42in. wide with a 5ft. dip. The engine cost £909 and the wheel, made by Gimson & Co. of Leicester, £483. The total cost of the plant was £2895 [156].

In 1940/41 this was replaced by two Ruston diesel engines each driving a 30in. Gwynnes pump delivering 160 tpm against a 9ft. head [157]. This was on a slightly different site over the Twenty Foot itself, and has since been demolished.

RAMSEY, MIDDLEMOOR, Hunts. (1757 Act)

An Act of 1757 [158] provided for drainage of land in the parishes of Ramsey, Bury, Wistow, Warboys, Farcet, Standground and Water Newton and Doddington. This area contained 9118 acres and was divided into the following districts (map 4, p.19):

1. Ramsey Hollow	3857 acres
2. Stocking Fen	250 acres
3. The Bill	234 acres
4. Middlemoor	2991 acres
5. Lodesend	543 acres
6. Mereside Lots	1213 acres

M21 FIRST DISTRICT – Ramsey Hollow (TL 335879)

This district originally contained five windpumps. Following construction of the Middle Level Main Drain in 1844, a further Act of 1848 empowered the Middle Level Commissioners to carry out a comprehensive programme of widening and deepening the main drains and rivers in the Level. Four of the Ramsey Hollow mills, standing on the bank of the Forty Foot Drain, impeded part of these works. In 1850 the Middle Level agreed to pay £1000 to the Ramsey Hollow Board as compensation for removal of these mills [159]. It was then resolved to remove the fifth mill as well, and to instal a steam engine. Extensive expenditure on repairs to all of these mills between 1842 and 1849 [160] indicates that this position had not been contemplated.

Tenders for the new plant were sought and that of J. & E. Headly of Cambridge in the sum of £2262 was accepted [161]. A 25 hp beam engine was installed on the south bank of the Forty Foot near the site of the demolished Ash Drain Mill. This drove a scoop wheel 28ft. in diameter by 18 ins. wide [162], which was lowered by 18in. in 1879 by Headlys. The machinery was started in December 1850. Two boilers were provided. These were renewed in 1879 [163] and again in 1908, when Lancashire boilers were chosen at a cost of £585 [164]. Delivery was 40 tpm against a head of 5ft. and coal consumption was 25 cwt per 12 hours [165].

This plant had been removed between 1910 and 1936 and replaced by a "horizontal with Corliss valves and a steam drifter type compound vertical" [166].

In about 1948 a pair of Ruston engines driving 33in. Gwynnes pumps were installed. Later an Allen-Gwynnes electric motor driving a 24in. pump was provided [167].

M22 SECOND DISTRICT – Stocking Fen (TL 286863)

The windpump serving this small fen was sold in 1855 and thereafter it seems to have had no powered drainage until 1890 when a water wheel was erected on the east side of High Lode, just north of Ramsey [168]. As payment was made to hire an engine to drive this, it may be assumed that no fixed engine was installed. By 1930 [169] a permanent station seems to have been established, and by 1953 this contained a 22 hp oil engine driving a Gwynnes pump [170]. This has since been demolished, and by 2004 only a pile of bricks marked the site.

M23 THIRD DISTRICT – The Bill (TL 286873)

In 1857 the windpump of this district was taken down and a centrifugal pump driven by hired engines installed [171]. In 1879 the Commissioners resolved to enter into an Agreement with the New Fen Commissioners and Edward Fellowes for the district to be drained through the New Fen District to the Ugg Mere Mill[172]. This does not seem to have been implemented, for in 1880 the Commissioners agreed to instal a scoop wheel to be provided by Green of Yaxley and driven by a portable engine [173].

In 1897 it was agreed to instal an 8 hp Ruston & Proctor semi-portable engine to drive the existing wheel by belt-drive. This cost £148 [174].

This district was incorporated into the newly-formed Ramsey Upwood and Great Raveley IDB in 1933, and the drainage was directed to the Ramsey New Fen pumping station (M30A). The scoop wheel seems to have been replaced at some stage by a pump, because this was removed in 1941 to the New Fen station and re-erected there. At that time the engine, boiler and buildings were sold. There are no remains of this plant.

M24 FOURTH DISTRICT – Middlemoor (TL 264873)

Until 1870 Middlemoor was drained by three windpumps, two discharging into Bevil's Leam and one into the Old River Nene, north bank. This was replaced in that year by a 25 hp [175] Easton, Amos & Anderson steam engine on the same site. This had two cylinders, each 13in. bore by 2ft. stroke. Steam was provided by two Cornish boilers supplied by Smithdales of Acle [176]. Each was 20ft. 1$\frac{1}{2}$in. long by 5ft. diameter, with a flue 2ft. 9in. diameter. The chimney was 50ft. in height. A house for the engine driver was incorporated into the building, as at Whittlesey Mere, (M38A), and at the surviving Westonzoyland plant in Somerset [177]. The entire plant, including buildings, cost £2350. The pump was a vertical centrifugal of the Appold type.

The date of demolition of this plant has not been traced, but was after 1936. In about 1941 two Ruston 9XHR diesel engines driving 27in. Gwynnes pumps [178] were provided, and there are now no traces of the original building. These diesel engines are now only used as stand-bys to an electric pump. In 1963 an electric plant was installed at Daintree Farm (TL 239902) to drain the western part of this district.

M25 FIFTH DISTRICT – Lodesend (TL 289875)

The windpump of this district was taken down in 1857. A centrifugal pump driven by hired engines was installed in its place [179]. This station survived until 1925 when a 25 hp Blackstone diesel engine was installed to drive an 18 in. Gwynnes pump [180]. Discharge was into the Old River Nene.

M26 SIXTH DISTRICT – Mereside (TL 302892)

A pumping station serving this district existed by 1877 [181], but no details of this have been traced. In 1938 two 54 hp Blackstone oil engines were installed, each driving a 27 in. Mirrlees pump housed in a new building (Fig. 27)[182]. These became a stand-by to an Allen-Gwynnes 21in. electric pump erected before 1977. Discharge is into the Old River Nene, west side. This district was amalgamated with Whittlesey Glassmoor before 1948 to form Glassmoor and Mereside IDB.

Fig. 27: Ramsey Middlemoor Sixth (M26) engine house

M27 RAMSEY, UPWOOD AND GREAT RAVELEY

This Board was created in 1933 by an amalgamation of the districts of Ramsey Upwood and Great Raveley with Ramsey Middlemoor Third (The Bill - M23) and the areas of Ugg Mere, Upwood Fen, Ramsey New Fen and School Farm (map 5, p.20) [183]. It contains the entire area south of the old River Nene between Ramsey High Lode on the east and Great Raveley Drain on the west. Initially it did not include the area of Upwood Common, but this was incorporated in 1936. The new Board inherited five pumping stations, of which three were privately owned. Great Ouse River Board instructed it to provide a new pumping station at Green Dyke Bank.

M27A Ramsey and Bury New Fen (TL 266872)

By Act of 1804 [184] a district was created to drain Ramsey New Fen, lying between The Bill and Ugg Mere Drain. It seems that at one time this area may have been drained by Ugg Mere Mill, but a windpump seems to have existed on this site at an early stage [185], and an engine by 1905 [186]. By 1935 the boiler needed repair [187]. In 1939 a horizontal single – cylinder Ruston diesel engine type 9HR (no. 198169) [188] was installed presumably to drive an existing pump, because in 1941 the pump from The Bill (M26) was resited at this station [189]. In 1949 Gwynnes supplied a 24in. pump to replace this [190]. This remained in good condition (Fig. 28), and was used as a stand-by for an electric pump, in 2004, but is now designated for demolition. Discharge is into the south side of the Old River Nene. This station should not be confused with New Fen pumping station (S8B) in Feltwell New Fen Southery District.

Fig. 28: Ramsey   New Fen (M27A) engine house in 2004

M27B School Farm (TL 272871)

By 1926 [191] a plant existed on the south bank of the old River Nene about a mile west of The Bill engine. This was clearly private [192]. Although it was regarded as still of some slight use in 1947 [193], the engine and shed were sold in 1951 [194], and there are no traces of this plant on the site.

M27C Ugg Mere (TL 249876)

In 1876 a 14 hp steam engine made by Smithdale of Norwich was installed inside an existing windpump. A new scoop wheel, 28ft. in diameter, was provided, and the engine only used when the windpump could not work [195]. This was erected by Lord de Ramsey, and was thus privately owned. It may have ceased to operate in 1916, but more probably survived until 1935, by which time it belonged to the IDB [196]. The shell of the windpump remains. Discharge was into the Old River Nene, south side.

M27D Green Dyke Bank (D) (TL 237863)

This station (Fig. 29)was established in 1934 on the east side of Great Raveley Drain at its junction with Green Dyke Bank. It contained an Allen two-cylinder diesel engine type S30 (no. K1/43187) coupled to a 22in. Allen Conqueror pump (Fig. 30). This was housed in a corrugated iron shed. In turn, this was replaced in 1954 by a Ruston three-cylinder vertical diesel engine type 3VCB (no. 369513) coupled to a Gwynnes submersible pump. This plant was housed in a separate brick building. Later an electric motor was mounted above the pump. The Allen engine was removed in 1993 [197]. This plant was also known as Ramsey Heights engine.

Fig. 29: Ramsey – Green Dyke Bank (M27D) engine house in 1993

M27E Lotting Fen (TL 240849)

This small fen, of some 500 acres, was constituted as a separate district by an Act of 1850 [198]. It lay between Ugg Mere Drove on the east, Great Raveley Drain on the west and the south bank of Green Dyke on the north. In 1874 a windpump was erected on the north bank of the catchwater drain feeding into Great Raveley Drain. This was destroyed in a gale within a year. Smithdale of Norwich was then employed to erect a new mill. This had a scoop wheel 28ft. in diameter and an auxiliary 16 hp steam engine with one vertical boiler [199]. This survived until after 1912, when the sails were removed and the wheel was driven by the steam engine [200]. This was possibly replaced by an oil engine [201]. The entire buildings and machinery were sold in 1935 [202].

M27F Upwood Common (TL 234843)

By 1902 [203] a water wheel existed on the east of Great Raveley Drain, presumably driven by a hired portable engine. By 1926 this was described as a pumping station belonging to Huntingdonshire County Council [204]. This probably contained a Blackstone diesel engine driving a 16in. Gwynnes pump [205]. In 1936 this was purchased by the new IDB for £700 [206], and was still operating in 1949 [207].

Fig. 30: Ramsey – Green Dyke Bank (M27D) - Allen engine

M28 RANSON MOOR

This district was formed as the Fifth District under the Ramsey, Doddington Act 1772, and only later became Ransonmoor IDB (map 4, p.19). Previously it had sometimes been called Doddington Fifth.

M28A Flood's Ferry (TL 354935)

A pumping station was established in 1850 at Flood's Ferry to replace a windpump. This discharged into the south side of the old River Nene. This contained a beam engine made by Beecroft Butler & Co. of Kirkstall Forge, near Leeds, and the engine house was built by R. Freeman of Ely. It was first started on 4 February 1851 [208]. The engine was fitted with Varlay's patent double-action eccentric motion, and drove a scoop wheel [209]. There were two boilers, of which one was replaced in 1891 by J. & J. Horsfield of Dewsbury at a cost of £399 [210].

This plant was supplemented in 1913 by a 75 hp Gwynnes steam engine driving a 30 in. Gwynnes pump delivering 75 tpm. This cost £1454, together with the cost of a separate building. A single boiler was provided [211]. The beam engine had been abandoned by 1917 [212] and was probably removed when a Blackstone diesel engine was installed in 1937 at a cost of £2047 [213]. The 1913 steam engine survived until at least 1945, when coal was still being ordered [214], but the entire plant seems to have been closed and sold in 1952. The 1850 building survives, altered and without chimney (Fig. 31), and now in use as a boat-builder's yard. By 2004 the building and yard had been securely fenced off so as to preclude any close inspection. This plant should not be confused with the other plant so named in March Fourth District, (M13E).

Fig. 31: Ranson Moor (M28A) engine house in 1972

M28B   Ransonmoor (D) (TL 358922)

In 1952 a new station was established on the east bank of the Old River Nene about one mile south of the original plant. This consisted of a vertical Ruston diesel engine driving a 30in. Gwynnes pump. In about 1966 a 120 hp Allen-Gwynnes electric motor was installed there to drive a 30in. axial-flow pump [215].

M29   STILTON – New Barn (TL 201908)

This district was created by Act of 1810 [216]. A pumping station, which must have been steam-powered, existed by 1887 [217] at a place called New Barn, discharging into the south side of Yaxley Lode. This may have been replaced in 1913 by an Allen steam engine driving a Smithdale pump delivering about 33 tpm, in turn replaced by a diesel engine in about 1934 [218]. This area was incorporated into Holmewood & Stilton IDB in 1920 [219].

M30   SUTTON AND MEPAL (TL 442822)

This district was created by Act of 1749 [220], and comprised some 10,500 acres (map 7, p.22) [221]. An 80 hp Butterley beam engine was installed in 1840 to drive a scoop wheel 34ft. in diameter by 48in. wide, said to discharge 120 tpm [222]. The building was similar to those at Ten Mile Bank and Hundred Foot (S14A and B) (Fig. 32). This replaced six windpumps. Discharge was into the Counter Drain running parallel to the Old Bedford River.

This plant was replaced in 1926 by two 250 hp Vickers-Petter four-cylinder vertical two-stroke hot-bulb oil engines driving 42in. Gwynnes pumps each discharging 150 tpm, and housed in a separate building (Fig. 32). These engines did not prove to be very reliable. On 21st January

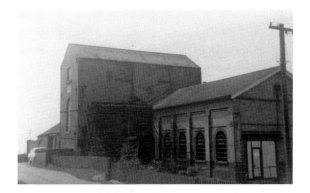

Fig. 32: Sutton &
Mepal (M30) engine
houses in 1972

Fig. 33: Sutton &
Mepal (M30) -
Ruston engine

Fig. 34: Sutton &
Mepal (M30) - Brush
engine

1939 the engine on no. 1 set disintegrated while being started, one whole cylinder breaking off, almost certainly due to water entering the cylinder overnight from a leaking head gasket. This was a known failing of these engines. It was replaced by a Brush four-cylinder horizontal opposed diesel engine type 4M13 having a bore of 13¾in. and stroke of 20in. (Fig. 34). This was purchased second-hand from the makers, having been made in 1939. The nominal rating was 380 bhp at 333 rpm, but this was reduced to 250 bhp at 250 rpm to be compatible with the existing pump, to which it was coupled direct. A wooden extension to the old building had to be constructed to accommodate this engine. It is not now used due to possible subsidence of a corner of the building.

The other Vickers-Petter engine was removed in 1947 and replaced by a Ruston five-cylinder vertical diesel engine type 5VEB (no. 282122) (Fig. 33). This is rated at 300 bhp at 500 rpm, and drives the 1927 pump by 20 V-belts. Although electric pumps were installed in about 1994, the Ruston is still required to supplement them during floods [223]. These engines are housed in the original building which remains, without chimney, and can be seen clearly from the A142 road.

Like Manea and Welney, this district declined to join the Middle Level in 1848 because it had its own pumping station, but in recent years it has been managed by the Middle Level.

UPWELL, Cambs. and Norfolk

The fens of this area were drained under an Act of 1801 [224]. This divided the land into two districts, partly in Norfolk and partly in Cambridgeshire, being separated by Popham's Eau (map 8, p.23). The first contained about 2400 acres, of which 180 acres was transferred to Churchfield and Plawfield IDB when that Board was formed in 1934. The second district contained about 9000 acres.

M31 UPWELL NORTH (TF 533009)

A beam engine driving a scoop wheel was erected in 1854 on the north bank of Popham's Eau, into which it discharged. The wheel was 22ft. in diameter. This was scrapped in about 1920 [225]. By 1936 there was a 45 hp Petter oil engine driving a 20in. pump on this site [226], This has since been demolished and there are no remains. In 1944 it was agreed that a new pumping station be constructed to pump into the High Level of the Middle Level Main Drain, at a cost of £5500. This seems to have been completed by 1946 [227] The district is now called Nordelph IDB.

M32A UPWELL SOUTH – Popham's Eau (TL 545010)

In 1877 a pumping station was erected on the south bank of Popham's Eau next to a windpump which had a scoop wheel 20ft. in diameter and 2ft. wide. The latter remained in use until 1887 [228]. The engine was a 40 hp horizontal high pressure condensing compound supplied by Appleby & Co., with a high pressure cylinder of 10in. diameter by 20in. stroke and a low pressure cylinder 20 by 20in. The flywheel was 9ft. in diameter. Steam was supplied by two Cornish boilers 20ft. by 5ft., fitted with Galloway tubes. Coal consumption was 2 tons in 12 hours.

This engine drove a wrought iron scoop wheel 24ft. in diameter and 4ft. wide, with 18 curved iron scoops (Fig. 35)[229], being the only such wheel in the Bedford Level known to have had curved scoops. The wheel discharged 120 tpm against a normal head and dip of 8ft. 6in. The chimney was 60ft. in height. The total cost of the plant was £2680, of which £700 was for the buildings [230].

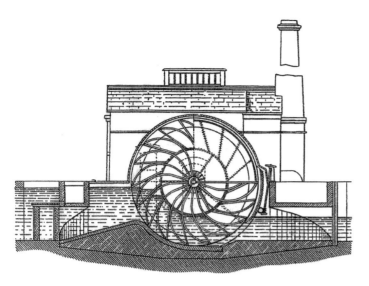

Fig. 35: Upwell South (M32A) – diagram of scoop wheel (Wheeler 1868)

Fig. 36: Upwell South (M32A) engine house in 2002

Fig. 37: Upwell South (M32A) - 1932 Allen plant (MLO)

This plant is said to have been scrapped in 1913, and replaced by a Marshall tandem horizontal [231]. By 1933 this was not being insured. The chimney was felled in 1936 and the engine sold in 1938 [232].

In 1932 a new building (Fig. 36) was constructed to house two Allen three-cylinder diesel engines driving Allen pumps (Fig. 37). This machinery was similar to that at March Binnimore Fen (M10). This plant had been removed by 2002, although the engine house remained in use as a store, and there were slight remains of the old engine house next to this [233].

M32B UPWELL SOUTH – Bedlam Bridge (TL 468947)

A windpump with auxiliary engine existed on the east side of the Sixteen Foot Drain near Bedlam Bridge in 1887 [234]. This was replaced in 1948 [235] by two Ruston horizontal diesel engines type 8HR (nos. 255275 and 260382), driving a 20in. Gwynnes pump. By 1988 [236] only one pump was connected, but the plant was well-maintained (Fig. 38). By 2003 one engine had been removed, and two electric 18in. pumps had been installed. The earlier plant may have been slightly south of the later.

Fig. 38: Upwell IDB, Bedlam Bridge (M32B) engine house in 1992

Fig. 39: Upwell IDB, north of Bedlam Bridge (M32C) engine house in 1992

M32C UPWELL SOUTH – North of Bedlam Bridge (TL 475957)

Another station existed on the east bank of the Sixteen Foot Drain, half a mile north of Bedlam Bridge by 1903 [237]. It replaced a windpump on this site [238]. This was disused and empty by 1988, but seemed to have contained a diesel engine and centrifugal pump [239]. By 1992 this had been converted into a house (Fig. 39). No further information has been obtained.

M33 WHITTLESEY MERE, Holme, Huntingdonshire

Despite its name, this mere lay as to two-thirds in the parish of Holme and one-third in the parish of Farcet in Huntingdonshire and had no connection with the parish of Whittlesey in Cambridgeshire. In 1786 the waters of the mere covered 1870 acres. It was $3^{1}/_{2}$ miles long from east to west and $2^{1}/_{2}$ miles broad from north to south, being between 2 and 7ft. deep [240]. The Middle Level Act of 1844 enabled construction of the Middle Level Main Drain from the Sixteen Foot Drain to the River Great Ouse at St. Germans, completed in 1848 [241]. This offered the facility to drain the mere.

Before this, an encroachment had been made upon the mere and a steam engine erected to drain a new enclosure of about 500 acres into the mere [242]. This almost certainly drove a scoop wheel, but no details of the nature of the plant or its position have been traced.

The 1844 Act also enabled the New Cut to be formed around the north of the mere from Conquest Lode in Yaxley to Bevill's Leam in 1851. Gravity drainage of the mere was achieved in the same year, but pumping was essential to maintain the drainage.

M33A   Whittlesey Mere Main Pumping Station (TL 237903)

In 1851, W. Wells of Holme Wood, owner of most of the land in Holme and Stilton and the mere, installed a pumping station on the eastern edge of the mere (Fig. 40). This discharged into the Old River Nene and thence to Bevill's Leam. The engine was a 24 hp double-cylinder Easton & Amos with steam supplied by one boiler at 40 psi and vacuum of $13^{1}/_{2}$ lbs.

Appold's centrifugal pump, as exhibited at the Great Exhibition of 1851, was driven by this engine. The fan was 4ft. in diameter [243]. At a 5ft. lift, this discharged 67 tpm. The pump was twice lowered until the lift was increased to over 9ft. The fan is now in the Science Museum, South Kensington.

This plant was removed in 1877. Wheeler [244] describes its replacement as follows:

> Easton & Anderson erected in their place a high-pressure compound condensing beam engine, with expansion gear, of 65 nhp making about 36 rpm with 60 psi steam. The boilers consist of one single-flued and one double-flued Cornish boiler. The pump, which is placed in a well outside the engine-house, is driven by a double set of motions, the first set consisting of a toothing on the fly-wheel driving a pinion, which actuates a horizontal shaft for driving a wheel geared into a bevil-wheel on the vertical shaft of the pump. This is hung by an onion-bearing to a cast-iron frame bolted to the top of the pump-well, which is formed with a wrought-iron cylinder fixed in the centre of the sluice connecting the main drain with the river.... This sluice is 12ft. wide on the inlet side and 6ft. on the delivery side. The fan is a single inlet fan of 6ft. diameter by 16in. deep, and is speeded to run up to 104 rpm when on a lift of 11ft. The quantity of water delivered is 96 tpm, or on a lift of 7ft. 6in., with a speed of 96 rpm of the pump, 155 tpm. The engine and boiler are contained in a brick building. The chimney shaft is 53ft. high and 3ft. diameter at the top inside. The cost of the machinery was approximately £3500, plus the value of the old machinery. [245]

Fig. 40: Whittlesey
Mere (M33A) engine
houses in 1972

Fig. 41: Whittlesey
Mere (M33A) - Allen
diesel plant (MLO)

This survived until 1924 when it was replaced by a pair of 24in. centrifugal pumps driven by Allen two-cylinder two-stroke hot bulb oil engines (Fig. 41), and in turn by an electric pump in 1962 [246]. The Allen engines were scrapped in 1971.

The original engine house survived until after 1972 (Fig. 40), but has since been totally demolished [247]. In 1920 the drainage of this land was taken over by Holmewood and Stilton IDB.

M33B Whittlesey Mere – Black Ham (TL 211903)

In 1893 a small pumping station was installed on the western side of the former mere to assist in its drainage. This was erected by Lord de Ramsey, then owner of the mere ground. By that date, the mere had become a basin, leaving the original pump at its highest point [248]. A new drain was cut from the lowest part of the mere to the north, discharging into the waterway called Black Ham or Ham River.

Fig. 42: Holmewood &
Stilton, Black Ham (M33B)
remains of engine house in
2002

Fig. 43: Whittlesey Second,
Blackbush (M35A) engine
house in 1993

The engine was a 20 hp Clayton & Shuttleworth steam engine supplied with steam by a single boiler at 60 psi [249], burning imported peat. [250]. This drove a scoop wheel 30ft. in diameter, made by Green of Yaxley.

This was partly demolished in 1913 – 14, and replaced by a Worthington-Simpson 18in. centrifugal pump driven by an oil engine. This was followed by a 30hp Allen diesel engine in about 1940, which last operated in 1967 [251] and had been demolished by 1980. By 2003 the only remains were one wall and the engine floor slab (Fig. 42).

WHITTLESEY, Cambridgeshire

Five drainage districts were created within the parish of Whittlesey by an Act of 1749 [252]. These contained a total of 9750 acres (map 6, p.21). The name of this parish is variously spelt with a 'y' or an 'a' at the end. The former spelling has been adopted throughout this work, except where a cited publication uses the variant.

M34 FIRST DISTRICT – King's Delph (TL 251962)

This district contained 350 acres. By 1886 it was served by a windpump on Canters Dole Drain [253]. This may have been supplied with an auxiliary steam engine. The plant was described as old in 1938, and was sold in 1941 for £20 [254]. It was not replaced. Discharge was into Canters Dole Drain and thence to King's Dyke by way of a sluice.

M35 SECOND DISTRICT

This district contained 1400 acres and was served by two drainage plants.

M35A Blackbush (TL 261925)

A horizontal steam engine was erected near Pondersbridge in about 1870. This was possbly made by Foster and had a single cylinder 10in. by 20in., and a flywheel 9ft. in diameter. Steam was provided at 40 psi from a Cornish boiler made by Hawksley Wild & Co. Ltd. of Brightside Boiler Works, Sheffield. The engine was geared 2.39:1 to a Smithdale turbine pump driven by gear drive until 1937 when chain drive was installed [255]. Discharge was into a long outfall drain leading to Bevill's Leam.

This may have been preceded by a beam engine of 1848, of which no details have been traced. The plant was often called Blackbush No. 2, but this seems to have been derived from the number of the district rather than having been the second engine on the site.

This plant was replaced in 1939 by Underwoods Farm Station (M 39A), but the machinery seems to have survived unused until after 1957 [256], but had been removed by about 1970 [257]. The old engine house remains in use as a store (Fig. 43). The chimney was demolished in about 1970.

M35B SECOND DISTRICT – Micklewaite (TL 291954)

By 1886 a pumping station existed on the south side of Whittlesey Dyke, into which it discharged, possibly being a windpump with an auxiliary steam engine. By 1940 this was reported as being unfit for use until the steam pipes had been repaired [258], and a tractor was being used to drive the pump. The date of removal is unknown, but was probably in 1942 [259].

M36 THIRD DISTRICT – Wype (TL 305957)

This district contained 1000 acres, and the pumping plant was called Wype Pumping Station. Until 1880 it was served by a windpump. In that year it was adapted so that the scoop wheel could be driven by a portable steam engine [260]. In 1897 [261] a 12 hp Marshall steam engine with one boiler was installed to drive the scoop wheel, which was replaced by H.J. Varlow of Benwick in 1900 [262]. In 1903 the scoop wheel was replaced by a pump supplied by Smithdale. This was reconditioned by them in 1947 [263]. Ministry consent to instal an electric motor to drive this pump was refused in 1948 [264] and the old plant continued in use until 1958, when the machinery was sold for £100 [265], although the engine had been uncoupled in 1956 and a pulley fitted to the existing pump to enable it to be operated by a 40 hp tractor [266]. This and Ironsides (M38) were most probably the last steam-powered drainage engines to operate in the Fens. Before 1977 an Allen-Gwynnes electric motor and 20in. pump had been installed on this site. The district was amalgamated with Kingsland (M41) in 1948 to form Whittlesey and Kingsland IDB, which is now part of March and Whittlesey IDB.

M37 FOURTH DISTRICT – The Turves (TL 338941)

This district contained 2000 acres. By 1886 [267] it was drained by two windpumps. In 1938 it was amalgamated with March Fourth District (M13) to become March and Whittlesey IDB, and the entire drainage system was redirected. It is now within Whittlesey IDB.

M37A Duncombe's or Beeby's (TL 341979)

A pumping station existed on this site by 1887. By 1930 this station contained an 18in. Dodmans Triton pump with belting, housed in a boarded and galvanised shed. No engine existed by 1942 [268] and the pump was probably driven by a tractor. This plant was sold in 1946 and the wheel race infilled in 1953 [269]. In 1992 an electric plant was installed at TL 347985. Discharge was into Bevill's Leam.

M37B Burnt House (TL 337941)

A pumping station seems to have existed on this site in 1903 [270]. By 1942 it contained a locomotive type steam engine direct coupled to a Smithdale pump said to date from 1921. It was housed in a galvanised engine shed [271]. This plant was sold in 1946, and there are no remains on site. Discharge was into Whittlesey Dyke.

M38 FIFTH DISTRICT – Ironsides (TL 321950)

This district formed the eastern part of the area called Glassmoor and contained 5000 acres. By 1834 it was drained by two windpumps called Ironsides and Low Mills respectively [272]. Low Mill was sold in 1868 [273].

In 1876 a 12 hp Clayton & Shuttleworth steam engine was installed at Ironsides as an auxiliary to the windpump. With engine shed, this cost a total of £439 [274]. This seems to have been a portable or semi-portable engine. In 1901 it was agreed that the sails be taken off the mill and sold [275]. The engine was scrapped in 1914 [276]. In the previous year a 30 nhp Smithdale horizontal condensing steam engine with one boiler had been installed. This drove a 22in. Smithdale pump claimed to deliver 67 tpm [277].

This was replaced in 1955 by two Ruston diesel engines each driving an 18in. Gwynnes vertical spindle axial flow pump in a new building [278]. The crankshaft of one of these engines broke in 1970 and the engine was replaced by a Perkins diesel engine [279], to be followed in 1975 [280] by the same occurrence and solution for the second engine. In 1979 electric motors were placed above the existing engines to provide alternative power [281]. The chimney survived until after 1967 [282]. The 1955 building survives, but appears to house only an electric pump [283]. Discharge was into Whittlesey Dyke.

M39 WHITTLESEY AND FARCET IDB

In 1937 the First and Second Districts were amalgamated with Farcet Fen and New Farcet Fen to form Whittlesey and Farcet IDB, the total area of the new district being some 10,000 acres. In 1941 all of the existing plant within the new district was scrapped and three new stations provided to replace them.

M39A Underwoods (D) (TL 272931)

This station contained two Ruston 9XHR engines each driving a 22in. Gwynnes pump discharging 40 tpm. Discharge was into Bevill's Leam. The area was originally a private estate.

M39B Tebbits Bridge (D) (TL 252918)

This station, established close to M7A, contained two 9XHR Ruston engines each driving a 22in. Gwynnes pump discharging 40 tpm. Discharge was into Bevill's Leam. See also M7A.

M39C Lords Farm (D) (TL 203909)

This station was established to drain Yaxley and Farcet Fens. It contained a 57 hp Ruston engine driving a 20in. Gwynnes pump discharging into Yaxley Lode.

M40 WHITTLESEY – Glassmoor (TL 275930)

This private district, being part of the Childers Estate, contained 5500 acres (map 6, p.21) [284]. In 1859 [285] a pair of single-cylinder Easton & Amos grasshopper steam engines of 25 hp each were erected on the south side of Bevill's Leam. Each cylinder had a bore of 15ins. and stroke of 24ins. These drove a vertical spindle centrifugal pump [286]. Steam was provided by two boilers, each 6ft by 20ft., at 30 to 40 psi. Average lift was 5ft., rising occasionally in floods to as much as 8ft. The engine made 47 rpm to the pump's 116 rpm. The pump had a 4ft. fan, 13$\frac{1}{4}$ins. deep. The chimney is about 70ft. high [287]. This machinery was scrapped in about 1942, without replacement on this site, but the building and chimney survive and were being converted into a house in 2003 (Fig. 44). By 1948 this area had been incorporated into Ramsey Sixth Mereside District (1757 Act) to become Glassmoor and Mereside IDB.

Fig. 44: Whittlesey, Glassmoor (M40) engine house.

M41 WHITTLESEY – Kingsland Coates (TL 343984)

The parish of Coates was originally within Whittlesey, only being created as a separate entity in 1850. It included an estate of 1486 acres called Kingsland, which was owned by the Childers family (map 6, p.21). This became Kingsland Drainage District in 1913 when the trustees of the estate conveyed all of the main drains and land used for drainage to the new Board [288].

In 1878 the estate built a pumping station on the south side of Bevill's Leam into which it discharged. This contained a single-cylinder Easton and Anderson grasshopper beam engine. The cylinder was 13in. by 27$\frac{1}{2}$ins. and the flywheel was 8$\frac{1}{2}$ft. in diameter. A slide valve with Meyer expansion valve was fitted. It ran at 65 rpm, with steam supplied by a single boiler at 65 psi. This drove an Easton and Anderson vertical spindle centrifugal pump by bevel gearing placed outside the engine house. The latter was the base of an old windpump [289]. In 1914 the boiler failed and was replaced by Barford & Perkins for £170 [290].

By 1946 it was considered necessary to instal a new drainage plant without delay, but the old engine was retained until the district was amalgamated with Whittlesey Third in 1949.

M42 WHITTLESEY – Feldale (TL 299989)

This small district, of some 418 acres [291], lying between Bassenhally and Eldernell north of Whittlesey (map 6, p.21), was drained by a windpump and scoop wheel with auxiliary steam engine by 1887 [292]. It may have existed before 1861 [293]. The engine was powered by one boiler working at 40 to 50 psi [294]. This plant ceased operation between 1942 and 1950, probably in 1948, and was sold in 1952 [295]. Discharge was into the Counter Drain which runs parallel to Moreton's Leam.

In 1952 a 65 hp electric motor coupled to an 18in. Gwynnes pump was installed at TL 301990 [296]. This discharged direct into Morton's Leam. At the same time the Board came under the jurisdiction of Nene River Board (later Welland and Nene River Authority) instead of the Middle Level. The site of the original engine was sold in 1955 [297]. The district had been constituted an IDB by 1950.

WIMBLINGTON PARISH, Cambs.

Until 1868 Wimblington was part of the parish of Doddington. It contained several drainage areas. That west of the Sixteen Foot Drain and north of Boot's Drove comprising Latches Fen and Stonea Grange was privately drained. To its south lay Wimblingon Common, first enclosed under the Act of 1791 relating to Curff and Normoor. To the east of the Sixteen Foot Drain lay the two districts called Wimblington First and Second (map 7, p.22).

M43 WIMBLINGTON – Stitches Farm (TL 451921)

In about 1850 an engine built by J. & E. Headly of Cambridge was erected on the west bank of the Sixteen Foot Drain, halfway between Boot's Bridge and Bedlam Bridge. This was to drain part of Latches Fen and Wimblington Hook, and replaced a windpump on the site [298]. It had a bore of 11in. and stroke of 24in., with a D-slide valve and 6ft. beam centres. The flywheel was 10ft. in diameter with six spokes and was cast in halves. Originally steam was supplied by a horizontal boiler, but this was later replaced by a Dodmans vertical. Initially the engine drove a scoop wheel. This was replaced by a Dodmans centrifugal pump driven by twin ropes via a countershaft fixed on the roof timbers of the scoop wheel race [299].

This plant ceased operation in 1933 and was derelict by 1937 [300]. It seems to have been replaced in 1938 by a small Ruston diesel engine driving the Dodmans pump [301]. Later a new station was established on another site, almost certainly electrically-powered. This area, previously privately drained, is now part of March East IDB.

M44 WIMBLINGTON, Stonea Grange (TL 445937)

A small steam engine known as Morris's Engine existed at Stonea Grange, Latches Fen, by 1886 [302]. It survived until after 1937, having been inspected by G. Watkins in that year [303]. This was a private plant, maintained by agreement between the various landowners [304], and is also known as Latches Fen Pumping Station.

Watkins describes it as follows [305]:

> This combination of an overtype engine and scoop wheel was probably unique in English land drainage; it is also modern, possibly made after the turn of the century. The engine was a standard non-condensing overtype design and with the boiler feed water heated by the exhaust steam. The scoop wheel was made by J. Varlow of Benwick [306] and was 27ft. outside diameter with paddles 5ft. long and 9in. wide and was made largely of rolled steel. It was driven by two-stage cast iron gearing with a total reduction of 24:1 giving a scoop wheel speed of around $5^1/_2$ rpm.

The engine was a 14 hp grasshopper beam engine having a cylinder about 8in. by 12in., possibly made by Marshall.

The date of removal of this plant has not been ascertained. In 1955 a 185 hp Ruston 6VCB diesel engine was installed to drive a Sulzer vertical-spindle mixed flow pump. The Ruston engine was replaced by an electric in 1997 [307]. Discharge was into a drain which fed into the Sixteen Foot Drain. This land, previously privately drained, is now within March East District.

M45 WIMBLINGTON COMBINED – Boot's Bridge (TL 448914)

An Act of 1768 [308] created two districts east of the Sixteen Foot Drain and west of the Manea and Welney District, containing a total of 2650 acres. The first or northern district contained

Fig. 45: Wimblington Combined, Boot's Bridge (M45) engine house in 1993

700 acres, and the second or southern 1950 acres. These were later amalgamated to become Wimblington Combined District [309].

A pumping station existed close to Boot's Bridge by 1887 [310]. In 1920 [311] two oil engines appear to have been installed, one a Campbell. One of the pumps was a Gwynnes, and the other an Allen. In 1938 a new Ruston engine was provided for the Allen pump [312]. By about 1948 it seems that the Campbell was replaced by a 47 hp Ruston engine driving the Gwynnes pump [313]. The plant was housed in a wooden building because it was thought that brick would settle badly [314]. By 1988 this was derelict and empty except for rubbish (Fig. 45)[315]. Another station existed at TL456927, near Poole's Bridge, by about 1930 (But not much earlier), of which no trace remains.

M46 WIMBLINGTON COMMON
(TL 442908)

The windpump which originally drained this district was abandoned in 1874, when a 12 hp Dodmans steam engine was installed to drive a pump [316]. This was replaced in 1912 by a 35 hp Campbell oil engine [317] driving an 18in. pump [318]. In 1956 this engine was superseded by a Ruston [319]. An electric pump has since been installed and there are no remains of the previous plant.

M47 WISBECH ST. PETER,
Cambs. – Hobbs Lot (TL 385011)

A private engine, presumably steam, existed near Guyhirn in 1886 [320]. The remains of a scoop wheel race still existing (Fig. 46) [321] confirm that it drove such a wheel, probably about 15ft. in diameter by 2ft. wide. This plant had been replaced in about 1943 by a 17 hp Ruston diesel engine (presumably type 3XHR) driving a 14in. Gwynnes pump [322].

Fig. 46: Wisbech St. Peter, Hobbs Lot (M47) scoop wheel race in 2000

In turn this has been superseded by an electric pump. Discharge is into the Twenty Foot Drain. This land is not within any drainage district and the pump and drains are maintained by agreement between the landowners [323].

M48 WOODWALTON, Hunts.

This area was bounded on the west by Monks Lode, on the east by Wheatleys Drain, and on the north by the New Dyke. By 1926 it had become Woodwalton IDB, comprising Woodwalton Fen and Higney Fen. The latter was a detached part of the parish of Ramsey until 1934 (map 5, p.20). Originally three windpumps operated in this area, probably all erected in the 1870s, and probably all later provided with auxiliary steam engines.

Fig. 47: Woodwalton, Higney Mill (M48A) – Dodmans pump in 2002

Fig. 48: Woodwalton, Higney Mill (M48A) – Ruston engine house in 2002

M48A Higney Mill (TL 216863)

This mill was erected in 1876 [324] on the east bank of Monks Lode. It had been provided with an auxiliary steam engine by 1887 [325]. By 1910 it appears to have had a marine steam engine driving a Dodmans pump (Fig. 47), this plant being housed in a separate building (Fig. 48). The windpump was demolished in 1936 [326]. In 1947 a Ruston diesel engine type 9XHR driving a 30in. Gwynnes pump was installed [327]. This was still in existence in 2002, in poor condition. By then, the Dodmans pump had been dumped in a nearby farmyard [328]. This plant remains in private ownership.

M48B Brick Mere (TL 229870)

This mere was drained by a windpump on the south bank of the New Dyke. By 1900 [329] this was marked as an engine house (as it was in 1986), but no further information about this plant has been obtained.

M48C Castlehill Farm (TL 223839)

Just north of Castlehill Farm a windpump was sited on the west bank of Wheatleys Drain. An engine existed there in 1887, which survived until at least 1927 [330]. In that year a 25 hp Blackstone engine driving a 16in. pump was installed. This was destroyed by lightning in 1972 [331].

YAXLEY, Hunts.

An area of 600 acres in this parish was first drained under an Act of 1773 [332], at which time there was a windpump in Cow Fen. This First District lay south of Yaxley village and west of Yaxley Lode. Later a Second District was created, south of the First and north of Stilton District. This contained 519 acres. These districts now constitute Yaxley IDB. In addition, the area between Yaxley Lode and Conquest Lode was constituted as Yaxley New Fen (map 6, p.21).

M49 YAXLEY FIRST DISTRICT (TL 193916)

This district was drained by an engine erected before 1887 [333], which must have been steam-powered. It discharged into Yaxley Lode. This, or its replacement, failed in 1941. A Ruston engine driving a Gwynnes pump was then installed, which was still working in 1961 [334].

M50 YAXLEY SECOND DISTRICT (TL 199912)

The Second District was drained by a steam engine erected before 1853 on the east side of the railway line near Yaxley village [335]. The district had the option of using this plant or that at Whittlesey Mere (M33A), on paying one shilling per acre for the facility. Plant on this site survived until at least 1937, and latterly also drained part of Yaxley New Fen through a culvert under Yaxley Lode [336]. In addition a farmer called Fielden had two pumps, probably driven by tractors, on the south side of Yaxley Lode in 1940 [337].

M51 YAXLEY NEW FEN

The area between Yaxley Lode and Conquest Lode was variously called Yaxley New Fen or Farcet New Fen. It became part of Whittlesey and Farcet IDB (now Whittlesey IDB) in 1937. Information about the early pumping plant in this area is sparse.

M51A (TL 205908)

By 1887 a pumping station had been erected on the north side of Yaxley Lode [338]. This seems to have survived until after 1938 [339].

M51B (TL 211910)

By 1926 another station existed near Black Ham Bridge stated to belong to Yaxley New Fen Drainage Commissioners [340]. Both of these stations seem to have survived until after 1941, possibly latterly driven by tractors.

NOTES

1. Of the many accounts of the drainage of the Middle Level, the best brief description is in Darby (1983), 155 – 159.
2. 7 & 8 Vict. c. 106
3. The extent to which this enabled Whittlesey Mere to be drained is recorded in Wells, W. "The Drainage of Whittlesea Mere" *Journal RAS*, First series, xxi, 1860, 138 – 139.
4. This information is derived from The Illustrated London News, 25 October 1862, which also contains a graphic description of the flood; Wheeler, 1868, 85; and Dempsey, 154 – 158. The Illustrated London News states the weight of each of the syphons as 45 tons, and the pump cylinders as being 14 ins. diameter and 2ft. stroke. Dempsey gives the hp of the engine as 10. Eaton, D. 2001, *Easton & Amos*, Westonzoyland Engine Trust, 36, states that the air pumps were designed by J. G. Appold.
5. Clark, R. G. "St. Germans Sluice and Pumping Station", *Journal of the Institution of Civil Engineers* (1935 – 6), Vol. 2, 377 – 392. This contains a full description of the construction of this plant.
6. Lambe.
7. *The Allen Engineering Review*, No. 21, February 1949, 6 – 15, contains a full account of this plant and its construction, with photographs.
8. 7 G3 c. 37
9. Clark: Engine no. 6, *English Mechanics*, 7 February 1936. Watkins SSE Vol. 9, 24 and Hills (2003): photograph, 136
10. Benwick White Fen Order Book, 1822 – 1937 (MLO). Their notes state that the later pump was a 22in. Allen.
11. 12 G3 c. 26
12. Darby (1936), photograph and caption opposite 278
13. Benwick IDB Minutes (MLO), 29 October 1968
14. This is referred to in the Minutes of Whittlesey Fifth District of 22 May 1897 (CRO R99/74) as the Mill belonging to Lord de Ramsey.
15. Filby – personal communication
16. OS 6 in. maps 1902 and 1926
17. Gibbs's Map
18. OS 6 in. map 1926 and map of Middle Level 1930.
19. Personal inspection
20. Minutes, note 13, 19 September 1946
21. Minutes, note 13, 21 August 1951 and 17 September 1954
22. Personal inspection in 1993

23. Filby
24. Minutes, note 13, 21 August 1951, 14 September 1956 and 17 September 1957
25. Heathcote, 7
26. Minutes, note 13, 19 September 1946 and 28 October 1954
27. Lambe
28. Westmoor and Beezlings Account book (CRO)
29. MLO list states a 70 hp engine and 26in. pump
30. See M17
31. Tebbutt, C. F. (1941): *Bluntisham-cum-Earith*, 114
32. Bloom, A. (1953): *The Fens*. Robert Hale, 7.
33. Doran p. 166 and *The Allen Engineering Review*, no. 14 (July 1946), 12 – 13.
34. Conington Estate Accounts (HRO)
35. Gibbs, 278
36. Heathcote, 13
37. Lambe and MLO notes. It had a bore of 11^1/$_2$in. and stroke of 13in.
38. Gwynnes 1977
39. 31 G3 c. 19. These areas should not be confused with Ramsey, Bury etc. (1775 Act) Second and Fifth Districts (M17 and M19), also called Chatteris and Doddington
40. Bensons Drainage District Minutes 1940 – 1979 (MLO) and Gwynnes 1943 and 1953 no. 106. The brick and slate roofed building was clearly a steam engine house and contained many 'drain bricks', possible re-used from the base of a windpump. The building is marked on the 6 inch OS map of 1887 and on Gibbs's map of 1888.
41. Date of personal inspection.
42. Normoor District Minutes 1923 – 1975 (MLO). These refer to the coal shed in 1929.
43. Gibbs's map.
44. Drain bricks were used in its construction – seen when inspected on 24 January 1988.
45. OS first edition 1824.
46. Name cast on pump. Dates are those when the firm was known by this name, according to Brian Hillsdon's list from Watkins's Notes. Clark states that the name was used from 1870 to 1878. Shown as a pumping station on the OS 6 inch map of 1887.
47. A brick building still existed in 2003, then derelict, of about this date with engine mountings. MLO Notes state the maker, but incorrectly describe the pump as a Dodmans. They state that the pump was driven by a tractor from 1966.
48. Minutes, note 40, 22 November 1972.
49. Filby
50. Chatteris and Doddington (Curff or Second District) Commissioners Minutes 1978 (MLO), which report that all records prior to 1928 had been destroyed by fire. In particular, see those of 8 May 1936, 13 and 27 May and 22 December 1937, and 1 April 1938
51. 13 G3 c. 39
52. Whittlesey & Farcet IDB Minutes 1937 – 1977 (CRO ref. 99/100)
53. Minutes, note 52
54. Gibbs's map.
55. Minutes, note 52
56. OS 6in. map 1926
57. OS 6 inch map 1900, and information from Paul Turner, present owner of Blackbush (M35A)
58. Minutes, note 52
59. Kelly's *Directory of Cambridgeshire* 1875

60. Kelly's *Directory of Cambridgeshire* 1916
61. Filby
62. CIP, 10 March 1877,7
63. Gwynnes 1943 and 1953, no. 95, and 1977
64. 11 G3 c. 83
65. 21 G2 c. 18 and 39 & 40 G3 c. 1
66. Gibbs, 265
67. CIP, 31 December 1842
68. Clarke J.A., 97
69. Clark, Engine no. 76, *English Mechanics*, 29 May 1936
70. Clark states before 1914, but the date of 1928 on the new pump outfall pipes suggests otherwise.
71. Gwynnes 1943 and 1953, no. 99
72. Personal inspection in 1995
73. OS, 1in., first edition
74. Searle, R. S. (1975): *Soils of the Ely District*, Memoirs of the Soil Survey of Great Britain, Harpenden, 55 – Fig. 16
75. 30 G2 c. 30 and 14 G3 c. 16. Other Acts followed, viz. 35 G3 c. 48 and 9 G4 c. 40 for the Fourth District and 50 G3 c. 78 for the First and Second Districts. The acreages are as stated in the Acts, and the later acreages from those stated in March and Whittlesey IDB Minutes (MLO), 27 July 1948
76. Clark, Engine no. 77, *English Mechanics*, 29 May 1936
77. CC, 29 November 1833. This stated that the engine was expected to start on 6 December 1833.
78. Personal inspection
79. Gwynnes 1977
80. Not listed by J. A. Clarke. Wisbech Advertiser, 9 April 1858, reported theft of brass fittings from this engine.
81. Clark, Engine no. 79, *English Mechanics*, 29 May 1936, stating that this plant was demolished in 1929, but this appears to be incorrect.
82. March and Upwell Second District Minutes (MLO), 24 May 1917
83. Minutes, note 82, 20 May 1919. It was then ordered that the old engine be sold.
84. Minutes, note 82, 7 March 1935 and 30 January 1936, when it was reported that the engine was not yet in running order. This plant was possibly on another site, since tenders were sought for an engine house and bungalow.
85. Minutes of Euximoor IDB (MLO), 21 August 1959
86. ADA Report 1947
87. Plaque on engine house
88. Gwynnes 1977
89. OS 6in. map 1903
90. March Third District Minutes (MLO), 29 November 1875
91. Gibbs's map
92. Minutes, note 90, 8 December 1875. An undated newspaper report in March Museum states that the original engine was installed in 1825, but this is clearly a confusion with March West Fen. It also stated that the oil engine was installed in 1911, but this seems to be incorrect. Allen, 802, wrongly states that the Campbell was 40 bhp
93. Minutes, note 90, 24 August 1892
94. Minutes, note 90, 14 November 1900 and 28 June 1901
95. Minutes, note 90, 1 March 1901 and Allen, 802

96. Minutes, note 90, 7 February 1902
97. Minutes, note 90, 31 January 1939
98. See watercolour in March Museum dated 14 March 1981
99. Personal inspection
100. Gibbs's map
101. MLO Notes
102. Gwynnes 1977
103. March and Whittlesey IDB Minutes (MLO), 11 January 1938
104. Minutes, note 103, 14 January 1942
105. Blawer, D. (1997): *John Peck of Parson Drove*, The Friends of the Wisbech and Fenland Museum, 21 establishes this date
106. Heathcote, p. 6
107. March Fourth District Minutes (MLO), 5 April 1899
108. Minutes, note 107, (MLO), 4 September 1940 – quotation for sale
109. Minutes, note 103, 24 July and 11 November 1942
110. Minutes, note 103, 3 June 1946
111. OS 6 in. map 1886 and Minutes, note 103, 2 July 1942
112. Minutes, note 103, 11 November 1942
113. Gwynnes 1943 and 1953 no. 96, and 1977. The Minutes, note 103, of 24 April 1936 refer to acceptance of Gwynnes' quotation for a pump with a Crossley engine at a cost of £2752 to replace the steam engine; and on 27 October 1937 it was reported that the new engine was running. The location of this plant is not stated. Clark, Engine no. 80, *English Mechanics*, 29 May 1936, gives little information.
114. Gwynnes 1943 and 1953 no. 94, and 1977
115. OS 6in. maps 1886 and 1924 and Minutes, note 103, 24 July 1942
116. Minutes, note 103, 24 July 1942
117. Gibbs's map and OS 6in. maps 1886 and 1924
118. CC, 4 August 1849 – particulars of sale of the estate. The engine was stated to be capable of draining 500 acres.
119. OS 6 in. map 1886
120. Personal inspection in 2000. Presumably the initials stand for Isle of Ely County Council. It is probably the engine of which a photograph is held in March Museum marked "Goosetree 1936".
121. March Fifth District Minutes (MLO), 15 June and 26 October 1920 and 3 October 1922. Those for 3 May and 4 October 1921 refer to sale of the old oil engine, which suggests that the mill may have been driven by an engine
122. Gwynnes 1953 no. 92A, and 1977
123. March Sixth District Minutes 1907 – 1953 (MLO), 21 May 1909, refer to the engine driver
124. Gibbs's map and OS 6in. map 1903. This mill still existed in 1945 (Minutes 6 February 1945)
125. Minutes, note 123, 19 May 1911 and 20 May 1915 refer to repairs by that firm
126. Minutes, note 123, 4 September 1939
127. Gwynnes 1943 and 1953, no. 92, and 1977
128. 15 G3 c. 65. Wells lists this under Sutton & Mepal, to which it did not relate.
129. Parts of the Second and Fourth Districts, and repealed the Act insofar as it related to these.
130. Part of this area was included in the Act of 31 G2 c. 19 called Chatteris and Doddington.
131. Gibbs's map and OS 6in. map 1900. The 1891 Census lists Fred Meadow, engine driver, Puddock Bridge.

132. OS 1in., first edition, Warboys United Act 1906 and Sunday Pictorial, 3 March 1962

133. Gwynnes c. 1936 and stone on engine house (since demolished)

134. *ADA Gazette*, Autumn 1992, 35 and Gwynnes 1943 and 1953, no. 107

135. Westmoor and Beezlings Letter Book (CRO), 26 April 1921

136. Gibbs's map. Westmoor and Beezlings Letter Book states on 25 July 1904 that it was then very old.

137. Westmoor and Beezlings Account Book (CRO), 12 October 1893, paid Ruston Proctor & Co. £229

138. Somersham and Pidley Fourth District Minutes 1790 – 1968 passim, papers regarding pumping machinery 1917 – 1919, and report by G. McLeod dated 4 October 1941 (all CRO ref. R80)

139. Gwynnes c. 1936

140. Plaque on engine house dated 20 May 1981

141. Curff and Normoor in Chatteris and Doddington – two districts, 31 G2 c. 19

142. Ramsey Bury Fifth District Minutes (MLO), 20 April 1874. The mill is illustrated in Hills (1967), 20 and Hills (2003), 29, but one or the other, probably the second, is the wrong way round

143. Minutes, note 142, 27 November 1924

144. Minutes, note 142, 29 March 1926

145. Minutes, note 142, 25 November 1926

146. Minutes, note 142, 15 July 1931: "roadway to Acre Fen Engine for delivering coal considered."

147. The engine is now in Prickwillow Engine Museum

148. OS 6in. map 1886. To confuse, the OS 6 in. map 1924 (1950 revision) marks the Chatteris Dock plant (M 20) as Nightlayers as well as this plant.

149. Minutes, note 142, 31 May 1876: "Nightlayers Mill to be lowered 18in. so that a portable engine can be attached to work the mill when necessary."

150. Minutes, note 142, 25 January 1883

151. Minutes, note 142, 6 April and 17 June 1904

152. Minutes, note 142, 22 September 1920

153. Gwynnes 1953, no. 108A – called Chatteris; and Lambe

154. Ramsey Bury Lower District Minutes (HRO), 13 June and 7 November 1862. Goodyear, R. (1989): *Chatteris in old picture postcards*, contains a photograph of this plant in 1900.

155. OS 6 in. map 1924 (1950 revision) – see note 21

156. Minutes, note 154, 22 May 1899 and 11 April 1901

157. Gwynnes 1943 no. 108 and 1977, and Doran, 166. The plant cost £4800 and the building £5000.

158. 30 G2 c. 33. The acreages are derived from this Act, which was repealed by 36 G3 c. 172 to create Ramsey, Middlemoor, Six Districts.

159. Ramsey First District Minutes, 28 March 1850 (HRO ref: 4247)

160. Minutes, note 159, passim

161. Minutes, note 159, 16 May 1850

162. CIP, 21 December 1850

163. Minutes, note 159, 4 June 1878

164. Minutes, note 159, 27 May 1908

165. Heathcote, 6, who states the diameter of the scoop wheel as 30ft., but this may have been in anticipation of the lowering

166. Clark, Engine no. 115, *English Mechanics*, 18 September 1936. He refers to the stone on the wall of the engine house reading "Ramsey First District 1850 J. & E. Headley, Engineers, Cambridge."

167. Gwynnes 1953, no. 105B, and 1977; and McLeod

168. Ramsey Second District Account Book (HRO), and OS 6 in. map 1902 marking "Water Wheel" and Filby
169. Map of Middle Level Pumping Stations c. 1930
170. Gwynnes 1953, no. 105A
171. Filby – personal communication
172. Ramsey Third District Minutes (HRO), 28 November 1879
173. Minutes, note 172, 30 September 1880
174. Minutes, note 172, 25 February 1897
175. Heathcote p. 20
176. Clark, Engine no. 114, *English Mechanics*, 18 September 1936, with photographs
177. Agreement dated 1 June 1870 with Easton, Amos & Anderson with supporting plans (HRO).
178. Gwynnes 1943 and 1953, no. 105
179. Ramsey FifthDistrict Accounts 1856 – 7 (HRO)
180. MLO Notes
181. OS 6 in. map 1886 and Gibbs's map; and Ramsey Sixth District Accounts 1877 – 1878 (HRO). The OS 6 in. map 1926 describes this plant as belonging to Mereside Plantation and Ramsey Mere Drainage Board.
182. MLO Notes
183. Ramsey Upwood and Great Raveley IDB Minutes 1933 – 1960 (HRO ref. 4314), 30 November 1933
184. 44 G3 c. 15
185. OS 1in. map, first edition
186. OS 1in. map 1905
187. Minutes, note 183, 11 September 1935
188. Lambe. Dated from serial number
189. Minutes, note 183, 3 October 1941
190. Minutes, note 183, 17 May 1949
191. OS 6in. map 1926, but not marked on 1902 map
192. Minutes, note 183, 24 July 1946
193. Minutes, note 183, 31 March 1947
194. Minutes, note 183, 29 June 1951
195. Heathcote, 7
196. Minutes, note 183, 16 May 1935, recording 14 tons of coal in stock
197. Information from E.M.S. Hinde, who assisted in its removal
198. 13 & 14 Vict. C. 12
199. Marshall, 6 & 7
200. Marshall, 71 and Filby
201. Darby (1936), illustration opposite p. 278
202. Minutes, note 183, 11 September 1935
203. OS 6in. map 1902
204. OS 6in. map 1926
205. Gwynnes 1977, called Upwood Estate
206. Minutes, note 183, 1 October 1936
207. Minutes, note 183, 17 May 1949
208. Plaque on engine house. See also Clark, Engine no. 78, *English Mechanics*, 29 May 1936, and CC 15 February 1851

209. Ransonmoor or Fifth District Minutes 1880 – 1945 (MLO). A Minute of 12 February 1913 refers to water wheel.
210. Minutes, note 209, 21 September 1891
211. Minutes, note 209, 15 April and 30 May 1913
212. Ramsey, Bury etc. (1775 Act) Fourth District papers regarding pumping machinery (CRO ref. R80) – report by Courtney in 1917 that by then the old wheel of the Ranson Moor plant was out of true and unworkable.
213. Minutes, note 209, 17 November 1937
214. Minutes, note 209, 23 May 1945
215. *Allen Engineering Review*, No. 61, (December 1966), 4, with photograph
216. 50 G3 c. 80
217. OS 6in. maps 1882 – 1887, and see Hutchinson, 238, footnote
218. Undated newspaper cutting in March Museum seen in 1987
219. See Whittlesey Mere (M33)
220. 22G3 c. 11 and subsequent Acts
221. ADA Report 1947
222. Clark, Engine no. 84, *English Mechanics*, 29 May 1936, who states the diameter as 32ft.
223. Lambe. For photographs, see Sly, 102 and 103
224. 41 G3 c. 34: Upwell, Outwell, Denver and Welney Drainage Board. Called Well District by Wells, Vol. 2, 786. Prior Acts were 22 G2 c. 16 and 13 G3 c. 19.
225. Clark, Engine no. 151, *English Mechanics*, 20 November 1936
226. Gwynnes 1953, no. 89A, called Outwell. This states that the pump was 18in.
227. Upwell Outwell Denver and Welney District Minutes (MLO), 8 June 1944 and 8 November 1946
228. Wheeler DF, 126
229. There were also two such at Sturton (T7) and Ravensfleet (T2B) in the Trent Valley. See Gibbs, 272
230. See Wheeler DF, 124 – 126 for a full description of this wheel with diagrams
231. Clark, Engine nos. 149 and 150, *English Mechanics*, 20 November 1936
232. Minutes, note 227, 1932 – 1959 – in particular those of 10 May 1933, 22 April 1936 and 31 October 1938
233. Personal inspection
234. OS 6in. map 1887 and Gibbs map
235. Date on engine house
236. Personal inspection and Lambe
237. OS 6in. map 1903 and map of Middle Level pumping stations c. 1930
238. OS 1in. map, first edition
239. Personal inspection
240. Heathcote, J. M. (1877): *Reminiscences of Fen and Mere*, Longmans, Green & Co., 27. Wells, W., "The Drainage of Whittlesea Mere", *Journal RASE*, first series, xxi 1860, 135, states that by 1851 the area was little more than 1000 acres.
241. Darby (1983), 158 – 159
242. Clarke, J. A., 101
243. Heathcote, note 240, 76 – 78
244. Wheeler DF, 118 – 119
245. Gibbs, 277, states that it was made from the same patterns as the Prickwillow Engine of Middle Fen (S 17), but this seems to be most unlikely
246. Hutchinson, 237

247. Personal inspection
248. The same problem was encountered in Waterbeach Level (S28) and Willingham West Fen (S29)
249. CIP, 27 February 1893, 7
250. Hutchinson, 238
251. Hutchinson, 238 and MLO Notes
252. 22G2 c. 19. This was followed by Acts of 1772 (12 G3 c. 27) relating to the third, fourth and fifth districts and 1797 (37 G3 c. 68) relating to all except the first district
253. OS 6in. map 1886
254. Whittlesey and Farcet IDB Minutes 1937 – 1977 ("W & F Minutes") (CRO ref. R99/100) – 20 June 1938 and 16 June 1941
255. Watkins SSE, Vol. 9, 48, who states that this engine was probably the oldest horizontal in the Fens; and Clark, Engine no. 158, *English Mechanics*, 27 November 1936. Heathcote, 14, quotes J. Easton as caustic about the effectiveness of this plant. The name on the engine may simply be that of the relevant part.
256. W & F Minutes, 15 January 1957
257. Personal inspection
258. W & F Minutes, 2 December 1940
259. W & F Minutes, 16 February 1942, being sold for £16
260. Whittlesey Third Minutes 1870 – 1948 ("W 3 Minutes") (CRO ref. 99/100), 22 October 1880
261. W 3 Minutes, 27 May and 16 June 1897
262. W 3 Minutes, 29 November 1899
263. W 3 Minutes, 11 June 1947
264. W 3 Minutes, 15 June 1948
265. W 3 Minutes, 14 February 1958
266. W 3 Minutes, 6 March 1956
267. Gibbs's map
268. OS 6in. map 1887 and March and Whittlesey IDB Minutes (MLO), 24 July 1942
269. Minutes, note 268, 12 February 1953
270. OS 6in. map 1903
271. Minutes, note 268, 24 July and 11 November 1942
272. Whittlesey Fifth Order (or Minute) Book 1833 – 1937 ("W 5 Minutes") (CRO ref. R99/74)
273. W 5 Minutes, 12 June 1868
274. W 5 Minutes, 25 February 1876
275. W 5 Minutes, 7 June 1901
276. W 5 Minutes, 12 June 1914. It was sold for £20
277. W 5 Minutes, 17 January and 13 March 1913
278. W 5 Minutes, 11 December 1952 and 7 March 1955. The old engine was sold for £50 in 1955
279. W 5 Minutes, 9 June 1970
280. W 5 Minutes, 17 June 1975
281. W 5 Minutes, 25 June 1979
282. W 5 Minutes, 15 June 1967
283. Personal inspection 2003
284. ADA Report 1947 states 4147 acres
285. Clark, Engine no. 160, *English Mechanics*, 27 November 1936
286. Clark, R.H., "Some Grasshopper Engines", *The Engineer*, 8 May 1942, 405, and photograph, 404. Wheeler DF states that each engine was 15 hp
287. Wheeler DF, 126

288. Kingsland District Minutes 1913 – 1949 (CRO ref. R99/100)
289. Clark, Engine no. 14, *English Mechanics*, 28 February 1936; Clark, R. H., note 286, 386 and photograph, 385; and Watkins SSE, Vol. 9, 48 which states that the flywheel was 7ft. 6in. diameter
290. Minutes, note 288, 29 May and 5 June 1914
291. Feldale District Minutes 1934 – 1942 (CRO ref. R99/99)
292. Gibbs's map
293. 1861 Census lists Thomas Anker as an engine driver at Bassenhally and in 1871 James Hilliard is listed as such
294. Minutes, note 291, 19 August 1938
295. Minutes, note 291, 5 October 1950
296. Minutes, note 291, 1952 passim
297. Minutes, note 291, 22 December 1955
298. CIP, 29 September 1849, containing an advertisement for sale of the windpump and stating that it belonged to J. & E. Headly, builders of the new engine.
299. Clark, R. H. (1950), *Some Steam Engine Builders of Suffolk, Essex and Cambridgeshire*, 138 and Clark, Engine no. 163, *English Mechanics*, 1 January 1937. Clark describes the builder as Headley & Edwards, by which name the firm was not known until 1885. He calls this the Wimblington Hook engine, and gives the date of erection as 1853.
300. Clark, note 299
301. MLO Notes
302. OS 6in. maps 1886 and 1903. It is called Latches Fen Pumping Station on the OS 6in. map 1924 (revised 1950).
303. Watkins SSE, Vol. 9, 48, with photographs
304. See Deed of Covenant dated 27 December 1901 (CRO ref. R76/15) containing the agreement between the landowners for maintenance of the pumping plant and drains. This contains a plan of the area, and evidences that this plant existed in 1898. The same arrangement still applies to Hobbs Lot M53.
305. Watkins SE1, 92, with photograph; and Watkins SSE, Vol. 9, p. 48, for all otherwise uncited information. The Morris family farmed at Stonea Grange from before 1896 until after 1937.
306. James Varlow was a blacksmith in Benwick in 1875, and Henry James Varlow in 1892 and 1896, but seems to have ceased to trade by 1916 (Kelly's'Directories of Cambridgeshire).
307. *ADA Gazette*, Autumn 1997, 21, which also calls this Latches Fen Pumping Station.
308. 8 & 9 G3, c. 30. Another Act of 1810, 50 G3, c. 143, related to the Second District only
309. Wimblington Combined District Minutes (MLO), 7 July 1938
310. OS 6in. map 1903. It replaced a windpump shown on Gibbs's map
311. Minutes, note 309, 24 May 1973
312. Minutes, note 309, 21 April 1938
313. Gwynnes 1953, no. 99A, and 1977
314. Minutes, note 309, 19 July 1938
315. Personal inspection
316. Wimblington Common Minutes (MLO), 10 July 1874
317. Minutes, note 316, 4 June 1912
318. MLO Notes
319. Minutes, note 316, 20 July 1955 and 29 October 1956
320. Gibbs's map and OS 6in. map 1886
321. Personal inspection in 2000

322. Gwynnes 1943 and 1953, no. 89, and 1977
323. Letter from the Clerk to the Middle Level to the author, 7 January 2002
324. Marshall, 7 and 71
325. OS 6in. map 1887 and Gibbs's map
326. Darby (1936), illustrations opposite p. 279. Tebbutt, C. F., "Huntingdonshire Windmills", *Transactions of the Cambridgeshire and Huntingdonshire Archaeological Society*, Vol. VI, 1947, 103, states that this was used until about 1924, when it was replaced by a steam engine, but this may not be correct.
327. Gwynnes 1953, no. 102A. Annis states that this was installed in 1945
328. Inspection by Edward Hinde
329. OS 6in. map 1900, and 2^1/$_2$in. map 1986
330. Gibbs's map and OS 6in. maps 1886 and 1927
331. MLO Notes
332. 13 G3 c. 46, followed by Acts of 1831 and 1852
333. OS 6 in. map 1887
334. Whittlesey and Farcet IDB Minutes (CRO ref. R99/100), 16 February 1942, 5 February and 5 December 1946 and 18 April 1961
335. CIP, 22 May 1853 – advertisement for farm sale. This plant was probably erected before 1842 and was rated at 25 nhp (CIP, 29 October 1842)
336. Personal communication by the farmer of Lord's Farm on 1 September 1981
337. Minutes, note 334, 26 February 1940
338. Gibbs's map and OS 6in. map 1902
339. OS 6 in. map 1926 and map of Middle Level pumping stations c. 1930; and Minutes, note 334, 11 April 1938 – "Mr. Burgess stated that the existing pumping plants were working very satisfactorily in the New Yaxley Fen area."
340. OS 6in. map 1926

4

MARSHLAND NORTH
OF MIDDLE LEVEL

CONTENTS

NM1   Downham West Fen
NM2   Magdalen
NM3   Marshland Smeeth and Fen
NM4   Stow Bardolph
NM5   Waldersea
NM6   Wisbech – Redmoor

The area between the Rivers Nene and Great Ouse lying north of the Middle Level was drained piecemeal (map 8, p.23). Except for Waldersea, it contained no separate drainage authorities until the late eighteenth century. The Middle Level Main Drain passes through it, but is unconnected to its drainage system, as is the pumping station at St. Germans. The early engines west of the River Great Ouse faced particular problems in discharging into a tidal river.

NM1 DOWNHAM WEST FEN,
Norfolk (TF 600052)

This district lay west of Downham Market, and was bounded by Tong's Drain on the west, Well Creek on the south, and the River Great Ouse on the east (map 8, p.23). It was created by Acts of 1802 [1], 1844 and 1851, and contained some 1680 acres [2]. Originally it was drained by two windpumps, working a double-lift. These stood on the bank of Well Creek, discharging the water through Salter's Lode Sluice into the River Ouse.

J.A. Clarke records [3] that "in 1840 an attempt was made to introduce steam-drainage; an engine was erected, and made to work neither a water-wheel nor a pump, but some of 'Hall's Patent Hydraulic Belts. After a trial, however, it was found that the scheme would not answer; and Downham Fen still continues under wind-drainage."

In about 1851 [4] a beam engine was installed on the west bank of the River Great Ouse to drive a scoop wheel 34ft. 3in. in diameter and $9^3/_4$in. wide. Steam was supplied by one Galloway boiler.

This plant was replaced in 1900, within the old building (Fig. 49). J. & H. Gwynne supplied a vertical compound condensing steam engine and an 18in. pump at a cost of £786 (Fig. 50) [5]. The old boiler was retained, but in 1902 an additional boiler was purchased from A. Dodman & Co. for £200. Another new boiler was supplied by the same firm in 1925 at a cost of £315. The working pressure was 90 psi. The chimney was lowered in 1892 and again in 1913 for no known reason [6]. The pump discharged 22 tpm at the maximum lift of over 17ft., and 36 tpm

Fig. 49: Downham West Fen (NM1) engine house in 1900 (J. & H. Gwynnes 1901)

Fig. 50: Downham West Fen (NM1) – Gwynnes steam engine and pump (Gwynnes 1901)

at lower lifts. Delivery was into the River Great Ouse, which is tidal at this point.

In 1931 a 66 hp Crossley oil engine was installed to drive the existing pump [6]. This plant survived until after 1953 [7], but has since been totally demolished and there is no trace of its site [8]. It was probably demolished in 1955 when the new diesel plant at Stow Bardolph (NM4) was erected by what had then become Downham and Stow Bardolph IDB.

NM2 MAGDALEN FEN, Norfolk

This fen is in the parish of Wiggenhall St. Mary Magdalen and parts of the other Wiggenhall parishes. It was first drained under Acts of 1757 and 1784 [9], and contained 5533 acres (map 8, p.23). McLeod, writing in 1950, stated that this district included some of the lowest land in the country with a surface level of minus 6.5ft. OD Newlyn and was likely to sink lower [10].

NM2A Magdalen – Steam (TF 582099)

In 1834 a 40 hp Butterley beam engine driving a scoop wheel [11] was erected over a mile west of the River Great Ouse, discharging into Simond Lode [12]. This plant was scrapped in 1914 [13] and replaced by twin 90 hp Gwynnes steam engines driving 24in. Gwynnes pumps each delivering 50 tpm [14]. Simond Lode consisted of a mile-long gravity channel with a tidal sluice at its junction with the River Great Ouse which, owing to its low level made the tide-locked period very long. In 1947 the sluice never opened for a week and one-third of the district was flooded [14]. Following selection of a different site for new plant in 1948, this plant was wholly demolished, and there is no trace of its site [15].

NM2B Magdalen (D) (TF 598099)

In 1948 a new station (Fig. 51) was erected on the bank of the River Great Ouse, into which it discharged direct. This contained two twin-cylinder Ruston diesel engines each driving a Gwynnes 27in. pump delivering 100 tpm (Fig. 52) [16]. This was supplemented in 1985 by an electric pump in a separate building.

Fig. 51: Magdalen (NM2B) engine house in 1994

Fig. 52: Magdalen (NM2B) – Ruston engines in 1994

NM3 MARSHLAND SMEETH AND FEN, Norfolk (TF 547110)

This area originally contained the common lands of the parishes of Walpole, Terrington, Tilney, Emneth, Walsoken, Walton and Clenchwarton. It lay west of Magdalen Fen and contained some 8000 acres (map 8, p.23) [17]. This land was first enclosed and drained under an Act of 1796 [18]. Wells comments that previously to the drainage, it was one waste of water [19]. The district was bisected in 1848 by the Middle Level Main Drain, and was eventually reconstituted in 1937 so as to contain 9500 acres wholly west of the Main Drain. The parts east of that Drain formerly within the district were passed to Magdalen and Stow Bardolph Boards. It has recently been amalgamated with Magdalen IDB.

Although installation of a steam engine had first been considered in 1814 [20], it was not until 1849 that a pumping station was erected at Tilney Fen End. A 40hp [21] beam engine made by Thompson & Stather of Hull was supplied by Simpson & Bennett at a cost of £2793. This had a bore of 33in. and stroke of 66in., with D-slide valves. The beam centres were 16ft. and the diameter of the flywheel 20ft. 6in. Speed was some 15 to 20 rpm [22]. This drove a scoop wheel 26ft. in diameter and 2ft. wide [23], making about 4 rpm. New boilers were purchased from Horsfields in 1876 for £792, and another from Dodmans in 1901 for £310 [24]. Pressure was about 30 psi. This plant became a stand-by in 1921 and was removed in 1938.

In 1921 a Dodmans horizontal steam engine driving a 36in. Triton pump (Fig. 55) was installed in a separate building. This delivered 100 tpm [25]. It seems that the existing boilers were retained, for in 1929 a new boiler with a capacity of 160 psi was purchased to replace No. 3 boiler [26]. This engine was replaced in 1950 by a three-cylinder Mirrlees, Bickerton & Day diesel engine driving the existing Triton pump. Before this, the beam engine and scoop wheel had been replaced in 1938. The old building was adapted (Fig. 53) to house two twin-cylinder 125 hp Crossley Premier diesel engines type KO2 (Fig. 54) each driving a 30in. Allen-Gwynnes pump delivering 75 tpm [27].

In 1941 the Lancashire boiler was sold to George Cohen & Co. of London for £345, and in 1949 the remaining serviceable boiler was passed to Waldersea IDB, whilst the other was sold for scrap. At the same time the chimney was demolished [28].

Four submersible electric pumps operating automatically were installed in a separate building in 1992 to replace the diesel engines and pumps, but these have been retained in preservation and form part of a museum of fen drainage.

Discharge is into a Mill basin, four miles in length, which joins the River Great Ouse at the Eau Brink just north of St. Germans Pumping Station. The tide allows for discharge from this channel for approximately seven hours in every twenty-four. Although the capacity of the Mill Drain usually enabled pumping to be continuous, at times the beam engine had to stop. It is said that, during the flood of August 1912, the water rose so high that it began to lift the scoop wheel off its bearings. It may not have been a coincidence that the 76 year old engine driver resigned within two months. In the 1990s an auxiliary electric pump was placed at the outfall of the Mill Drain to assist in the discharge of water into the river when the tide is high.

Fig. 53:
Marshland (NM3)
engine house in
2003

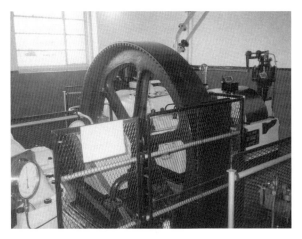

Fig. 54: Marshland (NM3) – Crossley engine in 2003

Fig. 55: Marshland (NM3) – Dodmans pump in 2003

NM4 STOW BARDOLPH, Norfolk (TF 598059)

This district lies north of Downham West Fen and was created by Act of 1798 [29]. It contained some 5235 acres (map 8, p.23).

A 50 hp beam engine made by J. & E. Headly of Cambridge [30] was installed in 1848. The cylinder was 36in. by 56in., with beam centres of 16ft. and a flywheel 20ft. 4in. in diameter. Two Lancashire boilers supplied steam at 15 psi. The scoop wheel was 32ft. in diameter with scoops 6ft. long by 24in. wide and a rising breast in front. Gearing was 5:1 [31]. Discharge was into Common Lode and thence to the River Great Ouse. This plant was only being used as a stand-by in 1936, and the machinery was scrapped in about 1937. The empty building, without chimney, survived until after 1974 (Fig. 56), but had been demolished by 1990 [32].

The original plant was replaced in a new building by a 200 hp Vickers-Petter oil engine driving a 36in. Gwynnes pump delivering 100 tpm [33]. In 1956 an unusual arrangement was provided. A 100 bhp electric motor and a 136 hp diesel engine were placed in the same station each driving a screw pump discharging 46 tpm against a 24ft. head. The electric unit was automatically controlled, whilst the diesel engine was operated manually [34].

Fig. 56: Stow Bardolph (NM4) beam engine house in 1972.

NM5 WALDERSEA, Cambs. (TF 433062)

Waldersea in the parish of Elm, near Wisbech, was the first internal drainage district to be established by Act of Parliament, in 1607 [35]. Thus it existed before Vermuyden commenced drainage of the Bedford Level. It contained some 5500 acres (map 8, p.23) [36]. In 1832 a pumping station (Fig. 57) was erected on the east bank of the River Nene, into which it discharged. Because this river is tidal at that place, a bucket-pump was selected instead of a scoop wheel [37].

The engine was a 70 hp Cornish single-acting beam engine, almost certainly by Harveys of Hayle [38]. The cylinder was 40in. bore by 96in. stroke and worked at 9 rpm on 35 psi cut off at a quarter stroke [39]. The bucket pump was 62in. bore by 90in. stroke [40]. It raised 63 tpm against a lift of between 10 and 24ft. [41]. The cost of this plant, including buildings, was about £3000. This was the only Cornish engine and bucket pump installed in the Fens south of Lincoln, and was not popular because the valves and working parts became blocked by mud and weeds which found their way into the inlet.

Fig. 57: Waldersea (NM5) engine houses in 1992

In 1883 this plant was supplemented by an Easton & Anderson single cylinder inclined condensing engine [42], the cylinder being 18 in. by 30in. and the flywheel 10ft. in diameter [43]. Steam was supplied at 65 psi by a single boiler 25$\frac{1}{2}$ft. by 5$\frac{1}{2}$ft. placed in the boiler house of the old engine. This drove a vertical-spindle Anderson pump having a fan of 3ft. 10in. diameter worked through one pair of bevel wheels geared 3:1. The engine was housed in a wooden building with the pump outside.

The Cornish engine was removed in 1900 and replaced by an Allen vertical compound double-acting open engine driving direct a horizontal-spindle pump (Figs. 58 and 59). The engine had cylinders 18 and 29 ins. in diameter by 16in. stroke, and was capable of developing 200 hp when running at 130 rpm. It was supplied with steam at 90 psi by two Lancashire boilers, each 29ft. by 7$\frac{1}{2}$ft. The diameter of the suction and delivery pipes was 36in and the pump was capable of discharging 100 tpm against a total lift of 15ft., the diameter of the disk being 4$\frac{1}{2}$ft. A jet-condenser was provided giving a constant vacuum of 26 to 27in. The air pump, 16in. in diameter by 9in. stroke, was worked from the high-pressure crosshead [44]. This plant was placed in the old engine house, its well being used for the suction pipes of the pump.

The two steam engines were removed in about 1945 [45] and replaced by two Ruston engines driving 36in. Gwynnes pumps [46], placed in a separate brick building following demolition of the old wooden shed (Fig. 57).

The surviving old buildings remain in very derelict condition, and are understood to have been sold in 2002 for redevelopment into a dwellinghouse.

FIG. 3.—*Waldersea Drainage District.*
Wisbech Pumping Station.

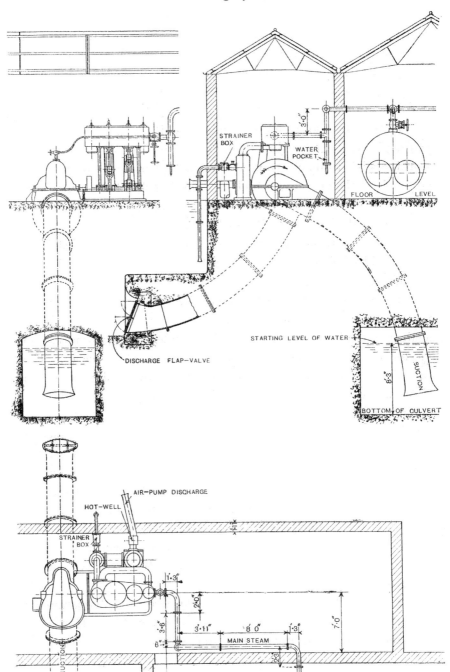

STRAINER
BOX

WATER
POCKET

3'-0"

FLOOR   LEVEL

STARTING LEVEL OF WATER

DISCHARGE FLAP-VALVE

SUCTION

8'·3"

BOTTOM OF CULVERT

AIR-PUMP DISCHARGE

HOT-WELL

STRAINER
BOX

1'·3"

20"

3'·6"

3'·11"

8'0"

1'·3"

6"

7'·0"

MAIN STEAM

SUCTION

Fig. 58: Waldersea (NM5) – diagram of 1900 Allen plant (Allen)

Fig. 59: Waldersea (NM5) – 1900 Allen steam engine (Allen)

NM6 WISBECH, Cambs. – Redmoor (TF 449073)

This area of 1780 acres [47] near Wisbech (map 8, p.23) was drained by a 14 hp [48] semi-portable steam engine driving a vertical-spindle pump in 1878 [49]. Discharge was into the River Nene. This had been replaced c. 1940 by a 35 hp Blackstone diesel engine driving an 18in. Gwynnes pump [50]. No traces of the original plant survive. This land is now within the Hundred of Wisbech IDB. It should not be confused with Redmore in Hockwold S1C or Redmoor Farm, Chettisham (S4).

NOTES

1. 42 G3 c. 19
2. Heathcote papers (HRO) state 1682 acres
3. Clarke, J.A., 105
4. This was when the mills on Salter's Lode were sold and a new Act obtained. It certainly existed in 1863, when coal was being purchased (Downham Fen District Accounts NRO). See also Clark, Engine no. 25, *English Mechanics*, 6 March 1936
5. District Accounts, note 4 , 1900 passim and Gwynnes 1901. The latter states that the wheel was unable to work when the tide reached a certain height, the extreme lift against which it would work being only 17ft.
6. Downham Fen Minutes 1899 – 1933 and Accounts 1863 – 1937 (NRO) , passim
7. Gwynnes 1943 and 1953, no. 87
8. Personal inspection in 1997
9. 30 G2 c. 32 and 24 G3 c. 9. The first of these Acts related only to 4000 acres
10. McLeod, 479
11. Glynn, 18. Clarke, J.A. states that it was erected in 1833 and the contract with the Butterley Co. is so dated (NRO ref. DB 11/8)
12. OS 6in. map 1881
13. Clark, Engine no. 161, *English Mechanics*, 27 November 1936. The Rural Life Museum at Gressinghall, Norfolk, holds an undated diagram entitled "Proposed arrangement of

pumping installation for Magdalen Fen Commission" produced by Alfred Dodman & Co., but this was clearly never implemented

14. McLeod, 476 and 479
15. Personal inspection in 1994
16. Gwynnes 1953, no. 86A and McLeod, 479. Gwynnes 1977 states 24in. pumps
17. Howling, 2
18. 36 G3 c. 100. Other Acts were obtained in 1849 and 1863
19. Wells, Vol. 1, 783
20. Howling, 7
21. Kelly's *Directory of Norfolk* 1900 and *Eastern Daily Press*, 11 October 1938
22. Howling, 14 and Marshland Smeeth and Fen Minutes (NRO) , 26 May 1849
23. Clark, Engine no. 142, *English Mechanics*, 13 November 1936
24. Minutes, note 22. Howling, 17, who states that there were three boilers, which seems to be an excessive number for this size of engine which was stoked by the engine driver
25. Clark, note 23, and Howling, 18
26. Howling, 18
27. Booklet on the history of the district 1937 – 1987 produced by the IDB
28. Howling, 20
29. 38 G3 c. 70. Ouse Outfall Act 1860, 68, entitles the district "Outwell, Stow Bardolph, Wimbotsham and Downham"
30. Clark, R.H. (1950) : *Steam Engine Builders of Cambridgeshire*, 138. This contains a photograph of the steam engine. The engine was first started in January 1849 (CIP, 27 January 1849). See also Watkins SSE, Vol. 9, 136 with photographs of engine and scoop wheel
31. Clark, Engine no. 161, *English Mechanics*, 27 November 1937 and Watkins, note 30, who states the stroke as 60 ins.
32. Personal inspection
33. Gwynnes 1936
34. Rigby, 14
35. 4 Jac 1 c. 13. The full text is printed in Wells, Vol. 2, 39
36. ADA Report 1948. Wells states 6000 acres
37. Hills (2003) , 1236, with photograph of the exterior. Others existed at Torksey (T1B) and Marton (T1C) in the Trent Valley. See Clark, "Engines of the Trent Valley", Engines nos. 2 and 3, *English Mechanics*, 24 December 1937
38. *Cornish Guardian*, September 1954, recorded installation of this plant by Thomas Burall, who then became the engine driver
39. Clark, Engine no. 152, *English Mechanics*, 20 November 1936
40. Allen, 796
41. Clarke, J.A., 113
42. Gibbs, 276 and Clark, note 39
43. Watkins SSE, Vol. 9, 52, which has a photograph
44. These particulars are taken almost verbatim from Allen, 794, which also contains diagrams
45. Possibly after 1949 – note acquisition of boiler from Marshland District (NM3) in that year
46. Gwynnes 1953, no. 85A, and 1977
47. Gibbs, 276
48. Heathcote, 20
49. Gibbs, but this may be incorrect, since Heathcote wrote in 1877
50. Gwynnes 1943 and 1953, no. 85, and 1977

5
NORTH LEVEL

CONTENTS

N1	NORTH LEVEL FIRST	Borough Fen and Newborough
N2A	WISBECH NORTHSIDE	Rummers
N2B	WISBECH NORTHSIDE	Mouth Lane
N3A	NORTH LEVEL SECOND	Dog-in-a-Doublet
N3B	NORTH LEVEL SECOND	Cross Guns
N4	NORTH LEVEL THIRD	(Thorney) French Drove
N5	NORTH LEVEL	Tydd or Protection Sluice

The North Level comprises some 75,000 acres including catchment areas [1] lying east of Peterborough and the River Welland, north of the River Nene and west of Wisbech (map 9, p.24). The northern boundary extends along the Welland north of Crowland to Brotherhouse Bar and then passes east to Postland and south to Dowsdale. From there it follows the county boundary to Tydd Gote and Gunthorpe Sluice where the North Level main drain discharges into the Nene.

During the eighteenth century this Level suffered regular flooding, not least because of the bad state of the estuary of the Nene from Wisbech to the Wash. This was improved by a straight cut (Kinderley's) from Wisbech to Gunthorpe Sluice, east of Tydd, made in 1773, but effective drainage of the Level was not possible until an outfall cut was dug from that sluice to the Wash in 1830. This was followed in 1834 by provision of the North Level Main Drain which enabled the Level to be drained primarily by gravity for over 100 years.

This Level was initially part of the Bedford Level, but was constituted as a separate entity by Act of 1753 (amended by an Act of 1771) [2] which formed it into five districts (map 9, p.24). In addition the Hundreds of Wisbech Court of Sewers administered the land east of the area of the Level, becoming Wisbech Northside Commission by Act of 1775 [3]. North of this area, Tydd and Newton Drainage Commission was constituted by Act of 1773 [4], Leverington and Parson Drove by Act of 1801 [5], and Sutton Common by Act of 1809 [6]. These districts, together with Holland Elloe Court of Sewers, were eventually taken into the Level. In 1973 the North Level IDB was formed to administer the drainage of the entire area.

The only steam pumping stations in the Level were the early and short-lived Borough Fen, followed later by Rummers. Sutton St. Edmund is included in South Lincolnshire, in which it was situated at the time of its existence.

From 1936, at least five diesel-powered pumping stations were installed, of which Tydd was a secondary station. Four of these contained the same makes of plant. The engines were supplied by Crossley-Premier and the pumps by Gwynnes. The non-existence of earlier plant afforded this rare opportunity to standardise, with all of its advantages in maintenance. In the 1970s, a major improvement scheme led to the erection of several new electric stations and upgrading of some existing plant, so that the entire Level is now pumped, and some 8000 acres are pumped twice [7].

N1 NORTH LEVEL FIRST – Borough Fen and Newborough (TF 260081)

The North Level First District, comprising some 6000 acres [8] was first enclosed and drained under an Act of 1812 [9].A steam engine of 30 hp [10] was erected in August 1820. It was made by Fenton & Murray of Leeds and drove a scoop wheel 21ft. in diameter and 36in. wide. The head and dip was 9ft. and the wheel revolved at 6$\frac{1}{2}$ rpm. Coal consumption was about 3 tons 16$\frac{1}{2}$ cwt. per 24 hours. The total cost of the plant was £7000 [11].

This discharged into the Old South Eau and became redundant in 1834 upon construction of the North Level Main Drain. The engine was sold in 1838, and the building demolished in 1840 [12]. Its site is still marked by the small hamlet called "The Engine".

N2A WISBECH NORTHSIDE – Rummers (TL 429063)

The parishes of Wisbech St. Peter and Wisbech St. Mary, containing some 7000 acres, were under the jurisdiction of the Hundreds of Wisbech Commission of Sewers until they became part of the North Level under the Wisbech North Side Act of 1775 [13]. There were then two mills in the district, the White Mill and the Red Mill. That part of the Hundreds of Wisbech lying east of the River Nene did not become part of the North Level.

In 1878 [14] a station was established on the north side of the River Nene to replace several windpumps [15]. It may not have been working until 1884 [16]. The engine was supplied by Easton & Anderson and had a cylinder 18 by 21in. Steam was provided by one boiler. The vertical spindle pump [17] had an impeller 44in. in diameter by 9$\frac{3}{4}$in and was bevel driven from the flywheel. At 75 rpm the pump discharged 36 tpm against a 13ft. lift [18]. This machinery was scrapped in August 1935 [19], and replaced by a diesel engine. Discharge was into the River Nene.

The building has been converted into a private dwellinghouse, and the chimney remains [20].

This station was also known as Rummers after the name of the mill which preceded the steam engine.

N2B WISBECH NORTHSIDE – Mouth Lane (D) (TF 419055)

In 1936 a diesel engine station was established south west of the Rummers plant to supplement it (Fig. 60). This consisted of a four-cylinder Allen type S30 146 bhp diesel engine driving a 26in. pump delivering 60 tpm against a 23ft. lift [21]. It still survives, albeit supplemented in 1978 by an Allen-Gwynnes electric plant in a separate building. Discharge is into the tidal River Nene.

N3A NORTH LEVEL SECOND –Dog-in-a-Doublet (D) (TF 275995)

This station was established in 1940 on the north bank of the tidal River Nene, into which it discharged. It contained a pair of Crossley-Premier diesel engines type HO4 (nos. 114865 and 114866) driving a pair of Gwynnes 30in. axial flow pumps (nos. 53734 and 53733) discharging 133 tpm. This plant was wholly replaced in 1983 by an Allen-Gwynnes electrically powered unit.

Fig. 60: Wisbech
North Side, Mouth
Lane (N2B) engine
house in 1992

N3B NORTH LEVEL SECOND – Cross Guns (D) (TF 345016)

This station was established in 1939 on the north bank of the River Nene. It contained three Crossley-Premier diesel engines type HO4, the cylinders being 11 by 16in. Each drove a Gwynnes 30in. axial flow pump (no. 53816) discharging 70 tpm. These became redundant in 1977 when a new station was built, but one of the engines (no. 114863) is preserved in the old building. The new plant consists of six 800 mm. pumps, each discharging 90 tpm. Three of these are driven by diesel engines and three by electric motors.

N4 NORTH LEVEL THIRD (THORNEY) – French Drove (D) (TF 311087)

This station was established in 1940 on the north bank of the New South Eau as a booster station. It contained a 160 bhp four-cylinder horizontal Crossley-Premier diesel engine, the cylinders being of 13$^{1}/_{2}$in. diameter by 20in. stroke. This drove a 30in. Gwynnes pump discharging 200 tpm. In addition there was a 60 bhp two-cylinder Crossley-Premier diesel engine, with cylinders 11 by 16in., coupled to a Gwynnes pump. This plant was scrapped as being redundant in 1982 [22].

N5 NORTH LEVEL – Tydd or Protection Sluice (D) (TF 460179)

In 1938 a station was established at Tydd [23] to discharge the waters of the North Level Main Drain into the River Nene. This housed four 350 bhp Crossley-Premier diesel engines with cylinders 13 by 20in. each driving a 48in. Gwynnes pump capable of discharging 200 tpm.

In 1948 a further 48in. Gwynnes pump was provided and in 1968 two of the original engines were replaced by electric motors and yet another pump driven by electric power installed. This brought the total number of engines and pumps to six, having a combined capacity of 1276 tpm. The total area drained is 38,000 acres.

NOTES

1. Grantham, 781, states 40,000 acres taxable and 36,000 acres of contributory areas. Morris, S.H. *North Level Internal Drainage Board* n/d c. 1990 published by the Board states 78,229 acres; but Charnley, 116, gives 97,000 acres as that for which the North Level IDB became responsible in 1973.
2. 27 G2 c.19 and 11 G3 c. 78. These Acts are set out in full in Wells Vol. 2 pp. 526-596 and 644-668.
3. 15 G3 c. 66
4. 13 G3 c. 60
5. 41 G3 c. 73
6. 49 G3 c. 119
7. Morris, note 1. Details of all of these diesel engines are taken from Morris and Charnley. The latter contains photographs of virtually all of these stations. No attempt has been made to list the new electric stations.
8. Blawer, D. (1997): *John Peck of Parson Drove*, 21, Wisbech Museum; and Charnley, 77.
9. 52 G3 c. 143
10. Charnley states 70 hp, but this cannot be correct having regard to the coal consumption.
11. Blawer, note 8. Hills (2003), 102, quotes Wing as giving a prime cost of £2500.
12. Newborough Fen Commissioners Minutes, Vol 2. (CRO R77/38)
13. 15 G3 c. 66
14. Watkins's Notes, no. 55, referring to the plaque on the engine house.
15. Charnley, 47, states that a windpump was at work on this site in 1592, and that by 1800 there were six in the district.
16. Clark, Engine No. 164, *English Mechanics*, 1 January 1937
17. Charnley, 78, quoting Northside Commissioners Minutes of 1885, states that this was an Appold pump.
18. Watkins's Notes, note 14
19. Clark; but Charnley, 118, states that the boiler and old steam engine were removed and sold for £50 in 1955. This is most likely a misprint for 1935.
20. Charnley, 127 – photograph.
21. *The Queen's Engineering Works Magazine*, no. 33, (1936), 69 and no. 34, (1937), 146 and 147 with photographs
22. Charnley, 136
23. Gwynnes map calls this station Protection Sluice, but it seems to be generally called Tydd.

6
SOUTH LEVEL

DISTRICTS

Serial No.	Name	Serial No.	Name
S1	Burnt Fen	S16	Methwold Severals
S2	Burwell	S17	Middle Fen
S3	Cawdle Fen	S18	Middleton
S4	Chetttisham	S19	Mildenhall or Burnt Fen Second
S5	Cottenham	S20	Northwold Severals
S6	Denver Parts	S21	Over
S7	East of Ouse Polver and Nar	S22	Padnal and Waterden
S8	Feltwell New Fen	S23	Soham Mere
S9	Feltwell Second	S24	Stoke Ferry
S10	Haddenham	S25	Swaffham and Bottisham
S11	Hilgay Great West Fen	S26	GORB (Swaffham District)
S12	Hilgay – Wood Hall	S27	Thetford
S13	Lakenheath	S28	Waterbeach Level
S14	Littleport and Downham	S29	Willingham West Fen
S15	Methwold and Feltwell		

This level, containing some 170,000 acres, lies east of the River Great Ouse between Horningsea near Cambridge in the south and the River Wissey in the north (map 10, p.25). For ease of classification, plant in Norfolk east of the Ouse and north of the Wissey has been included in this section. By 1936 there were 26 internal drainage districts in this level, as well as several privately drained areas. This number has been considerably reduced in recent years, particularly in the Southery area.

Whilst the Bedford Level Corporation was constituted in the seventeenth century to maintain the main river banks, it gradually ceased to be able to perform this function satisfactorily due to a diminishing income. A succession of separate undertakings to improve the River Great Ouse led to a proliferation of authorities and rates. These included the Ouse Outfall Board and the Denver Sluice Commission separately constituted by the Ouse Outfall Act 1860, Ouse Bank Commission under an Act of 1837 and, for the southern districts, the South Level Commission under an Act of 1827. Each were empowered to levy rates. This multiplicity of bodies was not eradicated until the Great Ouse River Board was formed under the provisions of the Land Drainage Act 1930.

Unlike most of the other areas in the Fens, the South Level has no secondary pumping stations and discharges into the sea through the River Great Ouse by gravity. Thus pumping in this Level is restricted to that undertaken by the Internal Drainage Boards or private landowners. It did produce one early and temporary use of steam power which deserves mention.

THE EAU BRINK CUT

The course of the River Great Ouse from Wiggenhall St. Mary to King's Lynn followed a circuitous route, some six miles long, to cover a straight distance of three miles. In some places it was half a mile wide, and had steep shifting sand banks [1]. This impeded the discharge of flood water and was a considerable hazard for the extensive barge traffic from Lynn to the south [2]. First suggested in 1751, the construction of a straight channel was not achieved until 1820, due to numerous difficulties and objections, not least from the merchants of Lynn, who feared damage to their harbour.

To assist in the construction of this channel, two steam engines were ordered from Boulton & Watt in 1818. One was a 40 hp [3] beam engine having a cylinder of 36in. bore and 84in. stroke [4]. This drove a pump, presumably of the bucket type, of 32in. diameter and 25ft. length [5]. The boiler was 13ft. 6in. long, 5ft. 4in. wide and 6ft. 10in. high [6]. The site of this plant is not known. The prime cost of the engine, boiler and pump was £1189. 6. 0d [7].

The second plant was a dredging machine worked by a 10 hp steam engine. It was fixed in a vessel 83ft. long and 21ft. wide, drawing 5ft. of water. "The machine works in a well, 45ft. long and 5ft. 2in. wide in the middle of the vessel, and will dredge to the depth of 14 or 15ft. The inclined plane is 38ft. in length. The buckets are 2ft. 10in. wide and there are 20 in number." [8].

Both of these machines were offered for sale in December 1823, although the Cut had been completed two years earlier. The purchaser is not known. The Cut did not eventually afford the relief to drainage expected [9], and the benefit to navigation was diminished when construction of the railways took much of the traffic from the water.

S1 BURNT FEN FIRST DISTRICT, CAMBS.

This district was constituted by Acts of 1759, 1773, 1797 and 1807 [10]. It comprised an area of 14,492 acres [11] and was bounded by the River Great Ouse, the Rivers Lark and Little Ouse, and Mildenhall Fen. Initially the latter was Burnt Fen Second District, but was later entitled Mildenhall, and is listed herein under that name (S19). The First District became Burnt Fen District in 1879 [12], and when its area was increased to 17,000 acres in 1962 it became Burnt Fen IDB [13].

Several windpumps were inherited or constructed when the district was first formed and by 1774 there were eight of these [14]. The first resort to steam power took place in 1831, and it seems that both the consulting engineer and the engine builder failed to provide an efficient plant. Eventually two steam engines were erected to serve the northern and southern parts of the district respectively.

S1A Little Ouse or Brandon (TL 619893)

The northern station was established on the south bank of the Little Ouse River about one mile upstream from Brandon Creek. In 1829, purchase of a gas vacuum engine was considered, but rejected [15]. Mr. W. C. Mylne was retained as consulting engineer [16]. He advised a 40 hp

Fig. 61: Burnt Fen, Little Ouse (S1A) engine house in 1972

steam engine, driving a pair of scoop wheels [17]. The engine was a marine side-lever type with a stroke of 42in. making 28 rpm to 5^1/$_2$ of the wheel. Steam pressure was at most 15 psi [18]. It was made by Boulton & Watt. One boiler was provided, which proved inadequate at an early stage [19]. It was repaired in 1837 and a new boiler was purchased to work with it [20]. The first boiler was replaced in 1848 by a Cornish boiler of 45 hp at a cost of £230 [21]. This worked to a pressure of 10/12 psi.

The two scoop wheels acted as a single or double lift [22], and it appears that one was in front of the other [23]. This differed from the arrangement at Ten Mile Bank Station where the wheels were side by side. These are the only known examples of two wheels being installed in the Fens, except for the "help" wheels later installed at Haddenham and Burwell engines. The system at Burnt Fen proved unsatisfactory and the front wheel was removed in June 1832. The remaining wheel appears to have been 28ft. in diameter with scoops 2ft. wide [24]. This was replaced by a new wheel in 1833 [25]. It was lowered by at least 20in. in 1847 [26], and increased in diameter by 4ft. in 1860, the width being reduced by 3in. [27]. At this time a rising breast was fitted in front of the wheel. By 1887 the wheel was 34^1/$_2$ft. in diameter with scoops 4ft. 9in. long by 2ft. wide [28].

The engine cost £1184. 4. 0d, the building £835.12. 6d and the scoop wheel shed £132.10. 0d, the total cost, including carriage of materials, being £2293.15. 9d.. This plant was removed in 1892 [29].

In its place a horizontal high pressure condensing engine with a single cylinder having a bore of 20in. and stroke of 36in. was installed. This drove a vertical spindle centrifugal pump delivering 75 tpm and made by Hathorn Davey & Co. A single boiler was provided to work at 80 psi. The plant was housed in the old building, altered for the purpose, and cost £1628 [30]. This machinery became redundant in 1925 and was removed in 1933.

In 1925 a Blackstone 250 hp diesel engine driving a 42in. Gwynnes rotary pump discharging 150 tpm housed in a corrugated iron building replaced this (Fig. 61) [31]. This was removed at some time after 1962 following construction of two electric pumps at TL 587889.

S1B Lark or Fish and Duck (TL 610826)

In 1842, a 40 hp side-lever engine driving a scoop wheel was installed on the north bank of the River Lark near Prickwillow [32]. This was made by Boulton & Watt and three boilers were provided. The scoop wheel was renovated in 1849 [33], and in 1852 one half of the scoops were removed to increase discharge [34], whilst in 1861 the wheel was lowered [35]. No other information about this plant has been traced [36]. It was replaced in 1883 by new machinery in the old building, which was adapted for the purpose (Fig. 63). The description of this by Wheeler [18] merits reproduction in entirety:

"The new engine is of the horizontal tandem type, high-pressure compound condensing, fitted with expansion gear, 60 nhp, the cylinders being 18in. and 30in. in diameter, with 3ft. stroke, provided with variable expansion valve working on the back of the high-pressure valve. Steam is provided by three Lancashire boilers, 25ft. by 7ft. diameter; working pressure 65 psi. Only two of the boilers are in use at the same time. The engine makes 70 rpm with steam at 65 psi, and cut-off in the small cylinder at half of the stroke, the pump at the same time 105 rpm with a lift of 14ft. and delivering 120 tpm.. The case of the pump is 9ft. 10in. in diameter; the diameter diminishing below the pump to 6ft. The outlet for the discharge is 9½ft. above the centre of the pump, and is 5½ft. high by 3½ft. wide. The pump is driven by a bevil wheel geared into a bevel pinion on the crankshaft, which is 11ft. long. The fan is single, made of gun-metal, 6ft. diameter by 12½in. depth at the periphery, with a short suction pipe attached to the case below the disc. The spindle is suspended by an onion bearing supported by a girder across the top of the cylinder of the pump well. When the pump is working it is found that little weight is carried by the onion bearing as the disc is so arranged that the water entering it supports the moving parts.

The pump was calculated to lift the following: 121 tons at 9ft.; 115 tons at 10ft.; 109 tons at 11ft.; 104 tons at 12ft.; 100 tons at 13ft.; 96 tons at 14ft.; 92 tons at 15ft.; 89 tons at 16ft. The engine bed occupies a space of 30ft. by 5½ft. The engine and pump were supplied by Hathorn, Davey & Co., Leeds. The contract price, including the well and fixing in the old building, the makers taking the old engine, was £2700.

Careful observations have recently been taken by Carmichael as to the consumption of coals by this engine under ordinary working conditions, the quantity of water delivered being ascertained by measuring the quantity passing through the outlet drain. With a lift of 11ft., the amount discharged was 120 tpm, with a consumption of 3 tons of coal in 12 hours. This equals 6¼ lbs/hp of water lifted per minute. One gallon of lubricating oil is used per 12 hours. In 1881 – 1883, with coal at 15/- (75p) a ton, amounts spent were: Coal £674; attendance, oils, etc. £252; total £926. Taking the average lift for both stations at 10½ft. , this is equal to 14.81d per acre, or per acre per foot of lift, 1.42d; or for coals only 1.02d. During this time both scoop wheels were in operation. The main drain is 20ft. wide at the bottom, with slopes 1½ to 1. The average depth of water when pumping varies at starting from 5½ft. to 3ft. at leaving off; the surface inclination also varying from 2½in. per mile to 4in."

In 1884 the crankshaft of this engine broke, smashing the cylinders and doing considerable damage [37].

Fig. 62: Burnt Fen, Lark (S1B) engine house in 1972

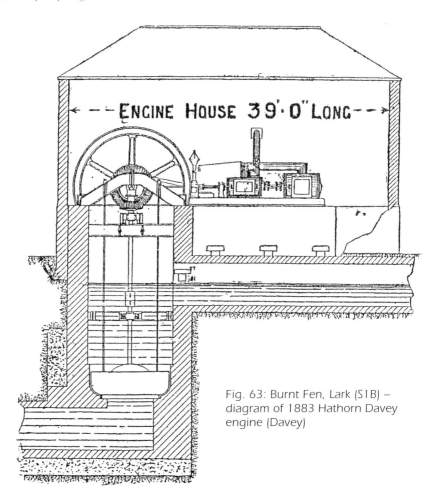

Fig. 63: Burnt Fen, Lark (S1B) –
diagram of 1883 Hathorn Davey
engine (Davey)

This plant was reduced to stand-by duty in 1925 and was last used in 1937. It was removed in 1945 and the building adapted for use as a workshop (Fig. 62). This was demolished in 1990. A shed now stands on the site, with two boilers, adapted for oil storage, outside.

On the outside of the 1842 building, a stone plaque bearing the oft-quoted verse by William Harrison, Superintendent of the district, was placed in the brickwork. This has now been removed to Prickwillow Museum (see Middle Fen), and reads as follows:

"In fitness for the urgent hour,
  Unlimited, untiring power,
  Precision, promptitude, command,
  The infant's will, the giant's hand,
  Steam, Mighty steam, ascends the throne,
  And reigns lord paramount alone."

A 250 hp Blackstone diesel engine driving a 42 in. Gwynnes pump was installed in 1926 in a separate building. This discharged 150 tpm against a total head of 18ft. [38]. This was supplemented in 1945 by a Crossley-Premier 300 hp type KO4 four-cylinder horizontal opposed diesel engine and 36in. Gwynnes pump in yet another building. Both were superseded by an automatic Dorman diesel engine and 33in. Allen-Gwynnes vertical-spindle pump in 1976 [39]. The Blackstone was sold in 1989.

S1C BURNT FEN – Redmore, Hockwold, Norfolk (TL 649869)

By 1863 [40] a pumping station existed on the south bank of the Little Ouse or Brandon River, into which it discharged. This replaced a windpump on a site nearby, which had been converted into two cottages by 1855 [41]. It consisted of a steam engine with one boiler driving a scoop wheel, and was housed in a brick and slate building. This drained Redmore (or Redmere) Farm, then belonging to Alfred Jones and let to F. K. Granger. This was a detached part of Norfolk lying between the present Little Ouse and its former course. It was almost certainly a private engine and survived until after 1898, but probably not for long [42].

This should not be confused with Redmore Farm, Chettisham or Redmoor near Wisbech.

S2 BURWELL FEN, CAMBS. (TL 538699)

This district contained 3288 acres in the parish of Burwell, and was created by Act of 1841 [43]. In the same year, a 35 hp [44] beam engine made by William Fairbairn of Manchester was installed at Upware to drive a scoop wheel. Two boilers appear to have been provided [45]. In 1884 an "assistant wheel" driven from the crankshaft by a chain was fitted behind the scoop wheel to increase the lift [46] It is said that for many years this engine was run on turf instead of coal [47]. There were extensive peat diggings in this fen.

Following failure of the boilers, this engine was replaced in 1895 by a 32 hp Hornsby-Ackroyd paraffin engine (no. 1289) (Fig. 66)[48] driving the scoop wheel. This arrangement was not found to be satisfactory, and the wheel was replaced by an Allen centrifugal pump in 1897 at a cost of £256 [49]. This seems to have been the first internal combustion engine to be applied to fen drainage.

A serious fire occurred on 24 January 1913 at a time of very high water, and the building was badly damaged. Two traction engines were hired to drive the pump until the engine had been repaired [50]. The latter was operating again by 26 March 1913, but it was then decided to instal an additional engine. A 50 hp Ruston & Proctor crude oil engine was purchased at a cost of £425.

Fig. 64: Burwell (S2) engine house in 1969

Fig. 65 (right): Burwell (S2) engine house being converted into a dwellinghouse in 2000

Fig. 66 (below): Hornsby-Ackroyd oil engine as installed at Burwell (S2) (*Engineering, 30 April 1897*)

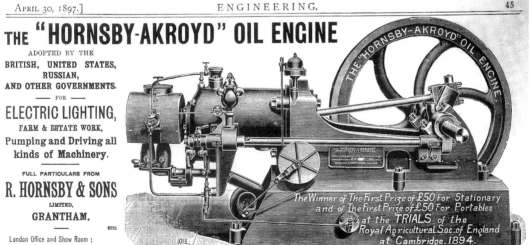

This drove the existing pump by belt drive, and was claimed to deliver 44 tpm with a 5½ft. lift and 31 tpm with a 7½ft. lift [51]. The chimney was demolished at this time.

By 1916 the Hornsby engine was not in working order [52]. It was sold in 1918 when a second-hand suction gas plant and engine, six years old, was purchased. By 1920 parts for the repair of this were unobtainable, and it was replaced by another suction gas plant supplied by Kynocks in 1921 [53]. The Ruston engine was retained and used for normal pumping. The suction gas engine was used in flood conditions because it was more powerful than the Ruston. It drove the same pump by belt-drive [54].

The entire plant failed in 1940 and the district was absorbed into Swaffham and Bottisham. Drainage was achieved by means of a culvert under Reach Lode [55].

For many years the engine house survived as a storeroom (Fig. 64), but was sold in 1995 for conversion into a dwellinghouse (Fig. 65). Discharge was into the River Cam.

S3 CAWDLE FEN, CAMBS. (TL 542788)

This small district was formed by an Act of 1738 [56]. It comprised some 300 acres [57] near Ely. A pumping station existed on the west bank of the River Great Ouse by 1887 [58]. This had been scrapped by 1936 [59]. By 1972 all that remained was a tin shed housing two old centrifugal pumps and traces of a brick building (Fig. 67) [60]. This plant discharged into the River Great Ouse and was next to the locks serving Ely Docks.

It may be surmised that this plant was installed after construction of the main railway line from London to Ely in 1845 and was a beam engine driving a scoop wheel. References to meetings with the Great Eastern Railway Company regarding pumping in 1921 suggest that the plant may have belonged to that company [61]. For this size of fen, it may be assumed that the engine was not above 10 hp.

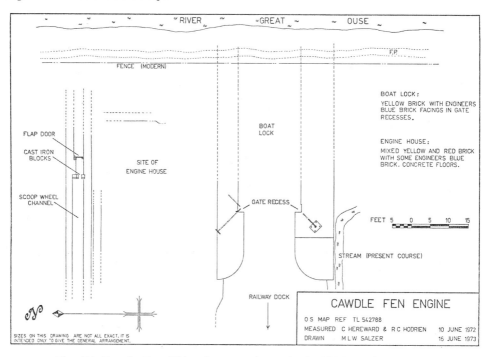

Fig. 67: Cawdle Fen (S3) – diagram of remains in 1972 (M. Salzer et al.)

S4 CHETTISHAM, ELY, CAMBS.
(TL 570834)

This is a small parish, formerly part of Ely, and entirely owned by the Bishopric of Ely [62] and later by the Church Commissioners [63]. In 1841 a station was erected on the west bank of the River Great Ouse, into which it discharged, by William Layton, then tenant of the land [64], to drain an area of 600 acres. This was most probably a beam engine driving a scoop wheel. In about 1870 a single cylinder vertical grasshopper engine replaced this. The bore was 13in. and the stroke 22in., whilst the flywheel was 7ft. 2in. diameter. Steam was supplied at 60 psi by a single boiler. This was replaced in 1915 by a Cornish boiler installed by T. Smithdale of Acle. The engine, rated at 12 hp, was made by Holmes & Sons of Norwich [65]. It originally drove a scoop wheel, but this was later replaced by a turbine pump [66].

This plant was replaced by a diesel engine and centrifugal pump in about 1937 [67]. This had become wholly disused and derelict by 1972 (Fig. 68) [68]. Before 1977 an Allen-Gwynnes electric 12in. pump had been installed.

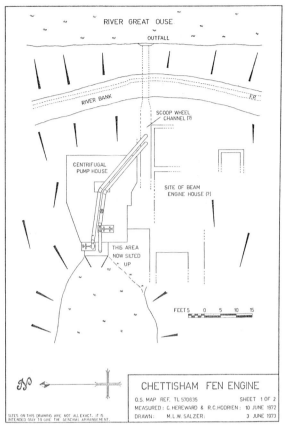

Fig. 68: Chettisham (S4) – diagram of remains in 1972 (M. Salzer et al.)

S5 COTTENHAM, RAMPTON AND WILLINGHAM, Cambs.

This district was formed by Act of 1842 [69], and comprised 3288 acres, later increased to 5000 acres. Its northern boundary extends along the south bank of the Old West River from the A10 road at Stretham Ferry in the east to Willingham Lode in the west, a distance of six miles. Because of this long river frontage, two stations were installed in 1842, being over three miles apart.

S5A Chear Fen (TL 497718)

One of these stations was placed near Stretham Ferry and contained a 30 hp beam engine made by J. Clarke of Deptford Iron Works, Sunderland. The cylinder had a bore of 30in. and a stroke of 60in. The beam was 20ft. 3in. in length and the flywheel 20ft. in diameter. The engine had slide valves and a speed of 18 rpm. There was one boiler. The scoop wheel was 28ft. in diameter with 40 scoops 5½ft. long by 1ft. 8in. wide. It was driven through cast-iron spur gearing with a 5:1 reduction [70]. This plant was last used in 1937 and was dismantled in 1948 [71]. In 1927 a 65 bhp single-cylinder Blackstone type KSI diesel engine driving a 24in. Gwynnes pump discharging 55 tpm was installed in a separate building (Fig. 70).

Fig. 69: Cottenham, Chear Fen (S5A) – Ruston engines

Fig. 70: Cottenham, Chear Fen (S5A) – Blackstone engine

In 1946 twin Ruston 5VCB diesel engines driving Gwynnes pumps having a discharge of 120 tpm (Fig. 69)were installed in yet another building. These engines were replaced in 1997 by Perkins automatic diesel engines type 1306-8TI, driving the existing two Gwynnes 600 mm vertical spindle pumps [72]. Part of the original building remained in 2003.

S5B Smithey Fen (TL 448719)

In the heart of this fen a plant almost identical to that at Chear Fen was also erected in 1842. This was by the same maker but was rated at 40 hp and had a bore of 32$\frac{1}{2}$in. and stroke of 64in. [73].

This plant was the scene of a dreadful accident in December 1860 when the engine driver, William Thoday, fell to his death from the beam loft whilst working the engine on his own at night. He was found in the morning, having been crushed by the crank of the flywheel [74]. This is the only known fatality caused in operating a fen pumping station. Whilst it was common for the smaller steam engines to be driven and stoked by one man, an engine of this size was sometimes staffed by two men.

In 1915 this plant was supplemented by a Ruston & Proctor type CC hot-bulb oil engine of 80 bhp driving a Ruston pump [75].

The steam engine was dismantled in 1942 and replaced by a 156 hp two-cylinder Ruston diesel engine type 10HRC driving a Gwynnes pump having a discharge of 120 tpm. Doran [76] gives a good account of the problems of installing new plant in a building which originally housed an old steam plant:

Fig. 71: Cottenham, Smithey Fen (S5B) engine house

"Owing to the conditions at the site, the only suitable location for the new plant was on the site of the old one. This necessitated the lowering of the engine room floor by four feet and the demolition of the partition wall between the scoop wheel compartment and the engine room. The original beam engine was housed in a lofty but narrow building and, in order to extend the roof over the site of the new pump, considerable structural alterations were necessary including the demolition of the high portion of the building above the new eaves level, the rebuilding of part of the gable wall of the scoop wheel house, and the provision of a new corrugated asbestos roof on steel trusses having a span of 38ft. On the suction side the intake flume had to be lowered by as much as 8ft. which strikingly illustrates the effect of fen shrinkage during the hundred years since the old plant was erected. This necessitated the demolition of part of the old brickwork and the construction of a new reinforced concrete flume in front of the old. At the termination of this flume the existing walls had to be underpinned. The centrifugal pump was placed in the line of the old scoop-wheel race and a new delivery flume constructed in reinforced concrete."

Part of the original building survives (Fig. 71). An electric pump has now been provided on a different site. Both of these stations discharge into the Old West River.

S6 DENVER PARTS (D) (TF 592016)

In 1897 a horizontal 9 bhp oil engine driving an 18in. horizontal-spindle pump [77] was installed on the north bank of St. John's Eau, which had been cut in 1653 from a sluice near Stow Bridge to Denver to convey water from a small area on the north side of the River Wissey. This plant probably replaced the Park Mill.

By 1953 this station contained a 17 hp Blackstone oil engine driving a 14in. Gwynnes pump [78]. This was eliminated upon construction of the relief channel between Denver Sluice and King's Lynn between 1954 and 1959.

S7 EAST OF OUSE, POLVER AND NAR (TF 604126)

This district existed prior to 1914 and contains some 10,000 acres (map 8, p.23). In 1914 [79] a Gwynnes pump and unidentified prime-mover were installed on the east bank of the River Great Ouse, being fed by the Polder Drain. There is no evidence of any earlier plant [80].

In 1944 [81] a pair of twin-cylinder Ruston type 9XHRC diesel engines were installed in a new building on the same site to replace the original plant (Figs. 72 and 73). Each of these drove a 36in. Gwynnes pump. Following serious damage by vandals, this entire plant was scrapped and the building demolished in 1994. An electric motor and pump were installed in its place in a new building.

Fig. 72: East of Ouse, Polver & Nar (S7) engine house in 1989

Fig. 73: East of Ouse, Polver & Nar (S7) - Ruston engines in 1989

S8 FELTWELL NEW FEN, Southery, Norfolk

Acts of 1757, 1773 and 1806 [82] constituted this district. It comprised some 7000 acres [83] in the vicinity of Southery, and is now within Southery and District IDB which contains a much larger area.

S8A Southery (TL 612932)

In 1842 a 60 hp beam engine made by Headly of cambridge was erected on the bank of the River Great Ouse, one mile south of Southery village. The cylinder had a bore of 42in. and stroke of 72ins. The engine moved at 24 rpm on steam at 12 psi. This drove a scoop wheel 32ft. in diameter and 20 tons in weight [84]. This was replaced in 1881 by James Watt & Co. by a wheel 40ft. in diameter with 52 scoops 7$\frac{1}{2}$ft. long by 2ft. 7in. wide, geared down from the engine at 6:1. A rising breast was fitted in front of the wheel [85].

Fig. 74: Southery (S8A) steam engine house c. 1990

Fig. 75: Southery (S8A) – Crossley engine house in 1993

Fig. 76: Southery (S8A) – Crossley engine in 1993

At some time after 1913, and most probably in 1917, the beam engine was scrapped and another building was erected at the side of the old engine house to contain fresh plant, possibly a 210 hp Campbell gas engine driving a 36in. Gwynnes pump [86]. Certainly in 1925 the old building was truncated (Fig. 74) and adapted to house a four-cylinder Mirrlees Bickerton & Day oil engine (no. 38197) driving a 36in. Gwynnes pump [87]. This plant was similar to that at Stretham (S28). In 1944 the other building (Fig. 75) was adapted to contain a Crossley-Premier three-cylinder horizontal diesel engine type KO3 (no. 126447) driving a 36in. Gwynnes pump (Fig. 76).

Both of these diesel engines became redundant when an electric plant was installed south of the A10 road in the 1980s. Following extensive damage by vandals, the old Mirrlees engine house was demolished in 1994. Subsequently the Crossley engine and its house were sold, and in 2004 planning consent was granted for the engine to be scrapped and the building to be converted into a dwellinghouse.

S8B New Fen (D) (TL 602949)

In 1943 a second station was installed on the east bank of the River Great Ouse about a mile north of the main station. This contained a single-cylinder Ruston diesel engine type 9XHR (no. 14750) driving a submersible pump and housed in a brick building. By 1993 this was in a neglected condition, but was still operational. It is still surviving. This station is also sometimes called Further Fen pumping station. It should not be confused with Ramsey New Fen (M27A).

S9 FELTWELL SECOND DISTRICT, Norfolk (TL 651869)

This district was formed by Acts of 1773,1802 and 1849 [88]. It contained 2400 acres [89], and was bounded on the south by the Little Ouse or Brandon River, on the north by Sam's Cut, on the west by Feltwell New Fen Cross Bank, and on the north-east by Feltwell and Hockwold. It is now within Southery & District IDB.

In 1838 a 20 hp [90] Butterley beam engine driving a scoop wheel was installed on the north bank of the Little Ouse River, into which it discharged. This is believed to have been demolished in about 1880, and was probably replaced by a vertical steam engine [91].

By 1936, and probably in about 1927, a corrugated asbestos building (Fig. 77) was erected to house a 170 hp Vickers-Petter hot-bulb oil engine driving a 40in. Gwynnes pump delivering 130 tpm [92]. This plant was similar to that at Lakenheath. This building had become ruinous by 1996 and the engine had been removed to Prickwillow Museum. Meanwhile, in 1942 a separate brick building had been constructed on the foundations of the old beam engine house to contain a type 9XHRF Ruston diesel engine driving a 36in. Gwynnes pump delivering 120 tpm [93].

In 1982 this district was amalgamated with Southery IDB and in 1987 the drainage was wholly reorganised so as to discharge into the new Cut-Off Channel on the east of the district, with a pumping station at Oulsham [94]. The original station must have become redundant at this time. This plant is often called Hockwold.

Fig. 77: Feltwell Second (S9) engine house in 1996

S10 HADDENHAM LEVEL, Cambs.

The Act of 1727 which constituted this district was the first district drainage Act within the South Level [95]. It contained some 9000 acres [96].

S10A Haddenham (TL 427728)

In 1831 a 60 hp side-lever engine made by Maudsley & Field of London [97] was installed on the north bank of the Old West River, into which it discharged. This was supplied with steam by two boilers and fitted with a patent coal supplying machine. The original scoop wheel was replaced in 1871 by Maudsley Sons & Field, the wheel itself being made by Savage of King's Lynn [98]. It had a diameter of 32ft. and width of 2ft. 9in. and delivered 100 tpm. The boilers consumed 2 tons 8 cwt of coal per 12 hours. Average lift was 6$\frac{1}{2}$ft. [99].

As an alternative to lengthening the scoops or lowering the wheel, an assistant wheel was fitted in a race behind the scoop wheel but dipping one to two feet lower than it and thus lifting the water on to the scoop wheel. It was a cast iron wheel with curved scoops driven from the toothed segments on the scoop wheel through gearing and belting. This device was patented by the engineer at this plant, Mr. Hamit, in 1872 and was also fitted to the Burwell Engine [100].

This plant was replaced in 1897 in the old

Fig. 78: Haddenham (S10A) steam engine house in 1949 (Cambs. Coll. – KH)

Fig. 79: Haddenham (S10A) – Allen steam engine in 1949 (Cambs. Coll. – KH)

building, lowered and adapted for the purpose (Fig. 78). Into this was placed an Allen vertical two-cylinder steam engine and centrifugal pump (Fig. 79) [101]. One cylinder only was normally used and two only in times of exceptional flood. Coal consumption was about 2¹/₂ tons per 12 hours. Although this survived until at least 1949, no further details of it have been traced [102]. This plant was almost completely submerged in March 1947. It was last used on 12 January 1948 [103], being replaced in the following year by two Mirrlees diesel engines and pumps in a separate building. These were removed in about 1990. An electric motor and pump now provides the drainage. Part of the old engine house survives in use as a barn.

S10B Sutton Gault (D) (TL 425784)

In 1924 an auxiliary station (Fig. 80) was established at Sutton Gault discharging into the New Bedford River. This contained a two-stroke Petter engine driving a 24in. Gwynnes pump (Fig. 81). This discharged 48 tpm against a head of 12.5ft. It was replaced in 1943 by an Allen two-cylinder type S30B diesel engine (no. K2/46809) driving the Gwynnes pump [104]. This plant was almost completely submerged in March 1947. This was abandoned before 1986 and removed in 1994.

Fig. 80 (above): Haddenham, Sutton Gault (S10B) engine house c. 1930 (CC)

Fig. 81 (right): Haddenham, Sutton Gault (S10B) – 1924 Petter engine (Cambs. Coll.)

S11 HILGAY GREAT WEST FEN, Norfolk (TL 597982)

This district consists of 615 acres [105] bounded on the south-west by Sam's Cut, on the west by the River Great Ouse, on the north by the River Wissey and on the east by Hilgay village, with some land west of the Ouse. The Commission was formed by Acts of 1768, 1831, and 1854 [106]. The grandiose title attaches to one of the smallest drainage districts in the Fens.

It was originally drained by a beam engine and scoop wheel [107] erected in 1854 [108] on the east bank of the River Great Ouse. This would have been a very small engine of about 10 hp, probably similar to that supplied for Willingham West Fen (S29).

By 1935 a vertical steam engine was in operation, [109] probably erected about 1900/1910. This was replaced in 1939, when the building was most probably truncated (Fig. 82). The new plant consisted of a Ruston & Hornsby 6HR diesel engine driving a Dodmans pump (Fig. 83) indirectly by V-belt. This drive suggests that the pump was installed with the previous vertical engine [110]. An electric pump was installed in 1971 and the old machinery was sold and the building demolished in the early 1980s.

Fig. 82 (above): Hilgay Great West Fen (S11) engine house in 1972

Fig. 83 (right): Hilgay Great West Fen (S11) - Dodmans pump after removal

S12 HILGAY, Wood Hall Estate, Norfolk (TL 643979)

The Wood Hall Estate near Hilgay was acquired in 1806 by William Lowton Jones [111]. In 1849 [112] he erected a beam engine and scoop wheel to drain his estate. The size of the boiler room suggests that this had two boilers. The estate was sold in 1878 to Major Michael Stocks and the plant was variously known as Jones's or Stocks's Engine.

This plant was removed in 1907 [113] and replaced by a vertical engine driving a Dodmans Triton pump [114]. The engine was replaced in about 1940 by a small Ruston diesel engine (type 5XHR?) driving the existing pump [115].

When E.P. Stocks died in 1974, drainage of the estate was taken over by Southery and District IDB and the plant was abandoned. The building and machinery remained in derelict condition in 2002 (Fig. 84). Discharge was into the River Wissey.

S13 LAKENHEATH AND BRANDON, Suffolk (TL 677856)

This district, formed by Act of 1768 [116], comprised 3586 acres [117]. In 1844 a 40 hp [118] beam engine, almost certainly by Butterley, was erected to drive a scoop wheel at Cross Waters, discharging into the Little Ouse River. The cylinder of this engine measured 27 by 48in. and the flywheel was 19½ft. in diameter. There were two boilers, one made by Butterley and the other by Charles Burrell of Thetford. Speed was 30 rpm. The scoop wheel was 30ft. in diameter by 19in. wide [119]. This plant was scrapped in about 1943, when the building (Fig. 85) was demolished [120].

Meanwhile, in 1926 [121] a 180 hp Vickers Petter oil engine had been fitted in a separate corrugated asbestos building (Fig. 86) to drive a 36in. Gwynnes pump delivering 100 tpm [122]. This was derelict by 1993 and has since been demolished. In about 1950 a 210 hp Ruston four-cylinder vertical oil engine was installed in a separate brick building. This was surviving as an un-maintained stand-by in 1996, having been superseded by an electric drive in yet another building.

Fig. 84 (left): Hilgay, Wood Hall Estate (S12) engine house in 1990

Fig. 85 (above): Lakenheath (S13) engine house c. 1920 (Cambs. Coll.)

Fig. 86 (left): Lakenheath (S13) – diesel engine house

S14 LITTLEPORT AND DOWNHAM

The largest drainage district in the South Level was constituted by Acts of 1756, 1800 and 1810 [123]. It comprises some 26,000 acres, but the catchment area for drainage purposes is over 30,000 acres. Although the majority of the district is in Cambridgeshire, the northern part lies in Norfolk.

By the early nineteenth century, there were 80 windpumps in this district. These were replaced by two steam-powered plants, placed seven miles apart. One was on the east bank of the Hundred Foot or New Bedford River near Oxlode, and the other on the west bank of the River Great Ouse at Ten Mile Bank. In 1847 a small private plant was installed at Martin's Farm, about 1½ miles north of Ten Mile Bank.

S14A Ten Mile Bank Station, Norfolk (TL 600963)

In 1818 the Commissioners decided to erect a steam engine to serve the northern part of the district. Before ordering this, they inspected the only steam-powered pumping station then existing in the Fens: that at Sutton St. Edmund (L1). This first plant was erected at Ten Mile Bank, by which name it became known, although early references call it Modney Court Pumping Station. Four successive sets of machinery stood on this site. The station is well-documented, although the log books which existed there in 1980 have disappeared. The engine was a 30 hp beam engine by Hague & Topham, having a cylinder 30 by 72in., and making 18 rpm. It was in operation by March 1820. The engine alone cost £1800 [124]. Although discharge was into non-tidal water, there was a considerable rise in the level of the river when Denver Sluice was shut. Therefore two scoop wheels were originally fitted so that one could be used against high water and both when the water was low. These were 26ft. in diameter and 2ft. wide and rotated at 6 rpm. Two wheels were only ever fitted at one other station, Burnt Fen – Little Ouse (S1A). A single boiler supplied steam, and this was renewed in 1830.

This plant was found to be inadequate to drain the large area involved. In 1842 the engine was sold [125] and the entire plant was demolished. In its place an 80 hp Butterley beam engine having a cylinder 44 by 96in. was installed in a new building (Fig. 87) which was very similar to those at Hundred Foot (S14B), Sutton and Mepal (M36) and Stretham (S28). This engine (Figs. 88 and 89) drove a scoop wheel 42ft. 8in. in diameter and 3ft. in width. The diameter was increased by one foot in 1879. This wheel had 50 scoops of 7ft. 6in. radial length. The engine was overhauled and refitted in 1881 at a cost of £2239. A circular slide valve to work from the parallel motion was substituted for the D slide valve and an internal expansion valve added to cut-off at from one-tenth to one-half of the stroke. In 1888 the average dip of the scoops was 3ft., but due to subsidence of the land this had fallen to 1ft. 10in. by 1912. The lift was 11ft. average and 14ft. maximum. At best discharge was 213 tpm [126]. Three boilers supplied steam, these being renewed in 1879 at a cost of £1372 [127].

In 1912 the entire plant was replaced. The engine house was reduced to the height of the boiler room, which was halved in width, and the roof of the latter was extended to cover the whole building. It is curious that this extensive building work should have been undertaken when the same Board retained the old building at their other station at Hundred Foot when replacing its plant only two years later. The new plant consisted of two sets of 200 bhp Allen double-acting open compound condensing engines having cylinders of 14 and 22in. bore and 13in. stroke. Speed was 200 to 250 rpm. These drove two 48in. horizontal-spindle Allen centrifugal pumps each capable of delivering between 150 and 190 tpm to a maximum lift of 15ft. Three Lancashire boilers supplied steam at 120 psi. This plant cost £6000 [128].

In 1935 one of these engines was replaced by a 340 bhp Allen three-cylinder four-stroke diesel engine type S60, and the other in 1948 by a 360 bhp Allen four-cylinder two-stroke

Fig. 87 (left): Ten Mile Bank (S14A) beam engine house c. 1900 (Cambs. Coll.)

Fig. 88 ((left): Ten Mile Bank (S14A) beam engine in 1912 (Allen)

Fig. 89 (above): Ten Mile Bank (S14A) beam loft in 1912 (Allen)

Fig. 90 (left): Ten Mile Bank (S14A) engine house in 1972

diesel engine type 47. The original pumps were retained. The chimney was demolished at this time (Fig. 90).

In about 1980 a completely new electrically-powered plant was installed some 1½ miles south of the old plant at TL 607940. The latter was retained for emergency use only until 1995, when all of the machinery was removed. The two engines were placed at Prickwillow Museum. The old building has since been converted into a dwellinghouse.

S14B Hundred Foot Station, Little Downham, Cambs. (TL 508891)

The first steam plant on this site was erected next to the site of the double-lift Westmoor Mills, which it replaced [129]. It was first operated on 10 April 1830.

The machinery consisted of an 80 hp Butterley beam engine having a cylinder 43½ by 96in. (Fig. 91) [130]. The flywheel was 26ft. 3in. in diameter and weighed 30 tons [131]. The beam was 26ft. in length and weighed 15 tons. Two boilers were originally supplied, a third being added in November 1843 [132]. The original boilers were replaced by Butterley in November 1869, and the third by James Watt in 1875. All three were replaced in 1911 by high-pressure Lancashire boilers supplying steam at 125 psi. These boilers remain in the building 2003. Coal consumption in the early years averaged 0.39 tons per hour, but this was reduced after a circular slide valve was substituted for the D slide valve in 1882, with an internal expansion valve to cut off from one-tenth to one-half of the stroke. The design of the engine house (Fig. 92) was followed at Ten Mile Bank (S14A) and elsewhere.

Originally steam was provided at 5 psi, but this was increased to 20 psi by extensive works carried out by Watt & Co. in 1881 to 2 at a cost of £4525. Similarly the original engine

Fig. 92 (above): Hundred Foot (S14B) engine house c. 1927 (COC)

Fig. 91 (left): Hundred Foot (S14B) beam engine c. 1913 (Cambs. Coll.)

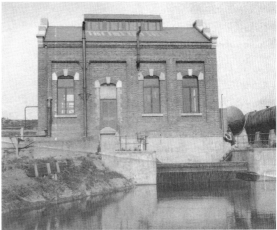

Fig. 94 (above): Hundred Foot (S14B)
Mirrlees engine house c. 1927 (COC)

Fig. 93 (left): Hundred Foot (S14B)
Gwynnes steam engine in 1949
(Cambs. Coll. – KH)

speed of 10/12 rpm was increased at that time to a maximum of 22 rpm. Gearing to the scoop wheel was 7:1.

The engine drove a scoop wheel originally 37ft. 5in. in diameter by 3ft. 4in. wide. This was increased to 41ft 8in. in 1844 by lengthening the scoops, the width then being 32in. 9. In 1881 a completely new wheel was installed. This was 50ft. in diameter and 42in. wide and weighed 75 tons, being the largest scoop wheel ever erected in the Fens [133]. The maximum recorded discharge was 197 tpm.

To deal with the problem of pumping into a tidal river, the engine was originally fitted with two gears. There was a sliding pinion on the engine axis, 4ft. in diameter, weighing 33 cwt., and turning at 13 rpm. At high tide, this was engaged with a wheel 24ft. diameter, with internal teeth, giving the ladles a velocity of 212ft. per minute and discharging 98 tpm. At low tide, the pinion, by the help of machinery, was made to slide into action with another wheel of 16ft. diameter discharging 146 tpm [134]. This mechanism does not seem to have been used very often, and never after 1853 [135]. By 1862 136 a rising breast had been installed in front of the scoop wheel, and by 1867 a shuttle or slacker on the inlet side. A trial with the rising breast in the latter year showed that with it down the engine made 10 rpm, and with it up 18 rpm [136]. A more precise trial was carried out in 1872 when a weir was fixed across the outlet. The dip was 3ft. 5in. and the head 15ft. 11in. With the rising breast down, the engine was unable to operate. When it was raised 8ft., the engine made 14 rpm [137].

The shrinkage of this peat fen is amply illustrated by the diminishing dip of the water wheel. Starting at 6ft. 4in. in 1830, it had fallen to around 4ft. by 1844, when the wheel was lowered. By 1872 this had fallen to about 3ft. The new wheel fitted in 1881 returned the dip to nearly 5ft. By 1911 it was falling to under 2ft. after a few hours pumping [135].

This plant was scrapped in 1914 when a 400 hp vertical Gwynnes steam engine (Fig. 93) [138] was installed in the old building. This drove a 50in. Gwynnes pump discharging 212 tpm against a total head of 21ft. Although supplemented in 1926 by a Mirrlees diesel engine driving a 36in. Gwynnes pump housed in a separate building (Fig. 94), the steam engine survived until 1951. It was then replaced by a 540 hp Ruston & Hornsby type 6VEBX vertical six-cylinder turbo-charged diesel engine (no. 313079) in the old building. The chimney was subsequently felled, but the old engine house remains, with the Ruston which is maintained as a stand-by, and the 1911 boilers. The Mirrlees engine was sold in 1965 and its engine house demolished in 1985, when a new electric plant was constructed on its site.

S14C Martin's Farm, Hilgay, Norfolk (TL 591986)

In 1847, about 1½ miles north of Ten Mile Bank Pumping Station, a beam engine driving a 34ft. scoop wheel was erected to drain an estate of about 800 acres. The cost of this was met by the Great Eastern Railway Company following successful litigation by the owner who claimed that the embankment of the new railway line from Ely to King's Lynn had stopped the wind from reaching his windpump.

This plant was replaced in 1909 in the old engine house (Fig. 95) by an Allen open double-acting single cylinder non-condensing engine driving direct an Allen horizontal-spindle pump (Fig. 96). The bore of the cylinder was 10in. and the stroke 9in. Steam was supplied at 60 psi

Fig. 95: Martin's Farm (S14C) engine house c. 1912 (Allen)

Fig. 96: Martin's Farm (S14C) – Allen plant (Allen)

to run the engine at 275 rpm. Discharge was 13$^1/_2$ tpm against a lift of 17ft. The pump was 14in. in diameter and placed in the scoop wheel race. The boiler was 20ft. by 5ft. diameter [139]. Discharge was into the River Great Ouse.

This was succeeded in about 1940 by a single-cylinder Lanz Bulldog diesel engine when the old building was demolished and a new engine house constructed from the old bricks. An electric plant had replaced this by 1972. This land is now within Littleport & Downham IDB.

S15 METHWOLD AND FELTWELL, Norfolk

This district lies between the River Wissey to its north and the Little Ouse to its south, being bisected by Sam's Cut. To its west it adjoins Feltwell New Fen and Hilgay. The drainage district was created by Act of 1855 [140] and was called Feltwell & Methwold. This Board was dissolved by an Act of 1909 which created a new authority called Methwold & Feltwell District. The area drained comprised 3718 acres in Methwold and 921 in Feltwell [141].

Until 1883 the district was drained by gravity through Sam's Cut to Hunt's Sluice, where the water was discharged into the River Great Ouse. Thereafter four stations were established at different places and times. There are no useful remains of any of these.

S15A Hunt's Sluice (TL599978)

In 1883 a 40 hp Edward Easton [142] semi-portable compound condensing engine was installed at Hunt's Sluice. This was coupled direct to a vertical spindle centrifugal pump discharging 100 tpm into the River Ouse [143]. Major Stocks, owner of the Wood Hall Estate in Hilgay, refused to participate because he already had a pumping plant on his land [144].

This plant was used less after the construction of the Decoy Bridge station in 1913 and by 1925 was deemed unfit for further service [145]. In that year an arrangement was made with Southery Fen District (Feltwell New Fen) to pass water out of Sam's Cut into that district through the Sandway Drain so as to render this station redundant. It was sold in 1931 [146]. The concrete floor of the plant is all that remains, mostly hidden by undergrowth (Fig. 98). The north-western section of Sam's Cut had been abandoned in 1928. The sluice remains, sunk into the ground and useless.

Fig. 97: Hunt's Sluice (S15A) – engine foundations in 2004

S15B Decoy Bridge (otherwise Harwins Bridge) (D) (TL 648943)

The station established at Decoy Bridge in 1913 contained a Campbell Gas Co. Ltd. 90 bhp two-cylinder oil engine driving a 30in. Gwynnes pump (Fig. 98) discharging 100 tpm into Sam's Cut. Each cylinder was 12$^1/_2$ by 22in. and only one was used for normal running to economise in fuel [147]. It is stated that this was the first crude oil engine to be installed in the Fens [148]. This plant was sold in 1931 and only the massive concrete foundations remain.

Fig. 98: Decoy Bridge (S15B) – Campbell engine in 1913 (Crocker)

S15C Catsholme Farm (D) (TL683971)

Following the arrangement with Southery District, the drainage of this fen was entirely changed in 1927. A new station (Fig. 99) was built to discharge into the River Wissey. Hathorn Davey & Co. supplied a 60 hp McLaren-Benz diesel engine driving a "Gill" pump having a capacity of 50 tpm. This engine did not operate satisfactorily, and in 1930 the supplier changed it for a 110 hp version. This cannot have been a success because in 1938 the plant was replaced by a pair of Allen type S30 diesel engines. One was a 108 bhp four-cylinder engine driving an Allen pump delivering 70 tpm, and the other a 155 bhp six-cylinder engine driving a pump delivering 100 tpm [149]. These were superceded in 1967 by two electrically-driven Allen-Gwynnes 27in. submersible pumps of 1.1 cumecs capacity each, but were retained as stand-by until 1998 when they were scrapped. The engines are understood to have been saved for preservation.

Fig. 99: Catsholme Farm (S15C) engine house in 1990

S15D Ammonia Plant

In 1904 the Crown sold some its land in this area. One of the purchasers built an ammonia plant about one mile downstream from the future Catsholme Farm engine site and installed a steam engine and scoop wheel to drain the land. In about 1924 this was replaced by a portable steam engine driving a centrifugal pump on the same site, and this operated until 1938 [150].

S16 METHWOLD SEVERALS, Norfolk (TL 660979)

This district was created in 1773 as the first district under Feltwell Drainage Act [151], which stated its size as 8000 acres [152]. It contained the land north of Sam's Cut and south of the River Wissey between the hard lands of Hilgay on the west and those of Methwold on the east. In 1854 part of the eastern section of this district known as Methwold Common was constituted as a separate district [153] called Methwold and Feltwell (S15).

In 1849 a beam engine made by J. & A. Blyth of London was installed close to the site of the present sugar beet factory at Wissington and near Five Mile House [154]. The cylinder was 27 by 48in. with beam centres of 14ft. and a D slide valve. The flywheel was $16^{1}/_{2}$ft. in diameter with six spokes and cast in halves. Steam was supplied at 15 psi from one Lancashire boiler. The engine drove a scoop wheel 30ft. in diameter with scoops 6ft. long by 18in. wide [155]. Discharge was into the River Wissey.

This plant existed in 1936, by then apparently disused, but has since totally disappeared.

As the Act of 1854 required the consent of the Duchy of Lancaster to be obtained before any steam engine draining into the River Wissey be installed, it is most likely that this plant was privately erected. The area is now within Southery & District IDB.

S17 MIDDLE FEN, Cambs.

This district is bounded on the north-east by the River Lark, on the north-west by a bank separating it from Upper Padnal District, and on the west by the Rivers Great Ouse and Cam. It was formed by an Act of 1758, followed by others of 1789 and 1800, and contains some 11,000 acres [156].

S17A Prickwillow (TL 597824)

In 1832 a Butterley marine side-lever of 60 hp was installed at Prickwillow [157]. This drove a scoop wheel $33^{1}/_{2}$ft. in diameter by 2ft. 1in. wide. Steam was provided at 6 psi [158]. Discharge which was into the River Lark was approximately 70 tpm. Coal consumption was 6 tons per 24 hours.

This plant was scrapped in 1897, but meanwhile had been supplemented in 1880 by new machinery in a separate adjoining building (Fig. 100). Wheeler's description [159] of this plant (Figs. 101 and 102) is so comprehensive as to deserve repetition in full:

"The new engine and pump were intended to relieve the old engine of the greater part of its duty, and to drain out the water to a greater depth than was practicable with the scoop wheel. The new machinery was erected by Eastons and Anderson. The engine is 60 nhp compound condensing beam engine, working on 65 psi from two Lancashire boilers. The high pressure cylinder is 15ins, and the low pressure 25in. in diameter with $4^{1}/_{2}$ft. stroke. The pump is of the vertical spindle type, with single inlet, with balance fan 5ft. 4in. diameter and 1ft. 2in. deep, placed at such a level that the lowest water in the drain will cover it. The inlet is 2ft. 8in. in diameter, formed on the lower side only, special provision being made for balancing the column of water above the fan being balanced by the fixed inlet piece, which also serves to steady the lower end of the fan spindle. The meeting faces between the fan and the fixed case are both turned in the same direction so that wear as it takes place can be taken up simply by lowering the fan spindle by means of an adjustment provided for the purpose. To take up the momentum of the water issuing at great speed from the fan, patent guide curves were fitted, which turned the water gradually into the vertical direction and at the same time assisted to bring it to rest. In this particular instance these guide curves were not found to be of much avail, as when the river was low the delivery was lower than the top of the blades, and consequently there was a churning action going on with the water in the well, which caused vibration in the spindle. They were therefore removed. The pump is placed at the bottom of a brick well, in one side of which is the outlet passage 4ft. wide by $4\frac{1}{2}$ft. high, fitted with self-acting doors and communicating with a cast iron outlet pipe $4\frac{1}{2}$ft. diameter and about 68ft. long. The upper end of the fan spindle hangs on an onion bearing, and is driven by a pair of bevel wheels from a horizontal shaft which passed into the engine house, on which is a pinion driven by annular gearing, bolted to the rim of the fly-wheel of the engine. The pump is calculated to lift 95 tpm at 8ft. lift, 88 tpm at 9ft., 83 tpm at 10ft., 78 tpm at 11ft., 74 tpm at 13ft., 68 tpm at 14ft. and 65 tpm at 15ft. The cost of the machinery including engine, pump and two boilers was £3853."

Fig. 100: Middle Fen, Prickwillow (S17A) – 1832 and 1880 engine houses c. 1900 (Cambs. Coll.)

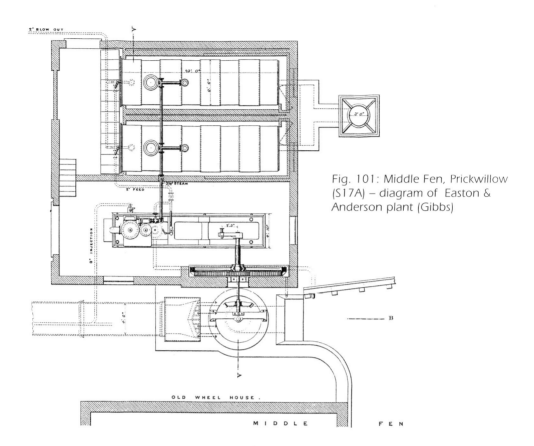

Fig. 101: Middle Fen, Prickwillow (S17A) – diagram of Easton & Anderson plant (Gibbs)

Fig. 102: Middle Fen, Prickwillow (S17A) – Easton & Anderson engine (Cambs. Coll.)

In 1897, new machinery was installed in the original engine house, which was adapted for the purpose. R.W. Allen describes this plant [160]:

> "The machinery consists of a vertical compound double-acting condensing open engine, driving direct an Allen Conqueror horizontal centrifugal pump. The steam cylinders are 21ins. and 35 ins. diameter each having a stroke of 20ins. The engine is capable of developing 300 ihp with steam pressure at 75 psi. The diameter of the suction and delivery pipes is 43ins. and the pump is capable of delivering 150 tpm upon a 16ft. lift at 130 rpm. The revolving disk is $5\frac{1}{2}$ft. diameter, and is made of cast-iron and keyed to a steel shaft, running in white-metal bearings. The pump is provided with steam-ejector, for the purpose of charging. The engine has fixed on the high-pressure crosshead a connecting-rod with reciprocating beam, the levers of which are connected to a single-acting air-pump, 20ins. diameter by 10ins. stroke. Attached to the air-pump is a jet-condenser, giving a constant vacuum of 26-27ins., steam being supplied by two Lancashire boilers , $23\frac{1}{2}$ft. by 8ft. diameter, with Galloway cross-tubes.
>
> From March 1912 to March 1913 this engine ran on 209 days (of 12 hours duration) the maximum non-stop run being 372 hours during the latter part of August. The average coal consumption was $3\frac{1}{2}$ tons for the 12 hours including the raising of steam in boilers."

The 1880 plant was removed in 1924 and replaced in the same building by a Mirrlees Bickerton & Day 5-cylinder marine diesel engine (no. 36650), developing 250 bhp at 250 rpm. This drove a 42in. centrifugal Conqueror pump made by W.H. Allen & Sons of Bedford. It delivered 140 tpm. This was superseded by an electric pump in 1958, but remains in preservation by a trust.

Gibbs comments that the drainage of this district in 1887 was performed by the two steam engines at Prickwillow and three large windpumps, two on the Lark bank and one on the bank of the Ouse at Ely, with thirty other small windpumps pumping into engine drains. These mills were eventually replaced by two stations, at Overfall and New Mills.

S17B Overfall (TL 560804)

The large mill called Overfall on the east bank of the River Great Ouse near Ely is fully described by Allen [161] and survived until about 1917, probably by then supplied with a steam engine, although the photograph in Allen suggests that it was in a poor state by 1913. A new brick building (Fig. 103), demolished in 2005 (Fig. 104) was then erected to house a Mirrlees three-cylinder vertical diesel engine (Fig. 105) driving a pump of unknown make. The engine was removed in 1971.

S17C New Mills, Isleham (D) (TL 628789)

By 1944 the drainage of the eastern part of Middle Fen had become wholly inadequate. A new plant was installed on the west bank of the River Lark in Isleham Fen. This consisted of a pair of 176 hp Allen type S30 vertical four-cylinder diesel engines (nos. K1/98946 – A and B) driving 28 and 30in. Allen Conqueror pumps each delivering 70 tpm [162]. These still existed, moribund, in 2004.

This district has now been amalgamated with Soham Mere and is called Middle Fen and Mere.

Fig. 103 (above): Middle Fen, Overfall (S17B) engine house c. 1930 (Cambs. Coll.)

Fig. 104 (left): Middle Fen, Overfall (S17B) engine house in 1993

Fig. 105 (below): Middle Fen, Overfall (S17B)Mirrlees engine (Cambs. Coll.)

S18 MIDDLETON, Norfolk
(TF 659179)

A small private plant was built in 1877 [163] to drain a few hundred acres belonging to the Middleton Towers Estate, then owned by Sir Lewis Whincop Jarvis [164]. This lay about two miles east of King's Lynn and discharged into a system of drains leading to Lynn (map 8, p.23).

The engine was a 10 hp vertical steam engine made by J.C. Baker of King's Lynn, with a cylinder $6^{1}/_{2}$ by $9^{1}/_{2}$in. [165] It ceased work in 1934 [166] and the engine had been removed by 1975. The building, chimney and scoop wheel remained in 1992, and are believed still to exist (fig. 106).

George Watkins provides a full description of this plant:

Fig. 106: Middleton (S18) chimney in 1992

"This little plant served to drain a low level area within the Ramsden Estate, transferring the water to the main drains in periods of very wet weather. Again it was as simple as possible with the non-condensing engine driving by single reduction gearing to the scoop wheel shaft. Steam was supplied by a vertical boiler $3^{1}/_{2}$ft. diameter by 8ft. high. There was no feed water heater, the exhaust steam pipe passing straight through the roof. The feed-water pump was originally driven by the engine and fitted on the bed-plate, but was replaced by an injector in later years. The scoop wheel was 16ft. tip diameter and fitted with 40 paddles each $3^{1}/_{4}$ft. long by $5^{1}/_{4}$in. wide. The gear reduction was one revolution of the wheel to 15 of the engine.

The scoop wheel framing consisted of a series of identical castings bolted together along the arms with slots in the rim for the paddles." [167]

An engine similar to this, but much earlier, is now exhibited at Stretham Engine (S28).

S19 MILDENHALL or BURNT FEN SECOND, Suffolk

This district, of some 6100 acres [168], was created by Acts of 1760 and 1807 [169].

S19A Mildenhall Original Station (TL 629790)

In 1844 [170] a 60 hp [171] Butterley beam engine having a cylinder 42 by 54in. was erected to drive a scoop wheel 32ft. in diameter. Steam was supplied at 10 psi by two boilers, replaced in 1886 by J. & J. Horsfield of Dewsbury. The wheel was geared down $5^{1}/_{2}$:1. The flywheel was 20ft. in diameter, and the beam centres 16ft. [172]. Discharge was into the River Lark.

This plant was last used in 1930 [173]. By then it had been replaced by a 145 hp Vickers-Petter oil engine driving a 40in. Gwynnes pump delivering 130 tpm [174]. The old engine survived in 1936 and is said to have been removed in 1944, but at some stage the building was truncated and the chimney felled. This plant was abandoned at some time after. The building remains in dilapidated condition (Fig. 107), with a pump but no engine inside. The drain has been infilled.

Fig. 107: Mildenhall (S19A) engine house in 1992

S19B Mildenhall (D) (TL 623801)

Before 1943 another station was established about ³/₄ mile north of the original station. This housed a four cylinder Ruston oil engine driving a Gwynnes pump. This remains, but has been superseded by an electric plant on the same site.

S20 NORTHWOLD SEVERALS, Norfolk (TL 701979)

This fen was enclosed in 1796 and contained 1500 acres [175]. In 1849 a small beam engine was erected by J.B.S. Bradfield [176] to replace a windpump [177]. The engineer responsible for installing the engine was W.D. Harding of King's Lynn.

The engine was of decorative A-frame design [178] and had a long D-slide valve [179]. This drove a scoop wheel 24ft. in diameter by 9ins. in width, built in eight segments with six start posts in each, the gear internal segments being cast with the rim. Discharge was into the River Wissey.

This plant was derelict in 1937 [180] and was scrapped in about 1942. It was replaced by an Allen diesel engine and pump, delivering 45 tpm, in the existing building. The latter was partially demolished in about 1990 (Fig. 108) [181]. This area is now within Northwold IDB.

Fig. 108: Northwold Severals (S20) – remains of engine house in 1996

S21 OVER, Cambs.

This district, in the parish of Over near Earith, was formed by Act of 1837 [182] and comprised 1498 acres [183]. The boundary between the parishes of Over and Willingham lies half a mile south of the River Ouse, and disputes over the drainage of the two parishes existed for centuries. Initially, therefore, any drainage plant serving Over had to be placed at least half a mile south of the river, with an outfall drain of the same length. The river is tidal at this point.

S21A Over original station (TL 390742)

In 1837 a 20 hp [184] beam engine made by J. Clarke of Deptford Iron Works was accordingly erected south of the river. The diameter of the flywheel was 14ft. and the beam centres 12ft. Speed was 33 rpm. This drove a scoop wheel 16ft. in diameter with 32 scoops 4½ft. long by 15in. wide, and was geared down 4:1 from the engine. This wheel was replaced in 1871 by Savage of King's Lynn (cf Haddenham). Steam was provided by a single Lancashire boiler by Dodmans of King's Lynn at a pressure of 10/15 psi. The original D-slide valve never seems to have been replaced. [185] This entire plant was scrapped in 1942 and there are no traces of it on the ground.

S21B Over (D) (TL 391747)

In 1942 it was possible to select a new site on the bank of the River Ouse just west of the Hermitage sluice at Earith. A 40 hp Ruston diesel engine type 7XHR driving a Gwynnes pump was installed in a brick building [186]. This survives as a stand-by, but has not been started since 1978. It was replaced by an electric pump in 1973, when Willingham West Fen was incorporated with the district to form Over & Willingham IDB.

S22 PADNAL AND WATERDEN FEN, Cambs.

This district was created by an Act of 1827 known as the South Level General Act [187]. This appointed separate Commissioners for the South Level main river (the Ouse from Hermitage Sluice at Earith to Littleport), and for Padnal and Waterden Fens. The South Level Commissioners were empowered to form a new cut, known as Sandy's Cut from Overfall Mill below Ely to Littleport, and to provide a new course for the Lark to flow directly into that Cut, which takes its name from an uncompleted part of Vermuyden's works. The new cut was opened on 19 April 1830 [188].

The new district of Padnal and Waterden consisted of the area between the new Cut and the old course of the River Ouse (which flowed to Prickwillow, where it joined the River Lark and then meandered to Littleport), together with land on the west side of Sandy's Cut near Littleport. By the 1827 Act, the Padnal Commissioners were given power to divide that Fen into separate Upper and Lower districts, which they did. In 1938 the acreages were given as 1732 for the Upper District and 871 for the Lower [189]. Each of these had its own drainage plant.

S22A Upper Padnal (TL 578839)

In 1831 this district erected a 12 hp steam engine made by Ryde of Leicester, driving a scoop wheel and costing £500. By November of that year Ryde was asked to supply an additional pinion wheel to increase the speed of the scoop wheel to 5 rpm when the head in the river was low [190]. The scoop wheel was replaced in 1842 by a cast-iron wheel dipping one foot deeper than the original wheel [191]. In 1850 a new metallic piston was fitted by J. & E. Headley at a cost of £20 [192]. A new Butterley boiler was purchased in 1873 for £147. 6. 4d [193].

This engine and boiler were sold in 1884 when a high pressure engine made by Hathorn Davey was installed in the old building, which was altered for the purpose. This had a cylinder 16 by 30in. and ran at 78 rpm. It drove a vertical spindle centrifugal pump 44in. in diameter, claimed to deliver 29 tpm against a 15ft. head. The cost of this plant was £941, and the alterations to the building £371 [194]. In 1926 the boiler was replaced by Alfred Dodman & Co. at a cost of £281. Discharge was into the River Lark.

Fig. 109: Upper Padnal (S22A) engine house in 1973

This plant was scrapped in 1937 and an Allen diesel engine and pump installed in its place. This had been removed by 1992, and the entire building (Fig. 109) had been demolished by October 1998. By 1977 an Allen-Gwynnes electric plant with a 12in. pump had been erected at the other end of the district at TL 568819, discharging into the River Great Ouse.

S22B Lower Padnal (TL 576857)

This district was originally drained by two windpumps erected in 1833, one on each side of Sandy's Cut. The western mill burnt down in 1858. A cast iron tube was then set in a channel in the river bed to take the water into the drain on the other side. For the eastern side, the Commissioners had purchased from the Littleport and Downham Commissioners the Westmoor Mill which had been replaced by the Hundred Foot Engine, but then decided that it would cost more to re-erect this than to instal a new pump. After a brief experiment in 1879 of using a locomotive engine to drive the wheel, a steam engine replaced the windpump in 1881 [195].

This was a horizontal Easton & Anderson condensing engine with a single cylinder of 12 by 26in. The flywheel was 8ft. 1in. in diameter. Steam was supplied at 60 psi by a single boiler supplied by the makers, which was replaced in 1925 by a Cornish boiler made by Dodmans of King's Lynn. The engine ran at 79 rpm. Clark states that:

> "the turbine pump was housed in an annexe outside and driven by bevel gearing, the wheel on the crankshaft having 106 wooden teeth and that on the pump spindle having 44 teeth of cast iron. The ratio of engine to pump was 2.4:1" [196].

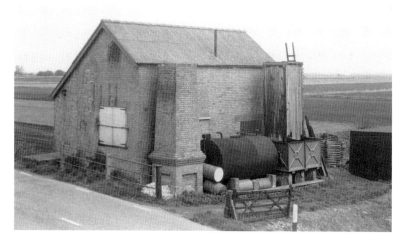

Fig. 110: Lower Padnal (S22B) engine house in 1973

This plant was scrapped in 1937 and an Allen twin-cylinder diesel engine type S27 driving an Allen pump installed in the old building. This has since been superseded by an Allen-Gwynnes 12in. electric pump in a new building; but the old building, less chimney, has survived (Fig. 110). Discharge was into the River Great Ouse.

S23 SOHAM MERE, Cambs (TL 570748)

An area of 1600 acres close to Soham was almost completely covered with water until the early nineteenth century. It was subsequently known as the Dunn Gardner Estate. In 1831 a gas vacuum engine was applied to its drainage [197] to supplement the existing windpump. This was abandoned in 1833 because the gas supply from the producer gas plant could not be maintained. Windpumps had been retained. One of these was replaced in 1839 by a 40 hp Butterley beam engine erected to drive a scoop wheel 36ft. in diameter. Glynn states that the power of this engine was dictated by the considerable lift involved [198].

This was replaced in 1910 by an open compound engine with cylinders 9 and 15in. bore by 9in. stroke, capable of developing 65 bhp at 250 rpm. Steam was supplied at 120 psi by a single Lancashire boiler 20ft. by 6ft. 3in. This drove a centrifugal pump 22in. in diameter delivering 35 tpm against a 17ft. lift. Coal consumption was from $2^{1}/_{2}$ to 3 tons in 24 hours. This machinery was placed in the old building [199]. Both engine and pump were supplied by Allens.

This plant was replaced in 1940 by a 90 hp Ruston twin-cylinder diesel engine (probably type 8HRC) driving a Gwynnes pump discharging 200 tpm in a new building [200]. This was scrapped in 1986 when an electric plant was installed in a separate brick building [201]. Discharge was into Soham Lode, south side. This area has now been incorporated into Middle Fen and Mere IDB.

S24 STOKE FERRY, Norfolk

This district was created by an Act of 1771 for the drainage of 2570 acres. By an Act of 1814, a further 1030 acres were added, and in 1834 a consolidating Act was obtained [202]. The district lay north of the River Wissey and comprised land in the parishes of Stoke Ferry, Northwold, Wretton, Wereham, West Dereham, Roxham, Fordham, Denver, Downham Market, Wimbotsham and Stow Bardolph.

Until the twentieth century, the district maintained no pumping stations and the individual landowners provided their own engines, some discharging into the River Wissey but most into the Commissioners' drains [203].

S24A Fordham (TL605992)

A small beam engine was erected in 1847 by Edward Roger Pratt of Ryston Hall to drain his estate. This was built by Overton & Wilson of Hull, and had a cylinder 21 by 48in. and a flywheel 18ft. in diameter. It drove a scoop wheel 28ft. in diameter by 15in. wide. There was one boiler, replaced by J. & J. Horsfield of Leeds in 1877. This supplied steam at 30 psi [204].

The engine and wheel were scrapped in 1936, when a small Allen diesel engine driving a centrifugal pump was installed in a separate building, whilst the old house was adapted to house a Ruston type 9HR (No. 204114) diesel engine driving a 24in. Gwynnes pump delivering 50 tpm. This was completed in 1942.

The Allen and its building were removed at some time after 1973. The chimney was demolished in about 1940 [205]. Until some time after 1972 the boiler stood outside the engine house and was used for diesel storage (Fig. 111).

An electric pump was installed in a separate building in about 1980. The old building and the Ruston engine are now preserved by a trust. Discharge is into a drain which joins St. John's Eau and discharges into the River Great Ouse four miles below Denver.

Fig. 111: Fordham (S24A) engine house in 1973

S24B West Dereham (TL 655978)

This station (Fig. 112) was erected in about 1860 to house a small beam engine on the north bank of the River Wissey opposite the present sugar beet factory. This drove a scoop wheel 2ft. wide. This was replaced in about 1942 by a 40 bhp Ruston vertical diesel engine (No. 478932) (Fig. 113) driving a Gwynnes pump delivering 45 tpm at a 10ft. lift [206]. This was placed in the old building. This building and machinery still existed in 1995, albeit in a fairly derelict condition. The scoop wheel house was then virtually unaltered. By 2003 the engine had been removed, but the remains of the single boiler (Fig. 114) and the pump were still surviving [207]. Discharge was into the River Wissey.

Fig. 112: West Dereham (S24B) engine house in 2003

Fig. 113: West Dereham (S24B) – Ruston engine in 1990

Fig. 114: West Dereham (S24B) – remains of boiler in 1990

S24C Wretton (D) (TL 687973)

In 1939 the Internal Drainage District erected a pumping station on the north bank of the River Wissey on a site where no such plant had previously existed. This consisted of two Allen diesel engines each driving Allen 24in. pumps each discharging 25 tpm [208]. This plant was removed soon after 1980, when an electric pump was installed in a separate building. The original engine house was then converted into a store [209].

S24D Oxborough (TL 719996)

A small private plant existed east of Stoke Ferry and north of Whittington in about 1883 [210]. This discharged water from a drain running from the south of Oxborough Hythe. It had become disused by 1907 [211]. Thereafter a hot-bulb oil engine, of which no details have been obtained, was installed. This was followed c. 1940 by a Ruston diesel engine, probably type 3XHR, driving a 12in. pump by belt-drive, which suggests that it was an existing pump [212]. This had become disused by 1989 [213] and the pump seems to have been removed soon after. The engine was sold and removed in 1998 [214]. A small electric pump has replaced it. Discharge was into the north side of the River Wissey.

S25 SWAFFHAM AND BOTTISHAM, Cambs.

This district was formed by an Act of 1767, followed by further Acts of 1779 and 1819 [215]. It comprised some 7000 acres [216] lying to the east of the River Cam between Horningsea in the south and Upware in the north.

S25A Upware first station (TL 537696)

In 1821 a 30 hp [217] Boulton & Watt beam engine was erected at Upware. Its cylinder was 30 by 60in. and speed 24 rpm. The scoop wheel was 27ft. 10in. in diameter with scoops 4ft. 10in. long and 18in. wide [218]. The entire wheel was lowered on its axle by $1^{1}/_{2}$ft. in 1832, and again by $1^{1}/_{3}$ft. in 1842. For the sake of economy, the wheel was not originally covered. One boiler was installed initially, a second being added in 1830 [219]. One of these was replaced by Butterley in 1843. The cost of the original plant was £6590 [220]. This plant was supplemented by three windpumps, one being sold in 1844, and the others in 1849 and 1850. Discharge was into the River Cam.

S25B Upware second station (TL 538697)

In 1850 the original plant was wholly removed and the engine sold [221]. For no known reason a new station was established on a new site, slightly north of the original site. The engine drain was straightened and a new shorter outlet to the River Cam was dug. This was an expensive and most unusual reconstruction because it involved the cost of a completely new building and foundations. The new plant was housed in a most impressive building (Fig. 115) and the engine was equally handsome. It consisted of a 70 hp beam engine by Robert Daglish of St. Helen's, having a cylinder of 42 by 84in. and a flywheel 25ft. in diameter. This ran at 15 to18 rpm, and drove a scoop wheel 36ft. in diameter with 48 scoops 5ft. 9in. long and 3ft. 6in. wide. Gearing was $3^{1}/_{2}$:1 [222].

Steam was supplied at 10 to 15 psi by two Galloway boilers fitted in 1887 to replace the original three. It was admitted through drop valves (Fig. 116) worked by two cams on the crankshaft. Coal consumption was approximately a third of a ton per hour [223]. The crankshaft of this engine broke during the flood of February 1897. The same accident had occurred at the Burnt Fen Lark Engine in 1884.

This plant was reduced to stand-by duties in 1927 when a diesel engine was installed. It remained in use until the flood of 1937 when one boiler burst and the self-acting gate in front of the scoop wheel failed to close due to lack of maintenance. The engine was then scrapped, and in 1939 the main building was demolished. The boiler room remained in use as a store until about 1969.

Fig 115 (above left): Swaffham & Bottisham (S25B) engine house from drain side in 1927

Fig. 116 (above): Swaffham & Bottisham (S25B) – drop valves of beam engine (COC)

Fig. 117 (left): Swaffham & Bottisham (S24B) – first diesel engine house under construction, 1927

A separate building was erected in 1927 against the old engine house (Fig. 117) to house new plant. This was a 140 hp Allen four-cylinder hot-bulb vertical diesel engine driving a 32in. Allen pump delivering 80 tpm. This engine never proved very satisfactory and was replaced in 1940 by a 174 hp Allen five-cylinder type S30 vertical engine (no. KI/92784) having a bore of 9in. and stroke of 11.8in. This engine was scrapped in 1993.

Meanwhile in 1939 a 194 hp Ruston & Hornsby horizontal four-cylinder type 8HRF engine (no. 184115) was installed in a new brick building on the site of the old engine house. This drove a 36in. Gwynnes pump delivering 100 tpm. This plant was sold in 1996. Both buildings are now used as stores.

In 1961 a third unit was installed in a brick building behind the 1939 engine house. This houses a 210 hp electric motor driving a suspended pump. In 1987 two 800 mm. mixed flow submersible pumps driven by 150 kW electric motors were sunk in a chamber on the river side of the existing engine houses against the discharge cut. The diesel engines, which had been in occasional daytime use up to that time, then became redundant [224].

S26 SWAFFHAM AND BOTTISHAM – The Lode Engines (D)

This district is crossed by three lodes, called Bottisham, Swaffham and Reach respectively. These run north-west from the chalk hard lands of the villages of Lode and the two Swaffhams and the hamlet of Reach to the River Cam. They were most probably constructed during the Roman period and may have been for drainage, but were certainly used as canals. They are now on a higher level than the surrounding land, being at river level in normal times. As part of the general drainage works completed in 1653 lock gates were placed at the head of each lode to prevent flood water from flowing back to the villages. Originally the Bedford Level Corporation was responsible for maintaining the banks of these lodes, but its performance became inadequate and the Act of 1767 entitled the Commissioners of this district to repair some of the banks and to levy tolls to meet the cost. In 1821 the Corporation decided that the lodes belonged to the District [225] and thus it became solely responsible for their maintenance. This position endured until 1940 when Great Ouse River Board took over the district. By then it had become apparent that pumping was necessary in flood times to evacuate the water from the lodes. Therefore the Board erected pumping stations at the head of each lode. They are not used frequently and can stand inert for several years in dry spells. Because of the shortage of engines during the Second World War, and a system of Government grants favouring portable and semi-portable engines, those installed to serve the Swaffham and the Bottisham Lodes were marine engines classed as semi-portable. These are now managed by the Environment Agency but have been designated as within this district because the Commissioners of Swaffham and Bottisham District undertook responsibility for the banks of the lodes until about 1930.

S26A Reach Lode (D) (TL 537699)

This station was built in 1941 at Upware on the north side of the locks at the head of Reach Lode. It contained a 94 hp Blackstone twin-cylinder horizontal diesel engine type GSK-T (no. 204922), having a bore of 10in. and stroke of 19in. This drove a Mirrlees Watson pump discharging 150 tpm against a 5ft. lift. The plant cost £3100 and the building £1520 [226]. This plant was removed on 7 June 1989 (Fig. 118) to be replaced by an electric plant in a new brick building. The Blackstone engine was moved to Prickwillow Drainage Museum (see Middle Fen).

Fig. 118: Reach Lode engine (S26A) being dismantled in 1989

Fig. 119: Swaffham Lode (S26B) engine house in 2000

S26B Swaffham Lode (D) (TL 522672)

This station (Fig. 119) was built in 1945 at the head of Swaffham Lode. It contained two 95 bhp Detroit supercharged two-stroke vertical engines type 6-71RC33A (one numbered 143672). The six cylinders each had a bore of $4^1/_2$in. and stroke of 5in. This drove a Worthington pump. The engines were replaced in about 2000 by Perkins 1006 diesel engines.

S26C Bottisham Lode (D) (TL 510658)

This station (Fig. 120) was also built in 1945 at the head of Bottisham Lode, which lies just north of Bottisham Locks, Waterbeach. It contains two 150 bhp Worthington five-cylinder vertical engines type BB5 (nos. VO 2460 and VO 2461) (Fig. 121). Each cylinder has a bore of 8in. and stroke of $10^1/_2$in. These drive Worthington pumps. This plant remains in active, if occasional, use. It has recently been refurbished. Apparently the cost of laying a cable from the distant mains supply is too great to make installation of an electric pump economically feasible.

Fig. 120: Bottisham Lode (S26C) engine house in 1955

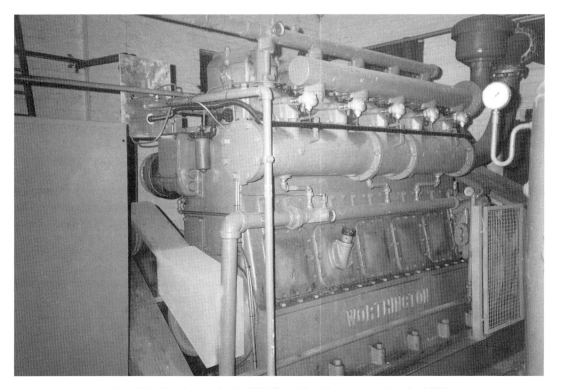

Fig. 121: Bottisham Lode (S26C) – Worthington engine in 1995

S27 THETFORD FEN, Cambs.
(TL 537760)

This district is situated at Little Thetford, south of Ely, and on the west side of the River Great Ouse. It was constituted by Acts of 1845 and 1852. The area was originally 471 acres [227], later rising to about 1000 acres when Stretham Common water was taken in 1929 [228]. This district was amalgamated with Littleport & Downham IDB in 1986.

Fig. 122: Thetford (S27) engine house with River Ouse in flood (Cambs. Coll.)

S27A   Thetford (TL537760)

In 1845 an A-frame 15 hp Boulton & Watt beam engine was erected on the bank of the River Great Ouse (Fig. 122). The cylinder was 23 by 36in. [229]. This drove a scoop wheel 27ft. in diameter [230]. This was removed in 1928 when two 60 hp Ruston type 2VXA double-cylinder oil engines (nos. 151948 and 151949) were installed in the existing building [231] to drive two 15in. pumps. This cost £1387. The chimney was demolished in 1940 [232], and the entire building in the 1960s, when an electric pump was installed. The machinery was sold, and one of the engines appeared at rallies for some years.

S27B Stretham Common (D) (TL520737)

At some time before 1916 a separate Commission was established to drain an area of some 500 acres north of the Old West River comprising Stretham Common. Of this only 297 acres were taxable. In 1917 a small paraffin engine was installed near Gravel Bridge to drive a 12in. Gwynnes pump discharging into the river by way of a tunnel under the bank [233]. This plant was, for no known reason, placed partly underground, and the flood of January 1928 caused it to be inundated [234]. It was then abandoned, and the drainage taken over by Thetford District. In recent years a small electric plant has been installed near the site of the original plant.

S28 WATERBEACH LEVEL, Cambs.

This district, lying north of Cambridge between Waterbeach and Stretham, was first drained under an Act of 1740 [235]. It contained some 5600 acres, since enlarged to about 7000 acres.

S28A Stretham (TL 516730)

In 1831 a 60 hp Butterley beam engine (Fig. 123) having a cylinder 39 by 96in. was erected on the bank of the Old West River one mile south of the village of Stretham. Originally steam was supplied at 4 psi by two boilers, believed to have been made by Butterley [236]. In 1846/7 a third boiler was added, the boiler house being extended to accommodate it. The original boilers were replaced in 1871, and the third in 1878, the new boilers all being Lancashire and supplied by Butterley (Fig. 124). The machinery cost £2900 and the building £2050 [237].

The engine drove a scoop wheel 29ft. in diameter by 3ft. wide. In 1850 the diameter was increased to 33ft. and the width of the scoops decreased to 2¹/₂ft. In 1896 this wheel was rebuilt and increased to 37ft. 2in. diameter. The scoops became 2ft. 4¹/₄in. wide. Discharge was into the Old West River.

In 1909 the old D-slide valve was replaced by an expansion valve supplied by Petrie & Co. Ltd. This gave variable cut-off [238].

In 1924 a 184 bhp four cylinder Mirrlees air-blast injection diesel engine (no. 37115) was installed in a separate building at the side of the old engine house. This was coupled to a 42 in.Gwynnes pump delivering 150 tpm. The old engine then became a stand-by and was last started in March 1941. The Mirrlees was last used in 1965. Both of these engines remain in preservation virtually as last used, being maintained by a trust.

Fig. 123 (left): Stretham (S28) beam engine c.1930 (COC)

Fig. 124: Stretham (S28) boiler house c.1960 (Stretham Engine Trust)

S28B Cam Engines, Dimmock's Cote (D) (TL 516730)

Behind Stretham engine lay a large mere, and the engine was sited to drain this. The mere bed was formed of silt, which did not shrink as much as the surrounding peat soil. Thus eventually it became a barrier preventing effective drainage of the southern part of the district [239]. This problem was addressed in 1944 by construction of a new plant on the west bank of the River Cam near Dimmock's Cote Bridge. This consisted of twin 120 hp four-cylinder Allen diesel engines driving pumps delivering 140 tpm., housed in a brick building. In 1979 an electric pump was provided at this station, but the diesel plant has been retained as a stand-by. Meanwhile continued problems in securing effective drainage of the southern part of the district were solved by erection of an electric pump at Bottisham Locks (TL 509658) in 1969.

S29 WILLINGHAM WEST FEN, Cambs. (TL 406735)

This fen contained a large mere, which had virtually disappeared by about 1800 [240], probably due to installation of a windpump, variously called the Weathersome [241] or Molly [242] Mill. By 1846 this mill had become dilapidated and useless, and a large part of the fen was partially inundated [243]. This led to enclosure in that year, and procurement of an Act [244] to drain that part of the parish lying west of Willingham Lode. This contained some 860 acres [245]. A pumping station was forthwith erected on the site of the mill on the south bank of the Old West River.

This engine, made by J. & E. Headly of Eagle Works, Cambridge, was a 10 hp beam engine with Bright parallel motion and one boiler driving a cast-iron scoop wheel 22ft. in diameter by 12in. wide. The flywheel was 12ft. in diameter and the chimney 55ft. in height [246]. This plant cost a total of £455. It was in operation by October 1847. The engine house, built by Mark Lucas at a cost of £500, had been completed a year earlier (Fig. 125). The boiler was replaced by a Galloway boiler by Smithdale of St. Ann's Iron Works, Norwich, in 1875 at a cost of £205 [247]. In 1857 the roof of the engine house had been burnt out. The cause of the fire was unknown [248].

This machinery was replaced in the same building in 1901 by a 32 hp Hornsby horizontal hot-bulb oil engine direct-coupled to an 18 in. Clayton & Shuttleworth centrifugal pump [249].

This engine broke down during the flood of January 1936. The cost quoted for its repair was such that it was decided to purchase a new engine. Meanwhile a traction engine and portable pump had to be hired to maintain the drainage (Fig. 126). The Commissioners' finances were in a parlous state and it was necessary for them to borrow £450 in addition to an existing loan of £400 [250]. The new engine was a 34 hp Ruston & Hornsby single-cylinder diesel engine type 6XHR (no. 178636) costing £340. This was placed at right-angles to the old pump which it drove by long belt and shaft. Such was the poverty of the Board that a second-hand threshing drum belt was used, and no auxiliary engine to charge the air bottle was provided for some years. The pump (Fig. 127) is the only Clayton & Shuttleworth known to have survived in the Fens. It has a curious vacuumiser built into the pump so that no separate exhauster is required.

The district was amalgamated with Over (S21) in 1973 and this plant and building were sold as redundant. It remains preserved in the care of a trust. It was last worked in the flood of May 1978. Since then shrinkage of the fen has left it incapable of pumping except when the level of water in the drain is very high. The chimney was felled in about 1941. Discharge was into the Old West River, south side.

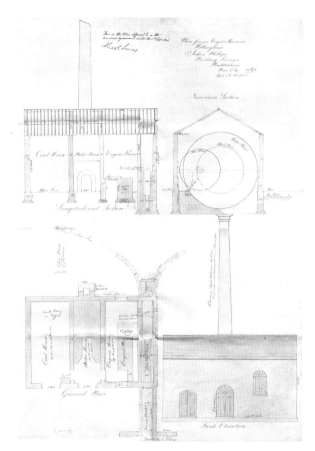

Fig. 125 (left): Willingham (S29) –
engine house plan 1846
(Willingham Pumping Station Trust)

Fig. 126 (below): Willingham (S 29)
engine house in 1936 with traction
engine in operation (Willingham
Pumping Station Trust)

Fig. 127 (inset): Willingham (S29) –
Clayton & Shuttleworth pump

Notes

1. Darby, (1983), 123 and 154
2. Summers, D. (1973), *The Great Ouse: The History of a River Navigation*, David & Charles, 99 – 100, This contains a graphic account of the perils of this passage.
3. Summers, note 2, and Hills (2003), 71, cite this as a 20 hp engine, but this was most probably the rating of the boiler. The size of the cylinder implies a rating of 40 hp.
4. Hills (2003), 71
5. Hills (2003) states 52 ins. by 60 ins., but the details given in the advertisement cited in note 6 agree with Mutton, N. "The use of Steam Drainage in the Making of the Eau Brink Cut", *Journal of Industrial Archaeology*, Vol. 4, No. 4, 353. He quotes a letter from Rennie, the Chief Engineer for the works, to Boulton & Watt dated 3 January 1818 stating that, as the Cut itself was 21ft. deep and, as the pump should be at least 1ft. above the surface and 3ft. below, the length of the pumps could not be less than 25ft.
6. CC, 5 December 1823, containing an advertisement for sale of these engines
7. Hills (2003), 55. The estimate of £6500 quoted in Wells, Vol. 1, 765, must have allowed for the cost of transport from the works and installation, and possibly the cost of the dredging machine
8. CC, 5 December 1823
9. Darby (1983), 155
10. 33 G2 c. 32; 13 G3 c. 20; 37 G3 c. 89; and 47 G3 sess. 2, c. 83
11. Heathcote papers (HRO)
12. Beckett, J.A. (1981): *The Urgent Hour – A History of Burnt Fen District,* 44
13. Beckett, note 12, 47
14. Beckett, note 12, 16
15. Beckett, note 12, 21 and Burnt Fen Commissioners' Minutes (CRO) ref. 96/15 dated 29 April 1830. See also Soham Mere (S23).
16. Beckett, note 12, 21
17. Minutes, note 15, 29 July 1830
18. Wheeler, W.H.: "The Drainage of Fens and Low Grounds by Steam Power", *The Engineer,* 2 September 1887, and Davey, 304-306
19. Minutes, note 15, 12 April 1832 and 23 May 1833
20. Minutes, note 15, 18 April 1837
21. Minutes, note 15, 5 May 1848
22. CC, 4 February 1831
23. Minutes, note 15, 14 June 1832, referring to the front and lower wheels. The discarded wheel was to be used for the Miles End Mill.
24. Minutes, note 15, 25 April 1833
25. Minutes, note 15, 27 June 1833
26. Minutes, note 5, 25 March 1847
27. Minutes, note 15, 16 June 1860
28. Wheeler, note 18
29. Beckett, note 12, 22
30. Beckett, note 12, 29
31. Beckett, note 12, 37 – 39 and Gwynnes 1943 and 1953, no. 104
32. Beckett, note 12, 22 - 23, and Ince, 120. Clark, Engine no. 12, *English Mechanics,* 7 February 1936, states that the Lark engine was made by Butterley, but this is probably a confusion in that a quotation was obtained by that company, but was not accepted.

33. Minutes, note 15, 21 June 1849
34. Minutes, note 15, 19 October 1852
35. Minutes, note 15, 28 March 1861
36. There are no remains
37. Journal of the Cambridgeshire Family History Society, November 1997, p. 122. A similar accident occurred at the Swaffham and Bottisham engine at Upware in 1897.
38. Beckett, note 12, 38 – 39 and Gwynnes 1943 and 1953, no. 113
39. Beckett, note 12, 48; and Lambe
40. Bidwells' Royal Exchange Policy Register CRO. It is also marked on the 6 in. OS map 1884, and on Gibbs' Map of 1888.
41. Filby, P. (2002): "The Windmills of Littleport 1750 – 1930", *Littleport Review*, 24
42. Bidwell's Policy Register, note 40. OS 6 inch map 1901 (revised 1950) does not mark this plant, but does show another engine house at TL 658864.
43 4 & 5 Vict. c. 57
44. Clarke J.A. states 30 hp, as do Burwell Fen Minutes, 20 August 1897 (CRO – ref. R71/7).
45. RCHM, North East Cambridgeshire (1972), 45 and Minutes, note 44, 16 September 1895.
46. Gibbs, 282 – 283 and Minutes, note 44, 21 April 1884.
47. Lucas, C. (1930) *The Fenman's World*, 36. Rouse, M. 1989: *The Villages of Old Cambridgeshire*, 20 contains a photograph of this engine, but with an incorrect description. See also Clark, Engine no. 147, *English Mechanics*, 20 November 1936, and photograph in Day, A. (1999): *Fuel from the Fens*, 30.
48. CWN, 31 January 1913, personal communication by Ray Hooley and Minutes 16 September 1895. The engine was supplied on 17 December 1895
49. Minutes, note 44, 20 August 1897 and 28 January 1898
50. Minutes, note 44, 31 January 1913
51. Minutes, note 44, 7 and 19 May 1913 and CWN, 3 October 1913
52. Minutes, note 44, 7 February 1916
53 Minutes, note 44, 9 May and 6 July 1921
54 C.O. Clarke, who viewed it, and said that the array of belts was frightening
55. Bloom, A. (1944): *The Farm in the Fen* p. 49
56. 11G2 c. 34, followed by an Act of 1810 (50 G3 c. 128). The area including Waterden, Redmoor and The Holts was 850 acres.
57. Heathcote Papers (HRO) and Cawdle Fen papers (CRO). The Act provided for drainage of a total area of 850 acres in Cawdle Fen, Redmoor and the Holts
58. Gibbs's Map
59. Clark, Engine no. 28, *English Mechanics*, 20 March 1936
60. Survey by C. Hereward and R.C. Hodrien 1972
61. Cawdle Fen papers in CRO contain several references to millwright's bills in the 1840s.
62. Kelly's *Directory of Cambridgeshire* 1875
63. Kelly's *Directory of Cambridgeshire* 1916
64. Clark, Engine no. 29, *English Mechanics*, 20 March 1936; and Clark, R.H.: "Some Grasshopper Engines", *The Engineer*, 15 May 1942, 402. This contains a diagram and photograph. He refers to a stone outside the engine house bearing the legend "W L 1841". Pigott's *Directory of Cambridgeshire 1838*, 57 lists William Layton of Woodhouse, which is in Chettisham. Watkins SSE Vol. 9, 28 suggests that a beam engine may have preceded this, but Clark does not appear to agree.
65. Clark, R.H. (1988): *The Steam Engine Builders of Norfolk*, Haynes, 128

66. Hills (2003), 164 and Watkins's SSE Vol. 9, 30 contain photographs. On 26 May 1842, Mr. Layton attended Padnal and Waterden Commissioners and proposed terms for draining the lands in the upper part of that district on the west side of Sandys Cut by the steam engine erected by him in Redmoor Fen (Padnal and Waterden Commissioners' Minutes CRO)

67. Clark suggests that the old plant still existed in 1942, but this seems to be unlikely

68. Survey by C. Hereward and R.C. Hodrien in 1972

69. 5 Vict. Sess. 2 c. 23 (Local and Personal)

70. Clark, Engine no. 16, *English Mechanics,* 6 March 1936, and Watkins, G. 1978: *The Steam Engine in Industry,* 1, 88 and Watkins SSE, Vol. 9, 24. These include photographs, as does Hills 2003, 107.

71. Cottenham District Minutes (CRO), 8 July 1947

72. *ADA Gazette*, Spring 1998, 18

73. Clark, Engine no. 17, *English Mechanics,* 6 March 1936. See also CIP 4 June 1842 and, for photograph, Hills 2003, 107.

74. CC, 15 December 1860, 5

75. CC, 21 June 1916, 8. The only other Ruston pump traced was at Pinchbeck South L4

76. Doran, 166 - 168

77. Allen, 802

78. Gwynnes 1953, no. 90A, and 1977

79. Plaque in engine house seen in 1989

80. Nar Valley District Minutes 1894 – 1903 (CRO ref. R79/104)

81. Plaque in yard seen in 2001

82. 30 G2 c. 35, which Wells wrongly lists under Feltwell Second; 13 G3 c. 45, which also relates to Feltwell Second; and 46 G3 c. 95

83. Heathcote papers (HRO) state 7484 acres, but it may have contained as little as 6550 acres.

84. CIP, 28 January and 18 February 1843, which states that the engine was made by Headly of Cambridge. See also Crocker, who includes photographs, but wrongly states that the maker was Headly & Hawthorn.

85. Clark, Engine no. 118, *English Mechanics,* 18 September 1936

86. Gwynnes 1936, 1943 and 1953, no. 100, and 1977. Clark states that the beam engine was scrapped in 1917. Crocker, 823, writing in 1913, states that plans had been prepared for a new installation, but it had been decided to postpone the installation because of high prices. This was to have been a pair of compound steam engines driving centrifugal pumps each delivering 100 tpm. The second building is clearly earlier than 1944 and closely resembles the architectural style of the 1926 diesel engine house at Hundred Foot. Gwynnes 1936 lists the Campbell engine as Feltwell and in 1943 lists a 400 hp plant, which cannot refer only to the Mirrlees. See also Clayton, C.H.J. (1919) *Land Drainage from Field to Sea* (reprint, Logaston Press, 2004), 150, referring to a 250 hp engine driving a 36in. pump.

87. Dated from the serial number. Doran, 166, lists this as a reconstructed building. Walker, R.V., "Southery Pumping Station", *Journal NIAS*, Vol. II, No. 5, 1980,49, sites the engines in the wrong buildings.

88. 13 G3 c. 45; 42 G3 c. 24; and 12 Vict. C. 7. Feltwell First District is described under Methwold Severals

89. Glynn, 19. Heathcote papers (HRO) state 6927 acres, but this may have included Feltwell New Fen.

90. Clarke, J.A., 94, states 30 hp. CIP, 29 October 1842, states 20 hp.

91. Clark, Engine no. 50, *English Mechanics,* 17 April 1936. It is assumed that the engine maker was Butterley because the plant was installed by Glynn, who was employed by that firm. Clark probably did not visit this plant, because the Vickers-Petter had almost certainly replaced any steam plant by the time he made his survey.
92. Gwynnes 1936
93. Gwynnes 1943, no. 109, and Doran, 166, who states the cost as £6300 for the plant and £6000 for the building, the latter being a reconstruction of an existing building
94. *ADA Gazette,* Autumn 1987, 18
95. 13 G1 c. 18
96. Heathcote papers (HRO) state 8145 acres but Heathcote states 9500 acres. Clarke J.A. states 7000 acres.
97. CC, 4 February 1831. Clark states that there were two side-lever engines, but this must be incorrect.
98. Braithwaite, D. (1975): *Savage of King's Lynn.* This contains a diagram of the wheel.
99. Heathcote, 6
100. Gibbs, 283 and Burwell District Minutes CRO, 21 April 1884.
101. Reeve, F.A. (1976): *Victorian and Edwardian Cambridgeshire in Photographs,* photograph no. 63; and CIP, 6 August 1897. Littleport and Downham District papers (CRO ref. 1971/12) contain two detailed drawings of a design for a horizontal condensing engine and scoop wheel for Haddenham by James Watt & Co. dated 24 June 1892. The wheel was to be 40ft. in diameter and 2ft. 7 ins. wide. The engine cylinder was to be 60in. by 43in. and the flywheel 14ft. in diameter, with a single boiler. Clearly this was never installed. It is surprising that this district should have contemplated a scoop wheel at such a late date, and to replace one only installed 20 years previously.
102. The present Clerk of this district informed the author that all of the old records have been lost. The author is not proud that he took the only known photograph of this engine in 1949, but failed to obtain any information about it
103. Engine Log Book 1910 – 1958, (CRO ref. R97/92A)
104 Gwynnes 1953, no. 112A and Lambe
105. Heathcote papers (HRO)
106. 8 G3 c. 47; 1 W4 c. 26; and 17 & 18 Vict. C. 172.
107. Clark, Engine no. 45, *English Mechanics,* 24 April 1936
108. Memorials and Petitions presented to the Bedford Level Corporation – No. 1770 dated 1854 (CRO): Peel, Edmunds and other owners in Hilgay Great West Fen requested permission to increase the outlet into the Ouse below Sam's Cut on the erection of a steam engine under the Act.
109. Clark, note 107
110. Trett, R.: "Hilgay Great West Fen Pumping Station" *Journal NIAS,* Vol. II No. 4, 1979, 74 – 76, which includes photographs.
111. Burke & Savill (1981): *Guide to Country Houses – East Anglia,* Burke's Peerage
112. Plaque on Engine House
113. Personal communication in 1997 from Mr. Brian Charlesworth, present owner of the estate
114. Clark, Engine no. 47, *English Mechanics,* 24 April 1936
115. Inspection in 1995
116. 8 G3 c. 47
117. Heathcote papers (HRO)
118. Clarke, J.A., 93

119. Clark, Engine no. 66, *English Mechanics*, 8 May 1936
120. Snelson, P. (1995), *Along the Cam and the Great Ouse,* Cambridge Library Publications, 99 with photograph.
121. Darby (1983), 199, with photograph.
122. Gwynnes 1943 and 1953, no. 111
123. 29 G2 c. 22; 39 & 40 G3 c. 26; and 50 G3 c. 194
124. Hills (2003), 97 – 100. This contains Boulton & Watt drawings of this plant
125. CC, 23 April 1842, containing advertisement for sale of this plant
126. Wheeler DF, 117 – 118
127. Littleport and Downham District papers (CRO ref. 1971/12)
128. Allen, 798 – 801 and District papers, note 127
129. Some years ago, the engine driver showed the author the remains of the windpump scoop wheel race in the south garden of his house, which is adjacent to the engine. See also Littleport & Downham District Minutes, 29 April 1829 (CRO).
130. Manuscript Notes of Ernest Stevens (Engine Driver 1911 – 1927) in the author's possession, and Wheeler DF, 114. Clark, Engine no. 68 *English Mechanics,* 15 May 1936 gives the bore as 42in. For plans, see Hills (2003), 119-121.
131. Wheeler DF, 114
132. Rough Log Book of James Stevens (Engine Driver 1830 – 1873) in author's possession.
133. Wheeler DF, 113 who gives a full description.
134. Glynn, 17
135. Rough Log Book, note 132
136. Notebook of James Stevens. It was later fitted at several of the larger pumping stations, such as Pode Hole (L2) (see Wheeler DF, 108) and Stretham (S28) where it can still be seen.
137. Wheeler DF, 114
138. Gwynnes 1943 and 1953, no. 103
139. Allen , 798, which contains photographs of the exterior and pump. See also Clark, Engine no. 46, *English Mechanics*, 24 April 1936
140. 17 & 18 Vict. C. 188
141. Methwold and Feltwell District Minutes 1909 – 1938 (CRO 79/104)
142. Edward Easton was a partner in Easton, Amos & Anderson. See Clark, note 65, 154
143. Crocker, 823
144. Feltwell & Methwold Separate District Minutes 1881 – 1890 (CRO). See Wood Hall Estate plant (S12)
145. Methwold & Feltwell District Minutes (CRO), 8 June 1925
146. Minutes, note 145, 23 June 1930 and 14 December 1931
147. Minutes, note 145, 7 December 1912
148. Darby, H.C. (1938), *The Cambridge Region.* CUP, 196. Crocker, 823 – 829 has a full description of this plant.
149. *The Allen Engineering Review,* no. 3, July 1939, 4 – 5. The four-cylinder engine is now at the Internal Fire Museum of Power, Wales.
150. Allison, G.: "Catsholme Pumping Station", *ADA Gazette,* Spring 2001, 10.
151. 13 G3 c. 45
152. Heathcote gives the area as 6927 acres.
153. 17 & 18 Vict. C. 188
154. Gibbs' Map and OS 6 inch map 1906 Edition.

155. Clark, Engine no. 165, *English Mechanics,* 1 January 1937 with photograph. He wrongly states the discharge as being into the Little Ouse. It has had to be assumed that these details refer to this plant and not to Northwold Severals. See also Watkins SSE, Vol. 9, 116 – 117, with photograph

156. 31 G2 c. 18, 29 G3 c. 22 and 39 & 40 G3 c. 90. Heathcote papers (HRO) state 11,628 acres and the ADA list of 1948 gives 11,498, but the district also takes much upland water. Glynn states that the original plant drained 7000 acres, whilst Gibbs states that the highland water increases the area drained in flood conditions to 25,000 acres. The first Act states 17,000 acres.

157. Glynn, 18. For Glynn's original drawings of this plant, see Hills (2003), 170 and 171.

158. Gibbs, 280 with plans. For plan of scoopwheel, see Hills (2003), 142.

159. Wheeler, W.H., "The Drainage of Fens and Low Grounds by Steam Power", *The Engineer,* 2 September 1887. His information was partly derived from a privately printed description of this plant dated 20 July 1880. The works were directed by G. Carmichael of Ely, Superintendent of the South Level Works. See also Clark, Engine no. 112, *English Mechanics,* 21 August 1936.

160. Allen, 793. The pump was almost certainly an Allen.

161. Allen, 789

162. Doran, 170 and 171 with illustrations, and Lambe

163. Clark, Engine no. 86, *English Mechanics,* 29 May 1936.

164. Burke & Savill's *Guide to Country Houses Vol. III – East Anglia* 1981, 160

165. Clark, note 163

166. Clark, note 65, 9

167. Watkins SE1, 92. See also Watkins SSE, Vol. 9, 116, 118 and 119 with photographs, and Hills (2003), 143 for photograph of scoop wheel

168. Papers of J.M. Heathcote (HRO)

169. 33 G2 c. 32 and 47 G3 sess. 2 c. 83

170. Plaque on Engine House

171. Clarke, J.A., 93. If R.H. Clark's statement, note 172, of the size of the cylinder is correct, it is unlikely to have been of such hp; yet Butterley's usual provision of 10 hp per 1000 acres suggests that this hp is correct.

172. Crocker, plate 23 and Clark, Engine no. 87, *English Mechanics,* 29 May 1936, both with photographs

173. Clark, note 172

174. Doran, 166 and Gwynnes 1943 and 1953, no. 114

175. Young, A. (1804): *General View of the Agriculture of Norfolk* David & Charles reprint 1969, 146

176. Plaque on Engine House now stored at the disused Wretton Pumping Station (S24C). Bradfield owned most of the land around Stoke Ferry at this time – see Directories of Norfolk of White 1845, Kelly 1853 and Harrod 1863.

177. OS 1 in., first edition

178. See photographs in Hills (2003), 137

179. Watkins's Notes no. 136. He calls the plant Adventurers Fen, Whittington.

180. Watkins SSE, Vol. 9, 120 – 122, with photographs

181. Letter from the Clerk to Northwold IDB to the author dated 17 December 1996

182. 7 W4 & 1 Vict. C. 90

183. Heathcote papers (HRO)

184. Clarke, J.A., 93

185. Clark, Engine no. 108, *English Mechanics*, 31 July 1936. See Hills (2003), 138 and Watkins SSE Vol. 9, 38 for photographs.
186. Gwynnes 1943 and 1953, no. 117 and personal inspection
187. 7 & 8 G4 c. 47
188. Fowler, G: "Fenland Waterways" *Proceedings CAS,* Vol. XXXIV, 1934, 19.
189. Padnal and Waterden District Minutes, 7 February 1938 (CRO)
190. Minutes, note 189, 2 July and 17 November 1831. This may have been similar to the device fitted to the Hundred Foot Engine (S14B)
191. Minutes, note 189, 26 May 1842
192. Minutes, note 189, 17 July 1850
193. Padnal and Waterden District Accounts (CRO)
194. Minutes, note 189, 24 April 1884
195. Minutes, note 189, passim
196. Clark, Engine no. 109, *English Mechanics,* 31 July 1936
197. CC 4 February 1831. Lenny's Map, 1853 and curiously R. G. Baker's Map of 1830
198. Glynn, 19
199. Clark, Engine no. 117, *English Mechanics,* 18 September 1936 and Allen, 796 which includes photographs and a plan.
200. Doran, 166 and Gwynnes 1943 and 1953, no. 115
201. Klee, C., "New Pumping Station for Soham Lode", *ADA Gazette*, Spring 1986, 17 – 18
202. 11 G3; 54 G3 c. 13; 4 W4 c. 63
203. Stoke Ferry Commissioners' Minutes 1875 – 1896. (NRO ref. DB 7.1)
204. Clark, Engine no. 33, *English Mechanics,* 20 March 1936. He states that there were two boilers, but this seems to be incorrect.
205. Walker, R.V., "Fordham Pumping Station" *Journal NIAS* Vol. 2, No. 5, 1980, 49
206. Doran, 166 and Gwynnes 1953. This plant is not listed by Gibbs. Evidence of the steam engine was deduced from inspection of the building in 1990, 1995 and 2003. The plate on the Ruston engine states that it is 40 bhp, but Doran and Gwynnes state 54 bhp.
207. Personal inspection
208. Walker, note 205, 50
209. Personal inspection, 6 October 1996
210. OS 6 in. map 1883 (revised 1904). Whittington is often mis-spelt Whitington
211. OS 6 in. map 1907
212. Gwynnes 1977
213. OS 2$^{1}/_{2}$in. map 1989
214. Information from E. M. S. Hinde who assisted the purchaser, Mr. John Littlechild, in its removal. The pump had been removed by then.
215. 7 G3 c. 53; 19 G3 c. 34 and 59 G3 c. 78
216. Act of 1767. Heathcote papers (HRO) state 6413 acres. The district has since been extended to contain over 8000 acres.
217. Swaffham and Bottisham District Minutes (CRO), 21 July 1832; but the advertisement for sale in CC 20 July 1850 states 26 hp. The table in Bourne, J. (1879), *Handbook of the Steam Engine,* 303, would place this as 32 hp. Ince, 116, states that it was 24 hp, with a 26$^{1}/_{4}$in. cylinder
218. Minutes, note 217. Hills (1967), 84 – 87 contains plans of this plant, but he confuses this with the later engine. This was corrected in Hills (2003), 103 – 110
219. RCHM, North East Cambridgeshire (1972), 132

220. Minutes, note 217, 21 April 1821
221. CC 20 July 1850. See also Hinde, K.S.G. "Swaffham Fen Engine" *Procs. CAS* Vol. LXIII, 1971, 87-89.
222. Clark, Engine no. 148, *English Mechanics,* 20 November 1936 and undated engine diagram held at Stretham Engine. Hills (2003), 178-179 contains photographs of this engine, as does Watkins SSE Vol. 9, 45-47.
223. Calculated over a fifty year period from coal delivery figures in the Minutes. The only other fen drainage steam engine known to have been fitted with drop valves was that at Torksey (T1A).
224. Sturgess, P. "Upware Pumping Station" *ADA Gazette*, Autumn 1988, 18-19, and Gwynnes 1943 and 1953, no. 122
225. Wells, Vol. 1, 729
226. Doran, 166
227. Heathcote papers (HRO)
228. Thetford Commissioners' Minutes 1920 – 1941 (CRO)
229. Ince, 120
230. Hills (2003), 92 and 144: plans of engine and scoop wheel
231. Day, A. (1993), *Fen and Marshland Villages*, S.B. Publications, for photograph of exterior.
232. Minutes, note 228, 14 December 1939
233. Notebook (in the author's possession) of I. Housely, Superintendent of Waterbeach Level, who supervised the installation, and OS 6in. map 1923
234. C.O. Clarke – personal communication
235. 14 G2 c. 24
236. Hills, R. H., "Joseph Glynn and fen drainage" *Journal RSA,* Vol. CXLIV, 1996, 69
237. Hills (2003), 131
238. Clark, Engine no. 133, *English Mechanics*, 23 October 1936
239. Hinde, K.S.G., "Meres and Mills in Willingham and Stretham", *Procs. CAS*, Vol. LXVI, 1977, 165 – 173, explains this problem
240. Hinde, note 239
241. Lenny's map
242. Willingham (West Fen) Minutes (CRO), 10 June 1846
243. Jonas, S. "On the farming of Cambridgeshire", *Journal RASE*, vol. 7, 1847, 69
244. 9 & 10 Vict. C. 9
245. Schedule of land subject to drainage rates 1847 (held by the trust)
246. Construction plan of the original plant (Fig. 125)
247. Minutes, note 242, 10 June 1846
248. CIP, 7 November 1857
249. See *The Implement & Machinery Review,* 2 June 1906, 210, for an illustration of this design of Clayton & Shuttleworth pump.
250. Minutes, note 242, 16 and 20 January 1936

7
South Lincolnshire from the Nene to the Glen

DISTRICTS

Serial
No.   Name

L1   South Holland
L2   Deeping Fen
L3   Pinchbeck Marsh
L4   Pinchbeck Fourth or South Fen
L5   Bourne South and Thurlby Fen
L6   Maxey IDB
L7   Surfleet
L8   Kirton Marsh

L1 SOUTH HOLLAND – Sutton St. Edmund (TF 378144)

South Holland is a large district lying between the rivers Welland and Nene. It contains some 36,000 acres. It was originally under Holland Elloe Court of Sewers for drainage purposes, but a Commission was constituted by Act of 1793 [1], which still exists as South Holland IDB. Only one early pumping station has been traced within this district, and its area was later incorporated in the North Level.

At the extreme south of both South Holland drainage district and the county of Lincolnshire lie the commons of Sutton St. Edmund, a chapelry of Long Sutton. These were enclosed in about 1797 and were drained at least partially under an Act of 1809 [2]. They contained about 1200 acres [3].

In about 1817 a 10 or 12 hp double-acting steam engine possibly made by Fenton & Murray of Leeds and driving a scoop wheel [4], was installed on the west bank of the Shire or South Holland Drain [5], into which it discharged (map 9, p.24). This is the first recorded instance of a permanent steam-powered pumping station being erected in the Fens. It became redundant upon construction of the North Level Main Drain and was removed in 1834/5 and not replaced.

L2 DEEPING FEN – Pode Hole (TF 214221)

Following general drainage schemes in the seventeenth century, the area known as Deeping Fen, including Pinchbeck North and South Fens and Crowland and Spalding Commons, together containing 34,000 acres, was first enclosed under an Act of 1801 [6]. This land lay between the rivers Welland and Glen (map 12, p.27). Prior to this, in 1800, a joint report by W. Jessop and John Rennie had recommended the erection of steam engines at Pode Hole, but this was not then carried out. By 1815 the district was drained by some 50 windpumps [7]. Eventually this area was combined with further land south of Boston and up to the outfall of the River Welland to form Welland and Deepings IDB. The plant listed under serial numbers L2 to L8 are all now within this district.

In 1824 two beam engines were erected at Pode Hole. These discharged into Vernatt's Drain and thence to the River Welland. Placed in the same engine house (Fig. 128), for some reason different builders were selected for each engine; and equally inexplicably they were not set to work until 1827. The entire plant cost £17,000 [8].

The larger of these engines, called the Holland Engine, was an 80 hp Butterley, having a cylinder 44 by 96in, and running at $16\frac{1}{2}$ rpm. The diameter of the flywheel, which weighed $21\frac{3}{4}$ tons, was 24ft. and the beam centres 24ft. 9in. This drove a scoop wheel 28ft. in diameter (increased to 31ft. in 1891) having 40 scoops 6ft. 6in. long and 5ft. wide and making 5 rpm. The lift was 6ft. [9].

The other engine, called the Kesteven Engine, was a 60 hp beam engine made by Fenton & Murray, and had a cylinder 45 by 78ins. This drove a scoop wheel identical to that of the Holland Engine except that the scoops were 5ft. 6in. long.

In about 1880, each scoop wheel was fitted with a rising breast on the delivery side and a shuttle behind the wheel. Total discharge of the two wheels was 563 tpm [10].

The Kesteven Engine was overhauled in 1881, and the Holland Engine in 1883. This work was carried out by Watt & Co. and included replacement of the D-slide valve by a long piston valve provided with a variable cut-off lever [11].

Originally each engine may only have been supplied with one boiler [12], but this arrangement is unlikely to have endured for long. In 1883 the old boilers were replaced by five double-flued Lancashire boilers, each 7ft. by 26ft. serving the engines jointly [13]. By 1928 these had been replaced by five Lancashire boilers 8ft. by 30ft. in size.

This plant was taken out of service in 1928 when the boilers became defective, and the scoop wheel of the Kesteven Engine was removed. The remaining machinery survived until 1952 when it was scrapped. The building, without chimney, survives in use as a workshop.

Fig. 128: Pode Hole (L2) – engine houses in 1920 (Miles, Ch. 8, note 9)

In 1914 these engines had been supplemented by a 100 hp two-cylinder Mirrlees air-blast injection diesel engine driving a 36in. Gwynnes pump, and in 1920 by another similar installation. Together these pumps discharged 200 tpm. They were removed in 1956.

When the steam engines were taken out of service, a 250 hp five-cylinder Mirrlees diesel engine was installed. This drove a 54in. Vickers-Gill axial-flow impeller pump discharging 260 tpm. This was joined by an electric pump in 1939. In 1957 three electric motors

Fig. 129: Pode Hole (L2) old engine house in 1994

driving axial-flow pumps replaced the two original Mirrlees plants. The old building, truncated and without chimney, has survived (Fig. 129).

In 1964 a new building was erected to house three Ruston vertical diesel engine. Two were 650 hp type VEBX engines driving 60in. Gwynnes vertical axial-flow pumps, and one a 410 hp engine driving a 50in. Gwynnes pump. At this time the 250 hp Mirrlees and the 1939 electric pump were scrapped [14].

L3 PINCHBECK MARSH
(TF 262262)

This area is known as Spalding and Pinchbeck District or Blue Gowt. It contains 4500 acres, although the area drained is 6000 acres. It is within Deeping Fen and was first, ineffectually, drained under the Act of 1801. In 1832 the proprietors obtained an Act creating a separate district [15]; but this has since been absorbed into Welland and Deepings IDB.

In 1833 a 20 hp A-frame Butterley beam engine was erected north-east of Pinchbeck. This plant has

Fig. 130: Pinchbeck Marsh (L3) engine house in 1994

survived. It has a cylinder 35 by 54in. and drives a scoop wheel 22ft. in diameter, having 40 scoops each 24in. wide and 5ft. 3ins. long. This wheel has never been lowered. Delivery was about 65 tpm. Engine speed was 28/30 rpm geared 4.46:1 to the wheel. The flywheel is 18$\frac{1}{2}$ft. in diameter, with six spokes, and weighs 5 tons. The beam is 14ft. long. The original D-slide valves were replaced in 1919 by a Worthington-Simpson piston valve. Steam was provided by a single boiler at 12 psi. This boiler was replaced in 1895. Fuel consumption was about 1 cwt. per hour [16]. Discharge was into Blue Gowt Drain, which met the River Glen at Surfleet Seas End.

This plant provided the sole drainage for the district until 1952, being the last beam engine and scoop wheel to operate in the Fens, and that which ran for the longest period. The chimney was later felled, but the remainder of the plant is maintained by Welland and Deeping IDB and is open to the public (Fig. 130). The engine is turned over by an electric motor.

In 1953 twin electric pumps of 75 and 45 hp were installed, driving pumps of 24 and 20in. diameter, discharging 55 and 33 tpm respectively [17].

L4 PINCHBECK SOUTH FEN or FOURTH DISTRICT (TF 215224)

This district is within Deeping Fen and was enclosed under the Deeping Fen Act of 1801 [18]. It contained 1425 acres.

In 1830 a 35 hp beam engine, possibly by Fenton & Murray, was erected at Pode Hole. This drove a scoop wheel 20ft. in diameter with 42 scoops $5\frac{1}{2}$ft. long by 1ft. 3in. wide. The average lift was 5ft. Steam was supplied at 6/7 psi. The engine ran at 30 rpm and the wheel at $7\frac{1}{2}$ [19].

This plant was scrapped in 1919 and replaced by a suction gas engine driving a Ruston pump (Fig. 131). By 1943 this had been superseded by a 30 hp Petter oil engine driving a 20in. Gwynnes pump [20]. In turn this was replaced in 1953 [21] by twin electric engines of 75 and 45 hp driving Gwynnes axial flow pumps, one of 24in. diameter and the other of 20in.

Discharge was into Vernatt's Drain. There are no remains of the old plant. This fen is now within Welland and Deeping IDB.

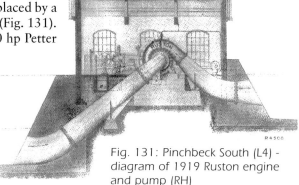

Fig. 131: Pinchbeck South (L4) - diagram of 1919 Ruston engine and pump (RH)

L5 BOURNE SOUTH AND THURLBY FENS (TF 148182)

This triangular area of peat fen containing 3240 acres is bounded on the west by the Carr Dyke, on the north by Bourne Eau and on the south-east by the River Glen. Early in the seventeenth century, Sir Gilbert Heathcote Bt. constructed a tunnel to drain the northern part of Bourne South Fen under the River Glen and into the Counter Drain (then called the Slacker Drain) which runs to Pode Hole. First enclosed by Act of 1772, the drainage of Bourne South Fen was originally under the general control of Deeping Fen Adventurers, using wind and horse mills.

In 1871, Bourne South Fen Drainage District was formed as a separate entity to drain 946 acres in the northern part of these fens. An 8 hp portable engine was immediately hired to drive a scoop wheel 12in. wide. In 1872, W. H. Wheeler, who had been appointed engineer to the Board, purchased a similar engine for £110 to replace this. In 1887 a centrifugal pump was obtained to work in addition to the scoop wheel. The function of this plant was to assist the flow of water from the fen into the tunnel.

A new 10 hp portable engine was purchased in 1893 for £90 to replace the old engine. The scoop wheel was replaced in 1904 by one made by Albert Freir of Pode Hole at a cost of £55.

In 1910 the district was reconstituted as Bourne South and Thurlby Fen Drainage Board so as to include 856 acres in Thurlby Fen belonging to Mr. Jonathan Ward. In 1912 a second-hand 50 hp gas suction engine driving a scoop wheel 2ft. wide was erected at TF 147181, i.e.

slightly nearer the tunnel, to handle the water from the enlarged area, and to replace the old plant. This engine broke down in 1942.

The entire fens of 3240 acres were taken over by Deeping Fen in 1943 and portable pumps were provided until 1949 when a new station was built at TF 151185, discharging into the River Glen. This contained two vertical spindle mixed flow pumps of 20 and 24in. diameter respectively, driven by 62½ and 100 hp electric motors. The pumps were lowered in 1973 [22].

L6 MAXEY IDB, Northants. – North Fen (TF 174074)

This district comprises North Fen, Northborough, in the Soke of Peterborough. A steam engine was erected in 1865 driving a pump of unknown type. This pump was replaced in 1887 by a 4ft. turbine pump (Fig. 132) made by Holmes at a cost of £150. This had applewood gearing. The engine was replaced in 1929 by a Blackstone oil engine [23]. Before 1977 this had been replaced by an Allen-Gwynnes electric motor driving a 16in. pump [24]. The Holmes pump was probably removed in 1911, but the top part is in Pode Hole old engine room, and the bottom half is exhibited at Pinchbeck Engine [25]. Discharge was into the River Welland. No trace of this plant remains. This area is now part of Welland and Deeping IDB.

L7 SURFLEET (D)
(TF 165315)

The fenlands of Surfleet bordering the east side of the South Forty Foot Drain contain 1280 acres and were enclosed in 1777. In 1923 a 34 hp Campbell single cylinder horizontal diesel engine (no. 11125), having a bore of 10⅝in and stroke of 20in., was installed to drive a 17in. Gwynnes pump by belt drive [26]. This delivered 25 tpm. This possibly replaced a windpump with auxiliary steam engine [27]. This plant survived until after 1953 [28], but seems to have been removed in the 1966 reorganisation and not replaced. This area is now within Welland & Deeping IDB

Fig. 132: Northborough (L6) Holmes pump at Pinchbeck (L3) in 1994

L8 KIRTON MARSH (D) (TF 345350)

This marsh was enclosed under an Act of 1772. In 1913 a single cylinder vertical hot-bulb two-stroke Robey diesel engine (no. 35192) was installed to serve some 800 acres in Kirton Marsh, previously drained by gravity through a sluice. This drove a submerged Smithdale pump by gear box drive through a clutch [29]. By 1943 there was a Gwynnes pump at this plant [30]. This was replaced in 1967 by an Allen-Gwynnes 27 in. electric pump. Discharge is into the north side of the River Welland. This area is now within Welland & Deeping IDB.

NOTES

1. 33 G3 c. 109
2. 49 G3 c. 119
3. Wheeler SL, 131. Hills (2003), 96, quotes Tycho Wing as stating 4000 acres, but this seems to be unlikely.
4. Hills (2003), 96 – 97 gives virtually all information known about this plant
5. OS 1in. map, first edition, 1824
6. 41 G3 c. 128. Further Acts followed in 1823 (4 G4 c. 76) and 1856 (19 & 20 Vict. C. 65)
7. A full account of the early drainage of this area is given in Wheeler SL, 312 – 332
8. Hills (2003), 147, and 112 and 113 for photographs
9. Miles, W.D. (1965), *History of Deeping Fen and Pode Hole Pumping Station*, Deeping Fen IDB, passim, including photographs. This wheel was lowered twice, lastly in 1883.
10. Wheeler SL, 383 – 386. Wheeler DF has a sectional drawing of this arrangement
11. Clark, Engine nos. 110 and 111, *English Mechanics*, 21 August 1936; and booklet of photographs of the engines in course of demolition produced by the IDB in 1952 called "Holland and Kesteven Pumping Engines at Pode Hole Spalding." Watkins SSE, Vol. 5, 128 – 131, contains photographs of these engines and one of the scoop wheels
12. Hills (2003), 138
13. Wheeler SL, 384
14. Miles, note 9, passim. He gives a full description of these engines with photographs
15. 2 W4. See Wheeler SL, 118 – 119
16. Pinchbeck Engine booklet: the maker is not otherwise substantiated. The building is not of the standard Butterley design, and this plant is not mentioned by Glynn, suggesting that it is not a Butterley engine. Wheeler SL, 119, gives the diameter of the scoop wheel as 24ft. Clark, Engine no. 123, *English Mechanics*, 25 September 1936, gives slightly different particulars, as does Watkins SSE, Vol. 5, 116
17. Gwynnes 1953, no. 77A and 1977
18. 41 G3 c. 128
19. Wheeler SL, 120. CC, 26 February 1830, states that this was a 25 hp engine and that the scoop wheel was 18in. wide.
20. Gwynnes 1943, no. 77
21. Miles, note 9, 28, and *Lincolnshire Free Press*, 6 January 1953.
22. Miles, W.D. (1976): *History of the Drainage of Bourne South Fen and Thurlby Fen,* Welland & Deeping IDB, passim. This contains, on p. 14, a photograph of the construction of the new scoop wheel in 1904. See also Wheeler SL, 333 and 335
23. Letter from W.D. Miles, Engineer to Welland and Deeping IDB dated 20 May 1975.
24. Gwynnes 1977
25. Personal inspection 1994.
26. Leafe, 31
27. Gibbs's map, but this is not mentioned in Wheeler SL
28. Gwynnes 1943 and 1953, no. 73, and 1977
29. Leafe, 31; but Robeys' records show the engine as ordered in 1917
30. Gwynnes 1943 and 1953, no. 68, called Kirton Sheldyke. Gwynnes 1977 records a Ruston engine driving a 20in. Gwynnes pump

8
THE WITHAM DISTRICTS

DISTRICTS

Serial No.	Name
WITHAM FIRST	
L9	Washingborough and Heighington
L10	Nocton Potterhanworth and Branston
L11	Branston Island
L12	Dunston and Metheringham
L13	Blankney Linwood and Martin
L14	Timberland and Thorpe
L15	Billinghay South
L16	Billinghay North
L17	Greetwell
WITHAM THIRD	
L18	Bardney Stixwould
L19	Stainfield
L20	Kirkstead
L21	Tattershall

Serial No.	Name
WITHAM FOURTH	
L22	Lade Bank and Hobhole Sluice
WITHAM FIFTH	
L23	Ruskington Dorrington and North Kyme
L24	Digby
L25	Anwick and North Kyme

The low lands lying on either side of the River Witham between Lincoln and Boston were first drained under an Act of 1762. This divided the area into six districts for drainage purposes. Within those districts, numerous sub-districts existed, created mostly for parishes and as a result of enclosure (map 12, p.27).

Witham First District lies west of the river and between it and Car Dyke. It extends from near Lincoln in the north to Kyme Eau in the south and contains 24,916 acres.

Witham Second District lies in Holland Fen south of the river from Kyme Eau to Boston and contains 19,101 acres. This district had no early drainage plant, and is within Black Sluice District.

Witham Third District lies east of the river, being a narrow neck of land between Stainfield in the north and Tattershall in the south. It contains 4621 acres.

Witham Fourth District lies east of the river and extends almost to the coast. It contains some 62,000 acres comprising the East, West and Wildmore Fens. The only early plant in this district was at Lade Bank.

Witham Fifth District lies west of the river between Billinghay Skirth and Kyme Eau and contains 5176 acres. It was amalgamated with the First District in 1953.

Witham Sixth District, containing 11,584 acres, lies on the south side of the river and west of Holland Fen. This district was included in the Black Sluice Level as was the Second District.

WITHAM FIRST DISTRICT

L9 WASHINGBOROUGH AND HEIGHINGTON

The fens of these parishes contain 1800 acres and were enclosed and drained under Acts of 1826 and 1828.

L9A Five Mile House (TF 082716)

In 1840 [1] an 18 hp [2] engine was installed about one mile below Five Mile Station. This drove a scoop wheel over 21ft. in diameter. In 1887, 32 new scoops were fitted and two new wrought iron hoops round the scoops which were 9in. longer than previously [3]. A single boiler supplied steam at between 15 and 20 psi. A new boiler 20ft. by 6ft. was supplied by Foster & Co. in 1910 [4].

This plant broke down in 1923 [5]. It was temporarily repaired [6], but replaced in 1924 by a horizontal tandem compound engine supplied by Robey & Co. This was coupled to a Smithdale pump delivering 40 tpm. The whole plant cost £1455 [7]. In about 1940, a pair of Ruston diesel engines driving 22 and 27in. Gwynnes pumps had replaced it [8].

Discharge was into the South Delph. No trace of the original building remains and an electric pump erected in 1975 now occupies the site.

L9B Sandhill Beck (D) (TF 042713)

Meanwhile at Sandhill Beck a Ruston & Proctor oil engine driving a 12in. centrifugal pump was installed as an auxiliary in 1910 [9]. This was replaced in 1930 by a Ruston 6HR 28 hp diesel engine [10], probably driving the original pump. By 1977 this had been replaced by an electric motor driving a 24in. Allen-Gwynnes pump.

L10 NOCTON, POTTERHANWORTH AND BRANSTON (TF 122662)

This district contains 5850 acres. The parishes were enclosed and drained under Acts of 1765, 1774, 1789 and 1832. In or soon after 1832, a 40 hp steam engine was erected on the north bank of Nocton Delph. This drove a scoop wheel 3ft. wide with scoops 6ft. long. Discharge was into Nocton Delph [11].

This plant was scrapped between 1896 and 1923 [12], by which date a 36in. Gwynnes pump discharging 120 tpm had been installed. This was driven by a 160 hp Marshall steam engine. In 1940 this was replaced by a 210 hp Ruston oil engine driving a 36in. Gwynnes pump [13]. In 1956 a 24in. axial flow pump was installed, driven by a 100 hp Allen-Gwynnes electric motor running at 585 rpm. Output was 56 tpm (34 cusecs) against a 17½ft. head.

L11 BRANSTON ISLAND (TF 102709)

When the South Delph was cut in 1812 to straighten the course of the River Witham below Lincoln, an area of 230 acres between the old and new courses was created, and this was called Branston Island. Previously it had formed part of Nocton, Potterhanworth and Branston District, within Witham First.

In 1883 a 16 hp steam engine made by Tuxford & Sons was erected on the west bank of the old River Witham to drain this area. It drove a centrifugal pump 20in. in diameter, handling a lift of 10ft. [14].

This was scrapped many years ago. In about 1941 a 15 hp Ruston diesel engine driving an 8in. Gwynnes pump was installed [15]. This remained in what appeared to be the old building (Fig. 133), somewhat truncated, until about 1995, when it was totally demolished. The land is owned by National Rivers Authority and was let on the basis that the owner operated the pump but the tenant was responsible for its maintenance [16]. Discharge was into the old River Witham.

Fig. 133: Branston Island (L11) engine house in 1993

L12 DUNSTON AND METHERINGHAM – Metheringham (TF 118630)

These fens were enclosed and drained under an Act of 1789, and contained 3400 acres within Witham First District [17]. By 1837 [18] a 20 hp [19] beam engine driving a scoop wheel had been erected on the north bank of Metheringham Delph, about two miles west of the River Witham. Steam was supplied by one boiler, consuming 3 cwt. 37 lbs. per hour, or 1 ton 7 cwt

Fig. 134: Metheringham (L12) engine house in 1992

in 12 hours. The coalyard held over 200 tons, a large quantity for a small engine. Constant replacement of scoops suggests some particular problem. A form of rising breast was fitted, but seems to have been in six sections or boards. The engine ran at 29 rpm, and had an ihp of 56 [20]. The maximum lift was 10ft. Discharge was into Metheringham Delph.

This plant was probably removed in 1913 [21] and replaced by a steam engine [22] driving a Smithdale pump [23]. Between 1933 and 1943 [24] this was replaced by a 100 hp oil engine driving a Gwynnes pump. In 1952 this was replaced by two electric motors driving 24in. Gwynnes pump on a different site against the River Witham [25]. Metheringham Delph was closed at the Carr Dyke inlet and became obsolete before 1974 [26]. A new electric submersible pump was installed at yet another site by the River Witham in 1990. The chimney of the original building has been felled, but the building itself remains in use as a barn (Fig. 134)[27].

L13 BLANKNEY LINWOOD AND MARTIN – Martin (TF 170609)

The fens of these parishes contain 1900 acres and were enclosed by an Act of 1787 and drained by an Act of 1832 [28].

In 1837 a 30 hp [29] beam engine built by George Leather & Son [30] and driving a scoop wheel was erected about half a mile west of the River Witham on the north bank of Timberland or Martin Delph, into which it discharged.

This plant was replaced after 1896 by a 160 hp Marshall steam engine driving a 36in. Gwynnes pump discharging 120 tpm [31]. This in turn was replaced by a pair of Ruston oil engines each driving a 30in. Gwynnes pump by 1943 [32]. Nothing remained by 1993 [33].

L14 TIMBERLAND AND THORPE – Timberland (TF 189583)

These fens, containing 2850 acres, were enclosed in 1785 and drained by an Act of 1839 [34]. In 1839 a 30 hp beam engine driving a scoop wheel 26½ft. in diameter [35] by 3ft. wide was installed on the west bank of the River Witham, into which it discharged. A single boiler supplied steam at 5 to 7 psi. This was a "long" boiler much favoured by Boulton & Watt c. 1800, with a central flue and made of wrought iron and hand-riveted. This was discarded in 1876 and became a hot well and storage tank for the two new boilers then installed [36].

Fig. 135:
Timberland (L14)
engine house in 2003

This plant was scrapped in 1881 and replaced by a 50 nhp high pressure condensing beam engine having a cylinder 36in. by 6ft. The flywheel was 24ft. in diameter and weighed 13 tons. The engine ran at 32 rpm and was geared 1:10 to the pump. This drove a centrifugal pump having a vertical fan 4ft. in diameter with a discharge pipe 14in. in diameter delivering 120 tpm at a lift of 11ft. This machinery was erected by Tuxford & Sons of Boston. The chimney was 106ft. high [35]. The two 1876 boilers were scrapped in 1910 and replaced by a single boiler, still in use in 1935 [36], and later converted for use as a fuel storage tank.

In 1924 this plant was replaced by a 124 hp Foster tandem compound horizontal steam engine driving a 33in. Gwynnes pump [36] delivering 100 tpm. The Foster engine was replaced in 1938 by a twin cylinder Ruston 9XHR diesel engine (No. 190605) [37] driving the Gwynnes pump. This generated 132 bhp at 265 rpm [38]. Since 1976 an electric pump has been used to drain the district, but the Ruston engine and pump is preserved and open to the public during the summer months (Fig. 135). The chimney has been demolished.

L15 BILLINGHAY SOUTH – Chapel Hill (TF 200540)

Enclosed in 1777, this district was effectually drained following an Act of 1840, and contained 4526 acres [39]. In 1841 a 30 hp beam engine, made by Green Atkinson, was erected at Chapel Hill. The cylinder was 78 by 28in. and the scoop wheel 28ft. in diameter and 27in. wide. The highest lift was 11ft. Steam was supplied at 25 psi. This plant cost £3600 [40] and was scrapped in 1935 [41]. It was replaced by two Ruston engines, a type 8HR and a type 8HRC respectively driving 30 and 22in. Gwynnes pumps [42]. These have long since been removed. Before 1977 a pair of Allen-Gwynnes 30in. electric pumps had been installed.

In 1941 a German bomb destroyed the old building and killed five members of the Richardson family one Sunday lunchtime. Richardson was the engine driver and a relative of the then driver of the Hundred Foot Engine (S14B)[43]. This led to the demolition of many redundant engine chimneys in the area, since they were believed to be used by enemy bombers for sighting.

L16 BILLINGHAY NORTH AND WALCOT DALES (TF 178560)

This fen contains 3150 acres and was enclosed in 1777 and drained under the Act of 1840 which also related to Billinghay South District [44]. In 1864 a 25 hp beam engine by Tuxford & Sons was erected on the north bank of Billinghay Skirth about 1½ miles west of the River Witham. This drove a scoop wheel 31ft. in diameter by 2ft. wide. The average lift was 9ft. and the maximum 13ft. The chimney was 90ft. high. The cost of this plant was £2500 [45]. Discharge was into Billinghay Skirth. This plant was scrapped in 1940 and replaced by two Ruston 9HR engines each driving 24in. Gwynnes pumps [46].

L17 GREETWELL – Fiskerton or Short's Ferry (TF 091711)

This fen contains 1410 acres of taxable land within Cherry Willingham, Barlings and Fiskerton, but receives the water from a much larger area of high land and also has the leakage from about 9 miles of river bank to contend with [47]. It was drained under an Act of 1861 [48].

In 1862 a pumping station was established at the junction of the old River Witham with Barling's Eau. It was called Fiskerton Engine, but is now called Short's Ferry. It was a 30 hp horizontal engine, made by Jarvis & L. Horsfield of Leeds [49], with a cylinder 22 by 42in. [50]. This drove a scoop wheel 31ft. in diameter and 28ins. wide, with a dip of 5ft.. The engine ran at 30 rpm with the wheel at 6½ rpm. Steam was supplied at 65 psi. The cost for the engine and wheel was £949.

Fig. 136: Fiskerton (L17) engine house in 2003

In 1893 an auxiliary plant made by Robey & Co. was installed. This consisted of a 50 hp horizontal engine driving two 21in. centrifugal pumps delivering 90 tpm in flood or 40 tpm from a level about 3ft. lower than that reached by the scoop wheel. This cost £644 [51].

These two installations were replaced in 1935 by two sets of twin-cylinder Ruston engines type 8HRC (nos. 17469 and 17470) each driving 30in. Gwynnes pumps lifting 75 tpm. This entire plant has survived as a stand-by (Fig. 136) [52]. By 1977 an Allen-Gwynnes electric motor driving a 27in. pump had been installed [53].

Discharge is into the old River Witham.

WITHAM THIRD DISTRICT

L18 BARDNEY STIXWOULD – Stixwould (TF 158652)

This district contains 2720 acres and was first drained under an Act of 1843 [54].

In 1846 a 30 hp beam engine was erected on the east bank of the River Witham near Stixwould Ferry. This had a cylinder of 32in. bore and 72in. stroke. It drove a scoop wheel 28ft. in diameter by 28in. wide, having 40 scoops each $5^{1}/_{2}$ft. long. This wheel revolved at 6 rpm whilst the engine made 18 rpm. Coal consumption was approximately $3^{1}/_{2}$ tons in 24 hours. The average lift was 4ft. [55]. This plant cost £3545.

Fig. 137: Stixwould (L18) engine house in 2003

This was replaced in about 1913 [56] by a Robey compound tandem steam engine driving a vertical spindle pump [57]. This was presumably demolished in 1936.

The present heavily secured brick building (Fig. 137) houses two Ruston & Hornsby oil engines driving Gwynnes pumps installed in 1936. One of these is a type 8HRC (no. 179699) engine driving a 30in. pump, and the other is a type 9XHRC (no. 179700) engine driving a 36in. pump [58]. This was a new building and the entire plant survives as a stand-by to an Allen-Gwynnes electric motor driving an 18in. pump installed before 1977.

This station is occasionally referred to as Southrey after a hamlet nearby and must not be confused with Southery (S8). Discharge was into the River Witham.

L19 STAINFIELD (TF 098714)

This parish, of some 2000 acres, was drained privately by the landowners. It was formerly part of Greetwell District. A 16 hp engine [59] was installed before 1881 near Barling's Lock. Discharge was into the River Witham.

After 1896 a 30 hp steam engine replaced this plant. It drove an 18in. Gwynnes pump discharging 25 tpm at 300 rpm [60]. This was scrapped between 1943 and 1953 [61]. By 1977 an Allen-Gwynnes 20 in. electric pump now serves the district and there are no remains of the old plant [62].

L20 KIRKSTEAD (TF 188603)

An area of 700 acres at Kirkstead was drained by a 30 hp [63] beam engine and scoop wheel installed before 1846 [64] about two miles south of Woodhall Spa on the east bank of the River Witham, into which it discharged,. The engine, when not used to drive the scoop wheel, was employed in driving a flour mill placed between the engine and the wheel [65].

This had been scrapped before 1936 [66]. In about 1948 an electric motor driving an 18in. Gwynnes pump was installed [67]. This was an axial-flow pump with an output of 25 tpm (25 cusecs.) against a $14\frac{1}{2}$ft. head. This was driven by a $37\frac{1}{2}$ hp squirrel cage induction motor at 720 rpm. The operation was automatic [68].

Fig. 138: Dogdyke (L21) engine house in 2003

L21 TATTERSHALL – Dogdyke (TF 207558)

This district was drained under an Act of 1796 [69] and contains some 2500 acres [70]. In 1855 a 16 hp A-frame beam engine made by Bradley & Craven of Wakefield was installed on the west bank of the River Witham about half a mile south of Tattershall Bridge. This still remains. The diameter of the cylinder is 24in. and the stroke 48ins. [71], with a flywheel 16ft. in diameter and beam centres of 12ft. 3in. This drives a scoop wheel 24ft. in diameter and 1ft. $3^1/_2$in. wide, with 36 scoops each 5ft. 5in. long. This delivered 25 tpm into the River Witham. Maximum speed of the engine is 28 rpm and gearing to the scoop wheel 4:1 [72].

The first boiler was a twin tube Cornish type which was replaced in 1909 by a Foster boiler $16^1/_2$ft. long and 6ft. wide. The front of this boiler has survived but it was replaced in 1976 by a Clayton cross-tube vertical boiler and this was replaced in about 2001 by another vertical. Steam was supplied at 15 psi. The chimney was originally 100ft. in height but was shortened after being struck by lightning in 1922 and felled in 1941.

This plant became redundant in 1940 when a Ruston type 7XHR diesel engine (no. 194833) driving a 22in. Gwynnes pump was installed in a separate building [73]. Both the steam and diesel plants remain under preservation and may be seen in operation on open days (Fig. 138).

L22 WITHAM FOURTH – East and West Wildmore Fens

Witham Fourth District consists of some 57,000 acres, with a catchment of some 88,000 acres [74]. It is bounded on the west by the River Witham between Dogdyke and Boston and on the south and east by villages close to the sea. It was created by Acts of 1762, 1801, 1803 and 1818 [75].

In 1803 considerable drainage works were carried out under a scheme proposed by John Rennie which included rebuilding the Maud Foster Sluice at Boston [76]. For this purpose a 6 hp Boulton & Watt bell-crank steam engine, possibly supplied by Bough Hollingsworth of Boston, was erected at TF 334431 [77]. This drove a water pump to drain areas for the sluice foundations. This engine remained until at least 1814, when it was broken into and badly damaged [78]. Another similar engine was also supplied, but may not have been used.

L22A Lade Bank (TF 379546)

Until 1867 drainage of the district was by gravitation. In that year an Act was obtained to enable a pumping station to be erected [79]. This was built in the same year. The plant was supplied and installed by Easton Amos & Sons. It consisted of two pairs of high-pressure condensing vertical direct-acting steam engines of 240 aggregate nhp driving two turbine pumps. The cylinders were 30ins. diameter by 30in. Stroke.

One pump well for each pair of engines contained a cast-iron cylinder 12ft. in diameter and $9^1/_2$ft. deep and having self-acting gates 12ft. wide. In each well was a double-inlet Appold pump having a fan placed horizontally. This was 7ft. in diameter and 2ft. $4^1/_2$in. wide with the mouth of the lower suction pipe $3^1/_2$ft. above the floor of the well and $4^1/_2$ft. below the surface of the water at ordinary drainage level. Each pair of engines could discharge 350 tpm at a 5ft. lift. Steam was supplied at 50 psi by six Lancashire boilers each 23ft. by $6^1/_2$ft. [80].

This plant cost £17000. It was scrapped in 1939, but the building and 90ft. chimney survives (Fig. 139). In 1939 a new building was erected against the old engine house to contain three Ruston engines driving 50 in. Gwynnes pumps (Fig. 140). These were supplemented in 1963 by a 36 in. electric pump [81].

Discharge was into Hobhole Drain, nine miles from its outfall into the Witham at Hobhole Sluice. This was because the low land lies between 10 and 13 miles from the outfall, and the drain acts as a reservoir when high tides prevent discharge through the sluice [82].

Fig. 139: Lade Bank (L22A) engine house in 1994

Fig. 140: Lade Bank (L22A) – Ruston engine in 1994

L22B Hobhole Sluice (D) (TF 365399)

In 1956/7 a pumping station (Fig. 141) was erected at the point of discharge of Hobhole Drain into the River Witham. This contained three six-cylinder vertical two-stroke Allen diesel engines (Fig. 142) driving three vertical 88in. mixed flow pumps, each delivering 267 tpm against a total head of 20.6ft. This plant was sited in a new cut just to the south-east of the redundant old sluices. In 1988 capacity was increased by installation of four 850 mm. Flygt submersible axial-flow electric pumps placed in the old outfall sluices [83].

Fig. 141: Hobhole (L22B) engine house in 2003

Fig. 142: Hobhole (L22B) - Allen engine in 2003

WITHAM FIFTH

Witham Fifth District lies west of the River Witham between Kyme Eau and Billinghay Skirth. It contains some 12,000 acres and was amalgamated with Witham First in 1953.

L23 RUSKINGTON DORRINGTON and NORTH KYME (TF 146533)

This district, containing 1300 acres, was first drained under an Act of 1832 [84]. In 1864 [85] a 16 hp engine was installed at North Kyme driving a centrifugal pump. This cost £1440. Discharge was into Billinghay Skirth. This was scrapped some years before 1935 [86]. The original building, without chimney, survives as a district store (Fig. 143) [87].

This district was amalgamated with Anwick and North Kyme when the old engine was scrapped. An electric plant was built across the main drain in 1986 (Fig. 143). This is called Farroway.

Fig. 143: North Kyme (Farroway) (L23) engine houses in 2003

L24 DIGBY (TF 142539)

This district contains 1440 acres and was formed into a separate drainage district in 1871 [88]. Previously the drainage had been private and the new district purchased the existing pumping plant from Lord Harrowby for £1000 [89].

Before 1869, a 14 hp steam engine had been installed on the north side of Dorrington Dyke between Billinghay and North Kyme. This drove a scoop wheel 24ft. in diameter and 12in. wide. The engine ran at 40 rpm and the wheel at $6^1/_2$ rpm. The lift was 5 to 6ft. [88]. This was replaced by a horizontal steam engine before 1936, which was scrapped in about 1940 [90] and replaced by a 57 hp Ruston diesel engine driving a Gwynnes 27in. pump [91]. This has long since been demolished and replaced by an Allen-Gwynnes electric pump. Discharge was into Dorrington Dyke, north side.

L25 ANWICK and NORTH KYME (TF 147532)

This area was enclosed in 1791 under an Act of that date [92.] In 1854 [93] a beam engine driving a scoop wheel was erected at North Kyme close to the Ruskington Engine. In 1926 a 75 hp Foster steam engine driving a 24in. Gwynnes pump delivering 50 tpm at 200 rpm replaced this [94]. This plant was scrapped in about 1948 when the district was amalgamated with Ruskington. Only a small part of the old building survives as a shed [95]. Discharge was into Billinghay Skirth.

NOTES

1. Washingborough & Heighington District Minutes (LRO) August to October 1839
2. Wheeler SL, 184
3. Minutes, note 1, 25 March 1887
4. Minutes, note 1, 27 May 1910
5. Minutes, note 1, 16 March 1923
6. Minutes, note 1, 23 November 1923
7. Minutes, note 1, 23 November 1923 to 14 July 1924
8. Gwynnes 1943 and 1953, no. 36, and 1977
9. Minutes, note 1, 8 April, 27 May and 10 June 1910
10. Minutes, note 1, 5 August 1930
11. Wheeler SL, 185. The Acts were 5 G3 c. 74; 14 G3; 29 G3 c. 32 and 2 & 3 W4 c. 96.
12. Minutes, note 1
13. Gwynnes 1943 and 1953, no. 40, and 1977
14. Wheeler SL, 185-186
15. Gwynnes 1943 and 1953, no. 39, and 1977.
16. Personal conversation with the tenant in 1993 and information obtained at Fiskerton Engine in 2003.
17. Wheeler SL, 186. He incorrectly states that this was within Witham Second District in Appendix 1 p. 27. The Act is 29 G3 c. 69. It was most probably an A-frame beam engine since the pedestal was replaced in 1900.
18. Metheringham District Account Books (LRO): "1837 September 15 – Slack for running steam engine 31 weeks to 19 April 1838".
19. Wheeler SL, 187. Clarke, J.A. states 30 hp, but White's *Directory of Lincolnshire* 1856 confirms Wheeler.
20. Engine Log Book 1896 – 1911 in author's possession.
21. Clark, Engine no. 85, English Mechanics, 29 May 1936
22. Minutes, note 18, record purchase of coal up to 1933.
23. Minutes, note 1, record such in 1923.
24. Gwynnes 1943 and 1953, no. 42, and 1977
25. Records at Timberland, where is also held a photograph of the exterior of this plant in 1906.
26. Robson, J.D. and others (1974): *Soils in Lincolnshire 1*. Soil Survey Record No. 2.
27. Personal inspection in April 1992
28. G3 c. 66 and 2 & 3 W4 c. 94
29. Wheeler SL, 187
30. Agreement dated 1837 held at Timberland Engine, which also holds a photograph of the exterior of this plant. For a picture of the scoop wheel, see Armitage, C.V.(N/D c. 1936): *Centrifugal Pumps*. Gwynnes Pumps Ltd. Publication No. 718, 21. Leather has not been traced: the firm may only have been the contractor.
31. Gwynnes 1936
32. Gwynne 1943, no. 43 and 1977
33. Personal inspection. See also Clark, Engine no. 82, *English Mechanics*, 29 May 1936, but his information appears to be inaccurate.
34. 25 G3 c. 14 and 2 & 3 Vict. c. 10
35. Wheeler SL, 189
36. Clark, Engine nos. 143 and 144, *English Mechanics*, 13 and 20 November 1936 and Gwynnes 1943 and 1953, no. 48 and 1977

37. Personal inspection
38. Old Glory no. 139 September 2001 p. 72
39. 17 G3 c. 70 and 3 & 4 Vict. C. 90.
40. Wheeler SL, 190
41. Clark, Engine no. 21, *English Mechanics*, 6 March 1936. Some of the details given by him are inaccurate.
42. Gwynnes 1943 and 1953, no. 53, and records held at Timberland Engine.
43. Wakelin, M.: ICE Panel for Historical Engineering Works Paper No. 774. See also Tattershall.
44. 3 & 4 Vict. C. 90.
45. Wheeler SL, 189-190.
46. Records at Timberland Engine and Gwynnes 1943 and 1953, no. 49 and 1977. This may be the plant described by Clark, Engine no. 7, *English Mechanics*, 7 February 1936, in which case it was scrapped before 1936.
47. Gibbs, 273
48. Wheeler SL, 192. The Act is 25 Vict. C. 149
49. Source unknown
50. Wheeler SL, 192. Gibbs states 48in. stroke by 24in. bore.
51. Wheeler SL,193. Gibbs states 32:5 and 60 psi for the original plant
52. Personal inspection in 2003. Gwynnes 1943 and 1953, no. 37.
53. Gwynnes 1977.
54. 6 & 7 Vict. C. 76
55. Wheeler SL, 193
56. Clark, Engine no. 124, *English Mechanics*, 25 September 1936. There is a photograph of the original engine house at Dogdyke Engine.
57. Gwynnes Pumps Publication no. 738 undated but post-1933.
58. Personal inspection in 2003 and Gwynnes 1943 and 1953, no. 41 and 1977
59. Wheeler SL, 193
60. Gwynnes 1943, no. 38.
61. Not listed by Gwynnes in 1953.
62. Personal inspection in 1993.
63. White's *Directory of Lincolnshire* 1856
64. Clark, J.A., 125
65. Wheeler SL, 196 and Gibbs, 274.
66. Clark, Engine no. 62, *English Mechanics*, 1 May 1936
67. Gwynnes' map 1943, no.44, marks this as steam-powered, but Clark states that the engine had been removed by 1936 and the building was derelict.
68. Rigby, W. (N/D c. 1963): *Land Drainage Pumping Stations in England*, Gwynnes, 13
69. 36 G3
70. Wheeler SL, 196
71. In February 2003 the Trust Chairman claimed that the stroke was 46 ins. and the bore 16$^{1}/_{2}$ins., but this seems to be unlikely.
72. Wakelin, M. (1990): ICE Panel for Historical Engineering Works HEW Paper No. 774. See also Clark, Engine no. 22, *English Mechanics*, 6 March 1936, and Watkins SSE, Vol. 5, 136, but neither give particulars which are wholly accurate. A photograph of the exterior of the engine house with chimney is held at the station.
73. Gwynnes 1943 and 1953, no. 50.
74. Wheeler SL, 198

75. 2G3 c. 32; 41 G3 c. 134; 43 G3 c. 118 and 58 G3

76. Wheeler SL, 197 – 240

77. Mutton, N. "The use of steam drainage in making the Eau Brink Cut", *Journal of Industrial Archaeology*, Vol. 4, no. 4, 1967, 353; and Hills (2003), 70

78. Dear, J. and Taylor, T. (1988), *Aspects of Yellowbelly History*, Chameleon International, Spalding, 75

79. Wheeler SL, 198

80. See Wheeler SL, 386-388; Hills (2003), 169 (plans – described as Hobhole Sluice) and 142 (photographs); and Clark, Engine nos. 64 and 65, *English Mechanics*, 8 May 1936 (including photographs).

81. Dear & Taylor, op. cit., 78 with photograph

82. Tomes, F.H. "Fen Drainage with particular reference to the Drainage of the Witham Fens", *Transactions of the Institute of Water Engineers*, Vol. XLII, 1937, 202 – 203. This contains a full explanation of this problem

83. Witham Fourth IDB brochure (undated)

84. 2 & 3 W4 c. 70. See also Wheeler SL, 241

85. Plaque on Engine House. Wheeler and Clark both state 1854, which must be incorrect.

86. Clark, Engine no. 24, *English Mechanics*, 6 March 1936

87. Personal inspection in 1986.

88. Wheeler SL, 242

89. Digby District Accounts 1869 – 1934 (LRO)

90. The Accounts show that coal was still being purchased in 1934. See Clark, Engine no. 19, *English Mechanics*, 6 March 1936.

91. Gwynnes 1943 and 1953, no. 51, and 1977

92. 31 G3 c. 93. See Wheeler SL, 240.

93. Clark, Engine no. 89, *English Mechanics*, 5 June 1936, who quotes date on engine house.

94. Gwynne 1937 and 1943, no. 55.

95. Personal inspection in 1986

9

BLACK SLUICE DISTRICT

This district contains some 112,000 acres, including 102,000 acres of fenland lying below the level of high tide. It consists of land bordering the South Forty Foot Drain which runs in a semi-circle from Gutheram on the River Glen to Boston.

The first effort at drainage of part of the area in the seventeenth century was thwarted by opposition from landowners, but did achieve excavation of a major part of the South Forty Foot Drain. The Black Sluice Commission was created by Act of 1765 [1]. Its first task was to build a new sluice at the lower end of the South Forty Foot in place of the old Black Sluice, and to scour the South Forty Foot and extend it to Gutheram. The Act provided for differential rating, settled by a further Act of 1770 as eighteenpenny, ninepenny, and sixpenny; and the areas so rated were long known by those amounts.

Within the district were many small internal districts (map 12, p.27). Their drainage was achieved by parish effort or separate Acts. Some of those included in Witham Second and Sixth Districts by the Act of 1762 were also placed within the Black Sluice area. These were Holland Fen, South Kyme, Great Hale, Little Hale, Heckington, Ewerby, Howell and Asgarby. The Black Sluice Commission only undertook a supervisory role over all of these 23 districts (of which 15 were pumped) [2] until the Land Drainage Act 1930 led to its taking over all of

Fig. 144: Black Sluice (L26) engine house in 2003

their responsibilities when the IDB was formed in 1935. In 1939 the South Forty Foot Drain itself and the Black Sluice were taken over by the Witham and Steeping Rivers Catchment Board, and are now managed by the Environment Agency. This led to the construction of the Black Sluice Pumping Station at Boston. Between 1964 and 1968 the Black Sluice IDB carried out a major reorganisation of the drainage of its district, replacing all existing machinery with electric pumps and, with new installations, providing a total of 33 stations. Only those previously powered by steam or oil engines are listed in this account.

Leafe states that a map of the Black Sluice area dated about 1856 showed 9 steam drainage engines and 8 wind drainage engines, draining an area of approximately 18,000 acres. There is no evidence to suggest that such a number of steam engines existed in this area by that date, or indeed by the time of the surveys by Wheeler and Gibbs. The latter states that 15 of the 23 districts were pumped by 1930.

Fig. 145: Black Sluice (L26) - Ruston engines in 2003

L26 Black Sluice Pumping Station (D) (TF 326429)

Until 1946, the South Forty Foot Drain discharged into the River Witham through the Black Sluice at Boston by gravity. In that year a pumping station (Fig. 144) was erected at the Sluice to house three 900 hp Ruston & Hornsby five cylinder turbo charged intercooled diesel engines each driving 100 in. mixed flow pumps through David Brown double reduction gear boxes (Fig. 145). Each pump was designed to deliver 668 tpm at 13ft. static head and 885 tpm at 5ft. static head. In 1966, capacity was increased by the addition of two similar pumps each driven by a 975 hp English Electric turbo-charged engine [3].

The installation of this station was a material factor in persuading Witham Fourth District to construct its Hobhole Pumping Station because it caused an additional flow in the Witham above the Hobhole Sluice.

L 27 BOURNE NORTH FEN (TF 173225)

This district lies in Lindsey Level and was within the Black Sluice Eighteenpenny District and contains some 4000 acres [4]. It was constituted under Acts of 1841 and 1843 [5].

In 1845 a 30 hp Butterley beam engine was erected at Gutheram Gowt. The cylinder was 45 by 72 in. The boiler pressure was 6 psi, later increased to 9 psi. The engine drove an iron scoop wheel 15ft. in diameter and 4ft. 3ins. wide, having 30 scoops each 3ft. 10in. long. The dip was regulated by a vertical shuttle placed near the wheel, the dip allowed being 2ft. The Act limited the height of the water lifted to 4ft. and, when this was attained, the engine was stopped. The engine ran at 19 rpm and the wheel at $4^1/_2$. At full head, coal consumption was $2^1/_2$ tons per 24 hours [6].

In about 1895 the wheel was replaced by a 20in. Easton & Anderson pump [7]. In 1918 the old engine was replaced by a 50 hp single cylinder Tangye horizontal magneto fired gas engine (no. B 14850). This had a bore of 15in. and stroke of 22in. It drove the Easton & Anderson pump by belt drive.

This was supplemented in 1933 by a Ruston two cylinder horizontal diesel engine (no. 166443) type 9XHRC coupled direct to a 36in Gwynnes pump [8].

An electric 24in. pump replaced this in 1968 and there are no remains of the old plant. Discharge is into the River Glen.

L28 PINCHBECK NORTH

L28A (TF 167265)

By 1887 an engine existed on the east bank of the South Forty Foot Drain, into which it discharged [9]. This was within the Black Sluice Eighteenpenny district. This probably drove a horizontal spindle centrifugal pump [10]. There is now no trace of this plant [11].

L28B Leaves Lake (D) (TF 169241)

In 1927 a 30 hp Vickers Petter single cylinder vertical two stroke diesel engine (no. 100110) driving a 20in. Gwynnes pump discharging 31 tpm [12] was installed at Leaves Lake. This was replaced by an electric pump in 1966.

L29 DUNSBY FEN (TF 165271)

This fen is in the Lindsey Level within the Eighteenpenny Black Sluice District, and contains 1329 acres [13]. Much of this was owned by the Charterhouse of London from at least the seventeenth century until the early nineteenth century.

In 1870 the tenant, Caswell, installed a centrifugal pump on the west bank of the South Forty Foot Drain just south of Caswell's Bridge. This cost £689 and was driven by a hired portable engine. It discharged about 25 tpm against a head of 17ft. In 1883 a permanent 16 hp semi-portable engine and centrifugal pump were installed at a cost of £1710 [14]. These costs were subsequently refunded by the Charterhouse.

This plant was replaced in 1921 by a Marshall semi-portable twin cylinder horizontal steam engine (no. 74843) having a bore of 9¼in. and a stroke of 14in. Steam pressure was 90 psi. The engine was coupled to a 20in. Drysdale pump by belt drive [15].

In 1958 [16] an Allen-Gwynnes electric motor driving a 20in. pump replaced this, and there are no remains of the original plant [17].

L30 MORTON FEN (TF 153246)

This district lies in the Lindsey Level within the Eighteenpenny Black Sluice District and contains 2613 acres [18]. It was enclosed in 1768 [19] and was formed into a drainage district in 1892.

A 16 hp steam engine driving a scoop wheel was erected between 1860 and 1870 [20] about one mile west of the South Forty Foot Drain at a place now called Engine Farm.. This discharged into an engine drain which eventually discharged into the South Forty Foot. The wheel was replaced before 1918 by a 30in. Ruston & Proctor centrifugal pump [21].

This plant was scrapped in 1932 when a Ruston & Hornsby two cylinder horizontal diesel engine (no. 168797) type 9XHRC was installed to drive the old pump by belt drive. The pump seems to have been replaced by Gwynnes by 1943 [22].

This station was scrapped in 1979 when a new station was established at Dyke Fen (TF 151227) to drain Bourne North Fen, Dyke Fen and Morton Fen . This contained two 700 mm. pumps discharging 2660 litres per second. The total area then drained was 4468 acres [23]. By 1990 there was no trace of the old plant [24].

L31 DOWSBY and ASLACKBY (TF155293)

These fens are within the Eighteenpenny Black Sluice District and contain about 1883 acres [25]. They were enclosed by an Act of 1765 [26].

In 1904 a Marshall semi-portable steam engine (no. 41892), having a bore of 9in. and stroke of 18in. [27] was installed about one-third of a mile west of the South Forty Foot Drain. This drove a 20in. Drysdale pump by belt drive.

This was replaced in 1965 when an Allen-Gwynnes electrically driven 24in. pump was installed against the South Forty Foot at TF 162293. The original plant discharged into a drain which fed into the South Forty Foot. There are no remains of the old plant [28].

L32 HACCONBY (TF 166257)

This district is within the Eighteenpenny Black Sluice District and contains some 1283 acres [29]. It was enclosed by Act of 1773. Until 1912 it was drained by a windpump.

In that year a semi-portable Clayton & Shuttleworth twin-cylinder horizontal steam engine (no. 45097), having a bore of 8⅝in. and stroke of 12in. was installed on the west bank of the

South Forty Foot Drain. This drove a 20in. Drysdale pump by belt drive [30]. It probably replaced the windpump [31].

This was replaced in 1951 by a type 7XHR Ruston diesel engine driving a 24 in. Gwynnes pump [32]. This is preserved, although an electric pump now serves the district.

L33 HECKINGTON FEN (TF 195468)

This fen lay within Witham Sixth District and the Black Sluice Ninepenny District. It contains 2572 acres and was enclosed under an Act of 1764 [33].

A pumping station existed on the north side of Heckington Eau and about a quarter mile west of the Carr Dyke in 1887 [34]. This discharged into Heckington Eau. By reason of date, this must have been a steam engine, but no records have been traced.

In 1928 a 35 hp Ruston single cylinder horizontal diesel engine (no. 150411) was installed to drive an 18in. Gwynnes pump by belt drive [35]. This was replaced by twin Allen-Gwynnes electric motors driving 30in. pumps in 1966.

This district also contained two other stations in the eastern part called the Rakes. These were probably sited at TF 217459 on the south side of Skerth Drain [36] and at TF 207426 on the north bank of the South Forty Foot Drain at Swineshead [37]. One contained a 20 hp, and the other a 30 hp, diesel engine. These drove Gwynnes pumps, but no further information about them has been obtained.

L34 QUADRING FEN (TF 168332)

This fen contains some 1400 acres [38] and was enclosed by an Act of 1775 [39]. A steam engine seems to have existed by 1887 [40] on the east bank of the South Forty Foot Drain. This was replaced in 1923 by a 52 hp Campbell single cylinder horizontal diesel (no. 11094) engine of 13in. bore driving a 21in. Gwynnes pump by belt drive. This was scrapped in 1967 when an Allen-Gwynnes electric motor driving a 20in. pump was installed [41].

L35 BICKER FEN (TF 188398)

This fen is within the Eighteenpenny District and lies in North Holland and Kirton Hundred. It contains some 2560 acres [42] and was enclosed by an Act of 1766 [43]. It was originally drained by a windpump. By 1886 this had been supplemented by an auxiliary steam engine [44] driving a Tuxford impellor sunken pump 8ft. by 24in. [45]. The windpump and engine were replaced in about 1903 by a Marshall semi-portable single-cylinder horizontal steam engine no. 40169, having a bore of 12in. and stroke of 24in. [46]. This plant survived until after 1935, but may have been replaced by a diesel engine before an Allen-Gwynnes electric motor driving a 30in. pump was installed in a new building in 1967. There are no remains of the old plant. Discharge was into the South Forty Foot Drain (east side).

L36 DAMFORD GROUNDS (TF 194507)

Damford Grounds is part of the parish of South Kyme and has an area of 1839 acres [47]. A pumping station existed in 1887 [48] north east of South Kyme, and was presumably steam powered. This was replaced in 1913 by a 30 hp Ruston single cylinder hot-bulb paraffin engine (no. 43451) having a bore of 11in. and stroke of 18⁷/₈in. This drove an 18in. Gwynnes pump by belt drive [49]. This was replaced in about 1954 by twin electric motors driving 20in. Gwynnes pumps [50]. Discharge was into Kyme Eau (north side).

L37 SOUTH KYME – Sandilands Farm (TF 208469)

This district contains 2874 acres and is within Witham Sixth District and the Ninepenny District. Up to at least 1896 it belonged to a single proprietor [51], Lord Brownlow [52].

Before 1874 [53] a 20 hp horizontal steam engine was installed near the junction of Head Dyke and Skerth Drain. This drove a scoop wheel 24ft. in diameter. The wheel was replaced in 1874 by a Tuxford centrifugal pump having the blades placed horizontally and driven by a vertical shaft geared to the existing engine. The pump had a disc 36ins. in diameter and discharged 56 tpm with a 5ft. lift [54].

In 1917 the engine was replaced by a 50 hp Ruston & Proctor single cylinder horizontal hot-bulb paraffin engine (no. 34789) having a bore of $14^{1}/_{2}$in. and stroke of 22in. This was belt driven to the old pump [55].

In about 1936 this plant was replaced by a 30 hp oil engine coupled to an 18 in. Gwynnes pump delivering 30 tpm [56]. This was scrapped during the Black Sluice major scheme of 1967 and not replaced.

L38 DONINGTON – Mallard Hurn (D) (TF 174356)

The fenland of this parish was formed into a drainage district under the 1861 Land Drainage Act in 1884, having previously been drained under the provisions of an enclosure Act of 1767 [57]. It is within the Eighteenpenny District and contains 980 acres. Three windpumps were erected and at least one survived until 1923 [58]. In that year a diesel engine was installed at Mallard Hurn to replace that mill. This was a 34 hp single cylinder horizontal Campbell engine no. 11111, having a bore of $10^{9}/_{16}$in. and stroke of 20 ins. It drove a 17in. Gwynnes pump by belt drive. This discharged 25 tpm [59]. Discharge was into the South Forty Foot. This plant was replaced by an Allen-Gwynnes 20in. electric pump in 1967 [60].

L39 EWERBY (TF 159484)

The low lands of this parish are within Witham Sixth District (Act of 1762) and the Ninepenny Black Sluice District, which also contains South Kyme, Donington, Bicker etc. [61]. The parish contains 2789 acres [62].

A pumping station, presumably steam-powered, existed in 1887 [63], discharging into Car Dyke.

In 1918 this was replaced by a 32 hp single cylinder horizontal hot-bulb Field & Platt oil engine no. 14456, having a bore of $10^{3}/_{4}$in. and a stroke of 20in. This drove an 18in. Gwynnes pump by belt drive [64].

By 1953 this had been replaced by an 80 hp electric motor coupled to a 24in. Gwynnes pump [65]. Two new electric pumps were installed in 1956 and 1967 respectively [66].

Notes

1. 5G3 c. 86.
2. Tomes, F.H., "Fen Drainage with particular reference to the Drainage of the Witham Fens", *Transactions of the Institute of Water Engineers,* Vol. XLII, 1937, 201
3. Leafe, 36; but *The Allen Magazine,* Autumn 1965, 14, states that these were 942 hp eight-cylinder turbo-charged intercooled diesel engines. See also Witham and Steepings Rivers Catchment Board booklet on the opening of this station on 12 December 1946
4. Wheeler SL, 281. Leafe states 5017 acres.
5. 4 & 5 Vict. C. 113 and 6 Vict.
6. Wheeler SL, 281 and Clark, Engine no. 8, *English Mechanics,* 7 February 1936
7. Leafe. Easton & Anderson ceased to use that name in 1895.
8. Leafe, 31, but Gwynnes 1936 states that the engine was a 160 hp Campbell. See also Gwynnes 1943 and 1953, no. 76.
9. Gibbs's map and map in Wheeler SL
10. Gibbs, 274
11. Personal inspection 20 May 1997.
12. Gwynnes 1943 and 1953, no. 74 and Leafe, 31. Gwynnes 1977 states the engine as a Ruston
13. Leafe, 31 states 1265 acres.
14. Wheeler SL, 276
15. Leafe, 31.
16. Plaque on engine house
17. Personal inspection 1992
18. Wheeler SL, 277. Leafe states that the acreage as 2349.
19. 8 G3 c. 41
20. Wright, N. (ed.) (2004), *Lincolnshire's Industrial Heritage – A Guide,* Society for Lincolnshire Histroy and Archaeology, Gibbs, 274 and Clark, Engine No. 88, *English Mechanics,* 29 May 1936.
21. Leafe, 31. Ruston & Proctor ceased to use this name in 1918.
22. Gwynnes 1943 and 1953, no. 73.
23. Leafe, 56
24. Personal inspection
25. Wheeler SL, 275. Leafe states 2483 acres.
26. 5 G3 c. 173
27. Leafe, 31.
28. Personal inspection 1999
29. Wheeler SL, 277. Leafe states 1290 acres.
30. Leafe
31. Marked on OS map first edition.
32. Gwynnes 1953, no. 74A.
33. 4 G3 c. 5. See also Wheeler SL, 284. Leafe states 1828 acres.
34. Gibbs's map and Gibbs, 274, which refers to three small horizontal spindle centrifugal pumps in the second and sixth Witham districts.
35. Leafe, 31, and Gwynnes 1943 and 1953, no. 62, and 1977
36. Gwynnes 1943, no. 64
37. Gwynnes 1943, no. 65
38. Leafe. Wheeler SL, 95 states 1100 acres.
39. 15 G3

40. Gibbs's map
41. Leafe, 31 and Gwynnes 1943 and 1953, no. 72.
42. Wheeler SL, 99. Leafe, 30 states 1650 acres.
43. 6 G3 c. 82
44. Gibbs's Map
45. Clark, R.H. (1955): *Steam Engine Builders of Lincolnshire,* 115 states that Tuxfords ceased trading in 1887.
46. Leafe, 30. A similar engine installed at Dowsby in 1904 was numbered 41892.
47. Leafe, 30.
48. Gibbs's map
49. Leafe, 30 and Gwynnes 1943, no. 56
50. Gwynnes 1953, no. 56 and 1977, and Leafe.
51. Wheeler, 283. Leafe states 3190 acres.
52. White's *Directory of Lincolnshire* 1856
53. Clark, Engine no. 119, *English Mechanics,* 18 September 1936, who describes this as an old beam engine, as does Gibbs.
54. Wheeler SL, 283
55. Leafe, 65
56. Gwynnes 1943 and 1953, no. 61. This states it to have been 22 hp, but the delivery suggests that it was a Ruston 6HXR.
57. Wheeler, 97-98
58. Leafe, 24-25 – diagrams of the Mallard Hurn windpump.
59. Leafe and Gwynnes 1943 and 1953, no. 70.
60. Plaque on engine house and Gwynnes 1977.
61. Wheeler, 283
62. White's *Directory of Lincolnshire* 1856, 540
63. Gibbs'sMap
64. Leafe, 31
65. Gwynnes 1943 and 1953, no. 59 and 1977
66. Leafe, 62

10
UPPER WITHAM

L40 Pyewype (SK 933737)

This district of some 50,000 acres includes the valley of the River Till between Lincoln and Peterborough, and the valleys of the River Witham and River Brant between Lincoln and Grantham. Thus it encompasses the area between Lincoln and the Trent Valley. It was first constituted as the Witham and Steeping Rivers Catchment Board in 1933.

A steam pumping station (Fig. 146) originally existed next to the White House, but no information about this has been obtained. In 1936 a new station (Fig. 147) was established on the south bank of the Fossdyke almost opposite the Pyewype Inn. This contained two single-cylinder Ruston class 9HR diesel engines (nos. 177899 and 177900) direct-coupled to 27in. Gwynnes pumps. In 1940 a third engine was installed. This was a twin-cylinder Ruston class 8HRC (no. 205215) coupled to a 30in. Gwynnes pump [1].

NOTES

1. Sheriff, T. "Treasures at Pyewype Pumping Station", *Old Glory*, May 2001, reporting a visit in 1987; and Gwynnes 1943 and 1953, no. 35, and 1977

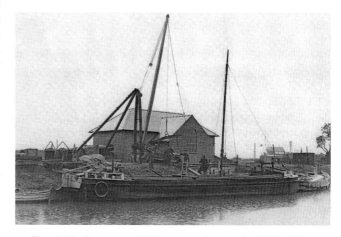

Fig. 146: Pyewype (L40) engine house in 1935 (RH)

Fig. 147: Pyewype (L40) engine house in 1988 (RH)

11
THE TRENT VALLEY

DISTRICTS

East of Trent

Serial No.	Name
T1	Newark
T2	Gainsborough
T3	Messingham
T4	Scunthorpe
T5	Althorpe
T6	Lindsey Marsh

West of Trent

Serial No.	Name
T7	Laneham
T8	South Axholme
T9	West Axholme
T10	Hatfield Chase
T11	Dun

The low grounds originally provided with pumped drainage into the River Trent stretch for over 35 miles on both sides of the river from above Torksey to the Trent Falls on the Humber (map 13, p.28). Gibbs states that a total of 59,000 acres of this area was drained by steam power, of which 21,000 acres lay on the east side of the Trent and 38,000 on the west side.

The main part of the west side contains the Isle of Axholme and Hatfield Chase, bounded on the north by the River Ouse and on the south by the Heckdyke. This area is some 19 miles from north to south and 7 miles from east to west. It was first drained by Vermuyden in the early seventeenth century by a system discharging most of the waters to the Trent at Keadby. Windpump drainage never seems to have been used in the Trent Valley area. It was not until 1828 that the first steam-powered pumping stations were erected. A total of 20 erected thereafter have been traced, of which Torksey LNER was not strictly a land drainage plant, and Redbourne was far east of the main catchment area. In the twentieth century, the installation of diesel and electrically powered pumps proliferated, so that by 1970 there were over 30 stations in the Isle of Axholme and Hatfield Chase alone. In addition, two large secondary pumping stations were provided at Keadby (T12) in 1940 and West Stockwith in 1981. The latter is an all-electric station at the outfall of the River Idle into the Trent and is therefore not included in this account. The Idle normally discharges by gravity and pumping is restricted to dealing with flood conditions.

Although not strictly within the Trent Valley, Kirk Bramwith has been included not least because it was the last steam-powered station traced as erected in the lowlands of Eastern England. Its proximity to coalfields must have been the major reason for this source of power being preferred to oil or electricity.

EAST OF TRENT

T1 NEWARK IDB

T1A   Torksey (SK 836781)

This is the most southerly pumping station on the Trent, being 35 miles from Trent Fall. It is situated on the south of the Foss Dyke and west of the lock on that watercourse. It drained some 13,000 acres [1].

In 1852 [2] a 60 hp [3] single cylinder condensing beam engine made by Davy Bros. of Sheffield was erected. This had a bore of 33in. and stroke of 60in. The flywheel was 19ft. in diameter [4] and the beam 15ft. long [5]. Steam was supplied at 10 psi by two Lancashire boilers sited below the engine and was admitted by drop valves [6].

This drove a scoop wheel 34ft. in diameter and 23in. wide, providing a maximum discharge of 40 tpm. In May 1932 the high level of flood water caused the wheel to be partially lifted off its bearings, as happened at the Marshland engine in 1912 [7].

This plant last worked in 1934, in which year it was replaced by two electric motors of 250 and 135 hp each driving Gwynnes pumps of 40 and 30in. diameter respectively [8]. These discharged 150 and 75 tpm respectively. The old engine was scrapped in 1936, and the chimney was later demolished, but the engine house remained in 2000 (Fig. 148). The electric plant was fully over-hauled in 1986 [9]. Discharge is into the Foss Dyke, almost at its junction with the River Trent, east side.

Fig. 148: Torksey (T1A) engine house in 2000

Fig. 149: Morton Carr (T2A) engine house in 2000

T1B Torksey LNER (SK 834781)

A second plant existed at Torksey close to the main engine and on the south side of Foss Dyke and west of the lock. This was erected by the L & NE Railway Company. It was a small beam engine with a cylinder bore of 18in. and stroke of 36ins, driving a double-acting bucket pump direct off the end of the beam. The date of erection is unknown [10] and it was broken up in 1936. The maker is believed to have been Davy Bros of Sheffield. Its purpose was to supply water to maintain the level of the Foss Dyke for navigation. Therefore it was not strictly a land drainage plant, but more of a canal service structure similar to the preserved Crofton engines on the Kennet and Avon Canal. There are no remains of this plant.

T1C Marton (SK 834813)

In 1864 [11] a station was established by the Lincoln Commissioners of Sewers on the east bank of the Trent near the village of Marton. This drained 1600 acres of taxable land and some 2000 acres of high land. It consisted of a 40 hp single-acting beam engine of the Cornish type, having a cylinder of 42in. bore and 90in. stroke [12]. It drove off the beam a bucket pump 5ft. in diameter and 7ft. 6in. stroke [13]. Steam was supplied by two boilers. The chimney shaft was separate from the boiler house and octagonal in section [14].

This plant ceased operation in 1923 and the engine was broken up in 1930 [14]. It was not replaced until Newark Area IDB was established in 1939. In that year two electrically driven Gwynnes pumps (of 24 and 36in. diameter) were installed in the old building which was adapted for the purpose. These together discharged 148 tpm.

In 1989 this plant was wholly scrapped and the building demolished. All that remains is the old outfall channel. In its place, three mixed flow submersible pumps driven by an electric motor were sunk near the site. These have a total discharge of 236 tpm and drain a total area of 5898 acres [15].

T2 GAINSBOROUGH IDB

T2A Morton Carr (SK 806915)

This is an area of some 2000 acres one mile north of Gainsborough on the east bank of the Trent. It was first drained under an Act of 1801, followed by another Act of 1841. In 1843 a 40 hp steam engine driving a scoop wheel was erected [16].

In 1868 Mr. Samuel Naylor, Superintendent of the District, patented a flap valve for fitting to the front of the scoop wheel to replace self-acting doors across the outlet, and a curved guide to cause the water to enter at the underside of the wheel [17].

This plant was removed many years ago, but the lower part of the building survives as a store (Fig. 149)[18]. Two upper floors have been removed. No replacement plant has been traced.

T2B Ravensfleet (SK 800960)

This area contains some 1850 acres east of the Trent about seven miles north of Gainsborough. In 1843 a 40 hp beam engine was erected. This drove a scoop wheel 35ft. in diameter and 2ft. wide, having curved iron floats (or ladles) on wooden starts. Clark [19] writes "at the back of the wheel was a casing of wood with an opening arranged in such a way that the water

Fig. 150: Ravensfleet (T2B) engine house in 2000

could not strike the floats until both were travelling in approximately the same direction. In front of the wheel was a door built of several wooden flaps which hinged together horizontally. When the wheel was discharging they floated horizontally but when it stopped they rose to a vertical position cutting off any return water."

This plant was replaced in 1902 by a steam engine of which no details have been obtainable [20]. It was superceded in 1953 by a Ruston type 4VCB (no. 359496) diesel engine driving a 30in. Gwynnes pump [21]. This was placed in the old building (Fig. 150). In 1962 the steam engine was removed and exported to India. In its place a Blackstone type EV3 oil engine (no. L70E13) driving a 30in. Gwynnes pump was installed. Both of these engines still exist [22].

T2C Jenny Hurn

This area of 1750 acres east of the Trent was part of the Lincolnshire estates of the Meynell-Ingram family, being situated in Laughton and Wildsworth.

Fig. 151: Jenny Hurn (T2C) engine house in 2000

Fig. 152: Jenny Hurn (T2C) – Ruston engine in 2000

Fig. 153: Jenny Hurn (T2C) - Gwynnes plant in 1897 (J. & H. Gwynnes 1899)

T2C/1 (SK 819985)

The estate was originally drained by a beam engine driving a scoop wheel 30ft. in diameter erected in 1867 [23]. In 1896 this plant was abandoned and a new plant established nearer the river (Fig. 151).

T2C/2 (SK 818986)

This comprised two sets of J. & H. Gwynne horizontal compound non-condensing engines each driving a Gwynnes 15in. centrifugal pump (Fig. 153). The suction pipes dropped into a pump-well below the engine room floor and the delivery pipes, each 18in. in diameter and about 90ft. long, passed first under a public road and then under the bank of the Trent. The pumps could be used together or independently. Steam was provided by a single boiler of locomotive type, possibly later supplemented by another boiler. Discharge was 20 tpm, presumably from each pump [24].

This plant was replaced in about 1940 by an 80 hp Ruston diesel engine, presumably type 7XHRC (Fig. 152), driving a Gwynnes pump situated in the old building [25]. Although an electric pump was installed in 1970, the Ruston plant remains as a stand-by [26].

T2D Susworth(D) (SE 832017)

No record of any early plant on this site has been traced [27]. In 1941 two Ruston 9HR diesel engines (nos. 208199 and 208200) were installed in a new building. These were coupled to 20in. Gwynnes pumps, but these were replaced in 1983 and 1985 by Bedford pumps. This plant remains, although an electric plant now undertakes most of the duty [28]. Discharge is into the River Trent, east side.

T3 MESSINGHAM IDB – East Butterwick (SE 838061)

This district contains 3250 acres north of Gainsborough and on the east side of the Trent. Until 1882 it was drained by gravity. In that year a pumping station was established in East Butterwick, next to the Trent. The engine was a double-cylinder semi-portable, almost certainly made by Hetts of Ancholme Foundry, Brigg, and fitted with Hartnell's automatic expansion valve gear. This drove by belt a "Hett's Improved Accessible" centrifugal pump with suction and delivery pipes 21in. in diameter. This discharged some 44 tpm. The total cost of the machinery and wooden engine house was £1432 [29].

This plant was removed in about 1940, and replaced by a twin Ruston oil engine driving a 27in. Gwynnes pump and placed in a new building which survives [30]. An electric pump was installed probably in 1956.

T4 SCUNTHORPE IDB – Burringham (SE 840085)

A 70 hp steam engine driving a Gwynnes pump existed about half a mile east of the Trent prior to 1943 [31]. This was replaced in 1944 by two Ruston type 8HRC diesel engines each driving a 30in. Gwynnes pump discharging 75 tpm. They were housed in a brick building placed across the main drain and built on piles [32]. In turn this plant was replaced in about 1968 by an Allen-Gwynnes electric motor driving a 15in. pump in a new building [33].

T5 ALTHORPE IDB – Redbourne (TA 009999)

Between 1880 and 1888 [34] a small pumping station was installed on the east bank of the New River Ancholme to drain 800 acres of low land on the estate of the Duke of St. Albans at Redbourne. The engine was a 14 hp semi-portable double cylinder engine which drove by belt an 18in. Hetts centrifugal pump. The cost of the engine and pump was £641 and of the brick and tiled shed £211 [35]. No further information about this plant has been obtained.

T6 LINDSEY MARSH

This Board manages the drainage of a large area of marshland on the coast of North Lincolnshire north of Skegness and was formed in 2000 through the amalgamation of Alford, Louth and Skegness Boards. It is not strictly fenland, but has been included because of two preserved pumping stations in the district which deserve mention. The information about these is derived from the material produced by the preservation trusts. The remaining 29 stations in this area are not within the scope of this work.

T6A Anderby (D) (TF 545760)

Lindsey Marsh itself has a catchment area of some 9000 acres, although the land subject to being periodically waterlogged is only about 4000 acres.

In 1946 a pumping station (Fig. 154) was established at Anderby Creek near the coast. No previous plant has been traced. This consisted of two Ruston type 10XHRC two cylinder engines, each driving a 42in. Gwynnes pump by belt drive. This was replaced in 1992 by three submersible mixed flow pumps driven by electric motors, but the original plant has been preserved (Fig. 155) and is open to the public.

Fig. 154: Anderby (T6A) engine house in 2003

Fig. 155: Anderby (T6A) - Ruston engine in 2003

Fig. 156: Gayton Marsh (T6B) engine house in 2003

Fig. 157: Gayton Marsh (T6B) – Petter engine in 2003

T6B Gayton (TF 458880)

Commissioners of Sewers established a station at Gayton-le-Marsh to drain the East Lindsey area in 1850. This discharged into the River Great Eau. It is known that this was a steam engine and the design of the engine house strongly suggests that it was a beam engine driving a scoop wheel (Fig. 156). It may later have been replaced, or supplemented, by a horizontal Robey steam engine driving an 18in. centrifugal pump [36].
This was replaced in 1945 by a 112 bhp Petter Atomic twin cylinder diesel engine (no. 222773) (Fig. 157), purchased second-hand. It drove a Gwynnes pump. This is sited in the old building, which is preserved together with the engine and pump. It is managed by a trust and is open to the public. This plant has not been used since 1956 when a new electrically-powered station was established at Theddlethorpe.

WEST OF TRENT

T7 LANEHAM IDB – Sturton (SK 815857)

In 1847 a 43 hp beam engine was erected on the west bank of the Trent, into which it discharged. This drove a scoop wheel 26ft. 6in. in diameter and 2ft 3in. wide, having curved iron floats [37]. It drained some 9000 acres. This was scrapped before 1937 [38] and the building has since been demolished. An Allen-Gwynnes 24in. electric pump now provides the drainage [39].

T8 SOUTH AXHOLME

T8A Misterton, Notts. (SK 779951)

Two impressive early steam engine houses (Fig. 158) still stand side by side on the south bank of the Mother Drain a quarter of a mile north of Misterton village, albeit now converted into a single dwellinghouse, but retaining their chimneys. These were erected to drain Misterton Carr and Gringley Carr, an area of about 10,000 acres [40]. They were respectively named *Kate* and *Ada*.

KATE: This was the first steam-powered pumping station to be erected in the Trent Valley. In 1828 a 40 hp [41] Butterley beam engine driving a scoop wheel 34ft. in diameter [42] was installed to drain Gringley Carr [43]. It probably had one boiler of the Butterley type [44].

In 1890 the scoop wheel was replaced by a 30in. Gwynnes centrifugal pump driven by pinion and spur wheel from the existing engine shaft [45], said to discharge 75 tpm. This was followed by replacement of the engine in 1895. J.&H. Gwynne of Hammersmith supplied a horizontal compound tandem jet engine, having two cylinders 12in. and 22in. by 18in. (Fig. 159) [46]. This ran at 75 rpm and was rated at 135 hp. A single Lancashire boiler provided steam at 100 psi, replacing one installed about 1855.

ADA: In 1839 the second plant was installed to drain Misterton Carr. This was a beam engine made by Booth & Co. of Park Iron-works, Sheffield. The cylinder had a bore of 33in. and stroke of 84in. [47]. The beam was 18ft. long and the flywheel 18ft. in diameter [48]. Speed was 18 rpm. The original D-slide

Fig. 158: Misterton (T8A) engine houses in 1899 (J. & H. Gwynnes 1899)

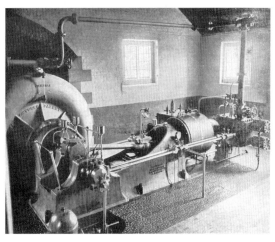

Fig. 159: Misterton (T8A) – Gwynnes plant in 1899 (J. & H. Gwynnes 1899)

valves were retained throughout its life. Steam was provided at 10 to 20 psi by one boiler made by Marshall & Co. [49]. This drove a scoop wheel 34ft. in diameter and 2ft. 2in. wide, having 49 ladles. The drive was by external gearing down from the engine in the ratio 1:4^2/$_9$ [50]. It was said to discharge 50 tpm. Photographs of these engines are contained in the works cited of Clark, Watkins, Hills and Gwynnes. Both became redundant in 1941, although *Kate* is said to have survived until the 1950s.

T8B   Gringley Carr (D) (SK 713949)

In 1941 a diesel plant was placed at Gringley Carr and the drainage system reorganised. This station contained twin Ruston engines, probably type 9XHRC, driving 40in. Gwynnes pumps [51]

T8C Heckdyke (SK 798960)

A beam engine presumably driving a scoop wheel was first erected at Heckdyke in 1828 [52]. It was replaced at some time after 1850 [53] by another beam engine made by T. Bradbury of Gainsborough having a cylinder of 18in. bore and 42in. stroke. This drove a scoop wheel 24ft. in diameter [54].

This plant was scrapped in 1933. In its place a 30 hp Marshall diesel engine driving a 16in. Gwynnes pump delivering 23 tpm [55] was installed in the old building, which remains without its chimney (Fig. 160). By 2000 this plant appeared to have been superseded by an electric pump.

Fig. 160 (right): Heckdyke (T8C) engine house in 2000

T8D Owston Ferry (SE 813005)

In 1910 a station was established on the west bank of the Trent at Owston Ferry to serve an area previously drained by gravity. Two Marshall 100 hp compoumd horizontal steam engines were installed each to drive a 27in. Drysdale of Glasgow centrifugal pump. The cylinders were 7 and 13in. bore by 20in. stroke. Steam was provided at 150 psi by two Cornish boilers (nos. 52765 and 52766), each measuring 20ft. by 6ft. [56].

One of these engines was removed in 1952 and replaced by two Ruston 9XHR diesel engines each driving by belt a Bon Accord pump [57]. In 1964 a Blackstone engine was installed in a separate building, but the surviving steam engine remains in preservation (Fig. 161), although rarely accessible.

Fig. 161: Owston Ferry (T8D) engine house in 2000

T8E Kelfield (SE 822012)

A pumping station was established at Kelfield on the west bank of the Trent probably in 1846, and certainly by 1856[58]. This discharged the water from Belton across Newlands Farm via the Black Dyke Drain. At some time before 1925 [59] this was replaced by a 20 hp steam engine driving an 18in. Gwynnes pump. In 1959 the entire plant was scrapped and an electric pump installed in a new building [60]. It should be noted that this plant has been variously named Newlands Farm, Kelfield, Belton and Black Dyke.

T8F West Butterwick (SE 833052)

In the Isle of Axholme, Manley Wapentake, the South Common area of Butterwick contained at least 700 acres[61]. In 1837 Sir Robert Sheffield installed a steam engine to drain his estate there [62]. This was replaced in 1854, probably on the site of the previous plant and possibly in a new building (Fig. 162). This was a twin-cylinder grasshopper engine made by Easton & Amos (Fig. 163). The cylinders were $14^1/_2$in. by 25in. Steam was supplied by a single Cornish boiler at 30 to 40 psi. This drove a vertical turbine pump, believed to have been made by T. Smithdale of Acle, delivering 60 tpm [63]. This plant was removed in about 1943 when the building was demolished. At that time a 114 hp Ruston diesel engine, presumably type 9HRC, driving a 20in. Gwynnes pump [64] was installed in a new building. This was surviving in 2000, presumably as a stand-by, because by then an electric pump was in operation. Discharge was into the west side of the Trent.

Fig. 162: (above) West Butterwick (T8F) steam engine house (RH)

Fig. 163: West Butterwick (T8F) – Easton & Amos engine (RH)

T9 WEST AXHOLME IDB – Rush Carr (SE 829087)

In 1846 Sir Robert Sheffield erected an engine at Rush Carr to drain part of his estate in the Isle of Axholme [65]. It was a single underdrive grasshopper engine driving a turbine pump. This was removed in 1926 when a later steam plant was installed [66]. In about 1938, a 20 hp Ruston diesel engine, probably type 4YHR, driving a Gwynnes pump was installed [67]. In turn, this was replaced before 1977 by an Allen-Gwynnes electric motor driving an 18in. pump. Discharge was into the west side of the Trent, south of Keadby.

T10 HATFIELD CHASE CORPORATION

The Corporation of Hatfield Chase, formed by Act of 1862 to take the place of trustees, comprised some 18,000 acres (later 21,180 acres). Most of Hatfield Chase is situated in Yorkshire. It is bounded on the east by the River Torne, on the south by the River Idle and on the north by the Stainforth-Keadby Canal, being divided into two districts, the South and the North. These are separated by the River Torne running westwards.

T10A South District – Bull Hassocks (SE 731017)

This district comprises 7270 acres. In about 1848, a steam engine was erected at a place called Little Hirst (SK 780098?), about 3½ miles from the outfall at the Trent; but this was found to be too far from the district. In 1858 [68] it was moved to Bull Hassocks, near Wroot. The engine, not new when purchased, was a 40 hp side-lever engine. It drove a scoop wheel 30ft. in diameter and 2ft. 11½in. wide at 4½ rpm [69]. The chimney was 120ft. high (Fig. 164)[70].

This plant was replaced in 1892 by two separate 175 ihp vertical condensing marine type engines each driving a centrifugal pump of 48in. diameter, delivering 150 tpm. Thus the total capacity was 300 tpm. Each engine and pump could be run separately. There were two boilers, each 27ft. by 7½ft. This entire plant was made by D. Steward & Co. of Glasgow [71].

In about 1940 this plant was replaced by a 300 hp Ruston diesel engine driving a 36in. Gwynnes pump. This was supplemented about a year later by a pair of Ruston engines each driving a 36in. Gwynnes pump [72]. Later an electric pump was added, and another in 1988, to bring the total output of the station up to 330 tpm from four pumps [73].

The chimney was demolished many years ago. Part of the old building, considerably altered, survives (Fig. 165). Discharge is into the South Engine Drain and thence to Keadby.

Fig. 164: Bull Hassocks (T10A) engine house c.1925 (Korthals-Altes)

T10B North District – Dirtness (SE 749098)

The northern part of the Level of Hatfield Chase contains 10,660 acres. Following passage of the 1862 Act, a large pumping station was established at Dirtness in 1864/5. This comprised two compound condensing 50 nhp beam engines operating in tandem to drive a scoop wheel. Each high pressure cylinder was 20in. bore by 52½in. [74], and each low pressure 35in. bore by 72in. stroke. Steam was supplied by four boilers working at 20/30 psi [75]. The scoop wheel was 33ft. 3in. in diameter by 6ft. wide with 36 paddles, and weighed about 80 tons. It was geared down from the engine 6:1 and delivery was about 330 tpm [76]. This plant was built by James Watt & Co. and replacement boilers by Ruston & Proctor [77]. The cost of the buildings was £4547, and of the plant £4340.

This plant was scrapped in 1928 [78] and replaced in the existing building by an electric motor driving a Gwynnes pump [79]. In 1951 two 36in. Gwynnes axial-flow pumps were installed, each discharging 110 tpm and driven by two 105 bhp electric motors [80]. The original building remains, without chimney [78]. Discharge is into the Double River and thence to Keadby.

Fig. 165: Bull Hassocks (T10A) engine house in 2000

T11 DUN IDB – Kirk Bramwith, Yorkshire (SE 628122)

The low lands of the villages of Fishlake and Sykehouse in Yorkshire comprise some 6500 acres about seven miles east of Doncaster. Drainage Boards were formed for both villages. These were amalgamated in 1974 to form the Dun Drainage District.

The first pump installed to serve this area was placed at Kirk Bramwith in 1876, on the north bank of the River Don, into which it discharged. This was a vertical spindle Appold pump driven by an Easton & Anderson beam engine. This delivered about 150 tpm [81].

In 1939 this plant was replaced by a 45in.. vertical spindle double suction centrifugal pump in the well which had previously held the Appold pump. This was driven through a gear box by a 304 hp compound steam engine with 12 and 23in. cylinders having a stroke of 10in. and a pressure of 150 psi. Steam was provided by one Lancashire boiler 24ft. long and 7½in. diameter. Maximum discharge was 230 tpm [82]. This steam engine was replaced in 1958 by a 306 hp diesel engine driving the existing pump.

In addition, a 204 hp Ruston diesel engine was installed to drive a 36in. pump [83]. In 1992 a new pumping station was constructed adjoining the existing one. This contains three submersible pumps made by the Bedford Pump Co. and driven by electric power. These deliver about 100 tpm.

T12 ISLE OF AXHOLME – Keadby (SE 834113)

In 1940 a large station was established at Keadby on the west bank of the Trent to provide secondary pumping for the entire lowland area between Doncaster and the Trent, comprising some 7,800 acres. Normally the water is discharged by gravity at this point, but pumping became necessary in times of flood. Six 420 hp Crossley Premier diesel engines were installed to drive 60in. Gwynnes pumps. In 1994 one of the engines was replaced by an electric unit and the others were completely refurbished by National Rivers Authority [84].

NOTES

1. Gibbs, 271, states 9260 acres and some high land.
2. Watkins SSE Vol. 5, 136, states 1850.
3. Gibbs, but compare Marshland engine (NM3) which was rated at 40 hp with a cylinder 33 by 66 ins. The article by G.L. Nutt, "An early rotary pump at Torksey", *Lincolnshire Magazine*, vol. 6, July/August 1933, contains much inaccurate information.
4. Clark, *English Mechanics,* 24 December 1937, states 20ft.
5. Clark, note 4, states 16ft. 3in.
6. As was the 1850 Swaffham & Bottisham engine (S25B)
7. Clark, note 4, with photographs, and Hills (1967), 115, for photograph of scoop wheel
8. Gwynnes 1943 and 1953, no. 32 and 1977
9. *ADA Gazette,* Summer 1989, 32
10. Clark, *English Mechanics,* 24 December 1937. He suggests that it was erected c. 1815, but this cannot be correct because the railway company did not then exist. It is more likely to have dated from about 1850.
11. Gibbs, 271
12. Clark, *English Mechanics,* 24 December 1937. Hills (2003), 123, contains an illustration of the valves. For another example of a Cornish engine and bucket pump applied to fen drainage, see Waldersea (NM5)
13. Gibbs, 271
14. Clark, note 4
15. *ADA Gazette,* Autumn 1990, 11
16. White's *Directory of Lincolnshire* 1856, 174
17. Wheeler DF, 79-80. Naylor is described as an engineman in White's Directory.
18. Personal inspection in 2000.
19. Clark, note 4. The source of Clark's information is not known. He must have visited this station long after the original plant had been removed. Other wheels with curved iron scoops existed at Sturton (T7) and Upwell South (M32A)
20. Information from the engine driver in 2000.
21. Gwynnes 1953, no. 27
22. Personal inspection in 2000.
23. Date on stone in engine house wall
24. J. & H. Gwynnes 1899, 44 and 45, with photographs and Gwynnes 1936
25. Gwynnes 1943 and 1953, no. 24. Gwynnes 1977 records the initial plant as two Ruston engines driving 15 in Gwynnes pumps, followed by another Ruston driving an 18 in. pump.
26. Personal inspection in 2000
27. Information from the engine driver in 2000
28. Gwynnes 1943 and 1953, no. 22, and personal inspection in 2000
29. Wheeler DF, 127 – 129 and Plate 2. For Hetts, see Clark, R.H. (1955) *Steam Engine Builders of Lincolnshire,* 49 – 51
30. Gwynnes 1943 and 1953, no. 17, and 1977
31. Gwynnes 1943, no. 16
32. Clay, C. "Pumping Stations with Special Reference to Land Drainage and Storm-water disposal" *Journal of the Institution of Civil Engineers,* March 1945, 54 – 55. This gives sectional arrangements of the new plant.
33. Personal inspection in 2000, and Gwynnes 1977

34. Clark, note 29, 49 – 51. Charles L. Hett of Brigg was in business c. 1880 to 1896.
35. Wheeler DF, 129.
36.   Information from Mr. T.H. Heys, Chairman of the Preservation Trust, who informed me that they believed the engine to be a single-cylinder horizontal Robey engine with a locomotive-type boiler, driving two pumps, one deep and one shallow; and that these consisted of one 18in. pump and one wooden paddle wheel. The original engine is unlikely to have been by Robey, since that firm did not commence business until 1854.
37. Gibbs, 272
38. Clark, note 4
39. Gwynnes 1977
40. Glynn, 15 states 6000 acres, but this probably refers to Gringley Carr only. Watkins gives 10,000 acres, and Gwynnes (1899) 9109 acres.
41. Glynn, 15
42. Watkins SSE Vol. 5, 172, but Gwynnes 1899, 42 states 31ft.
43. Clark, note 4
44. Hills (2003), 122
45. Gwynnes 1899, 42
46. Watkins (1978), 96
47. Watkins SSE Vol. 5, 168. Clark states the stroke as 90ins.
48. Watkins , note 8, but Clark states the beam as 21ft. long.
49. This must have been a replacement because Marshall did not start trading until 1842 – see Clark, note 29, 62.
50. Clark and Watkins SSE, note 47, Watkins (1978), 88, wrongly states the width of the scoop wheel as 4ft. 6in. Both of these sources contain photographs
51. Cory, 90 and Gwynnes 1943 and 1953, no. 26, and 1977.
52. Clark, note 29, 8
53. Clark, note 52, states that Bradbury commenced trading in 1849
54. Clark, *English Mechanics,* 31 December 1937
55. Gwynnes 1936, 1943 and 1953, no. 25
56. Watkins SSE Vol. 5, 116, and Hayes, G. *Guide to Stationary Steam Engines* 1981 (2nd Ed. 1990), Moorland, 137
57. Gwynnes 1943 and 1953, no. 23, and personal inspection.
58. Cory, 90, refers to a steam unit built at Newlands Farm on Sir Robert Sheffield's estate in 1846. White's *Directory of Lincolnshire* 1856, 619, notes this engine.
59. Korthals-Altes, 147, and Gwynnes 1943 and 1953, no. 21, called Black Dyke
60. Plaque on new engine house.
61. Watkins SE1, 98 and Watkins SSE Vol. 5, 140, both with illustrations. He probably understates the acreage.
62. Cory, 90
63. Clark, note 4, and Clark, R.H. "Some Grasshopper Engines", *The Engineer,* 8 May 1942, 385. This gives a full description of the engine, with a diagram and illustration.
64. Gwynnes 1943 and 1953, no. 18, and 1977.
65. Cory, 90 and 115.
66. Clark, *English Mechanics,* 31 December 1937. A turbine pump is unlikely to have been provided in 1846: it probably replaced a scoop wheel, if the date of construction is correct.
67. Gwynnes 1943 and 1953, no. 15, and 1977.

68. Wheeler DF, 130, states 1857, but Clark, *English Mechanics,* 31 December 1937, quotes the plaque on the engine house as marked 1858.
69. Wheeler, note 68
70. Clark, note 4
71. Korthals-Altes, Appendix, 140-141 and photograph, 145.
72. Gwynnes 1943 and 1953, no. 20, and 1977.
73. *ADA Gazette,* Summer 1991, 36.
74. Clark, *English Mechanics*, 7 January 1938, states 49in.
75. Clark, note 74, states 36in.
76. Wheeler DF, 130-131 and Gibbs, 272
77. Korthals-Altes, Appendix, 141
78. Cory, 91
79. Gwynnes 1953, no. 13A
80. Rigby
81. *ADA Gazette,* Spring 1988, 27 and Autumn 1992, 16
82. Clay, note 32, 53 - 54
83. Gwynnes 1977
84. *ADA Gazette*, Autumn 1987, 5 and Autumn 1994, 7 and 18, and Cory, 108 - 109

APPENDICES

APPENDIX 1

CONVERSION TABLES

For the sake of consistency, all statements of discharge have been expressed in tons per minute, lineal measurements in feet and inches, and areas in acres. Conversions are as follows:

1 ton per minute = 0.5983 cubic feet per second (cusec)
1 cusec = 374.1 gallons per minute
1 cusec = 1.67 tons per minute
1 cumec = 0.985 tons per minute
1 ton of water = 224 imperial gallons
1 foot = 0.3048 metres
1 inch = 2.54 centimetres
1 acre = 0.404667 hectares
1 hectare = 2.47 acres
1 square mile = 640 acres

APPENDIX 2

MAKERS OF ENGINES AND PUMPS

STEAM ENGINES

Maker	Site Serial Numbers
Allen, Bedford	M29, NM5, S10, S14A, S14C, S17, S23
Armitage & Ruston, Chatteris	M8, M12A, M17?
Appleby, London	M32A
Baker, W.P., King's Lynn	S18
Beecroft Butler, Leeds	M28A
Blyth, J. & A., London	S16
Booth & Co., Sheffield	T8A
Boulton & Watt, Birmingham	S1A, S1B, S25, S27
Bradbury, T., Gainsborough	T8C
Bradley & Craven, Wakefield	L21
Butterley Co., Derby	M2, M9, M10, M13A, M30, NM2, S9, S13, S14A, S14B, S17, S19, S23, S28A, L2, L27, T8A

Clarke, I., Sunderland	S5A, S5B
Clarke, J., Deptford	S21
Clayton & Shuttleworth, Gainsborough	M5, M7C, M15, M33B, M38, L32
Daglish, R., St. Helens	S25
Davy Bros., Sheffield	T1A
Dodmans, King's Lynn	M7C, M46, NM3
Easton & Amos ,London	M1A, M33A, M40, T8F
Easton Amos & Anderson	M6C, M24, M33A, M41, N2A, L22A
Easton &Anderson	S17A, S22B, NM5, T11
Easton, Edward	S15A
	N.B. Eastons also supplied at least 10 engines and pumps to the Somerset Levels and at least 6 to the Norfolk Broads.
Fairbairn, Manchester	S2
Fenton & Murray, Leeds	N1, L1, L2
Foster, Lincoln	M35A, L14, L25
Green Atkinson, Wakefield	L15
Gwynnes, J. & H., Hammersmith	NM1, T2C/2, T8A
Gwynnes, London	M16, M18, M28A, NM2, S14B
Hague & Topham, London	S14A
Harveys of Hayle	NM5
Hathorn Davey, Leeds	S1A, S1B, S22A
Headly, J. & E., Cambridge	M21, M43, S8A, S29, NM4
Headly & Manning, Cambridge	M43
Hetts, Brigg	T3
Holmes & Son, Norwich	S4
Jarvis & L. Horsfield, Leeds	L17
Leather, George & Son ?	L13
Marshall, Gainsborough	M13A, M13B, M32A, M36, L10, L13, L29, L31, L35, T8D
Maudslay & Field, London	S10
Overton & Wilson, Hull	S24A
Robey & Co., Lincoln	L8, L9, L17
Ruston & Proctor, Grantham	M17, M18, M19B, M20, M23
Ryde, Leicester	S22A
Smithdale, Norwich and Acle	M27C, M27E, M38, T8F
Steward, D., Glasgow	T10A
Thompson & Stather, Hull	NM3
Tuxford & Sons, Boston	L11, L14, L16
Watt, James, Birmingham	T10B

DIESEL ENGINES

| Allen, Bedford | M1B, M1C, M3G, M4, M10, M12A, M14, M27A, M32A, M33A, M33B, N2B, S10B, S14A, S15C, S17C, S20, S22A, S22B, S24A, S24C, S25B, S28B |
| Blackstone, Stamford | M2, M12A, M12B, M25, M26, M28A, M48C, NM6, S1A, S1B S5A, S6, S7, S26A, L6 |

Brush, Loughborough	M30
Campbell, Halifax	M3C, M3H, M11, M12A, M19B, M45, M46, S8A, S15B, L7, L34, L38
Crossley, Manchester	NM1, S1B
Crossley - Premier, Nottingham	M1B, NM3, N3A, N3B, N4, N5, S8A, T12
Detroit	S26B
Dorman, Stafford	M1C
Fielding & Platt, Gloucester	L39
Hornsby - Ackroyd, Grantham	S2, S29
Lanz Bulldog	S14C
Marshal, Gainsborough	T8C
McLaren – Benz	S15C
Mirrlees, Stockport	NM3, S8A, S10A, S14B, S17A, S17B, S28A, L2
Parsons, Newcastle-upon-Tyne	M13A
Perkins, Peterborough	M38
Petter, Yeovil	M31, S10B, T6B
Premier Gas Co.	M1B
Robey, Lincoln	L8
Ruston & Hornsby, Grantham	M3D, M6A, M6B, M6D, M8, M9A, M13E, M14,M15, M18, M19A, M21, M27A, M28B, M30, M38, M39A, M39B, M39C, M43, M44, M45, M46, M47, M48A, NM2B, nm5, S5A, S5B, S8B, S9, S11, S12, S13, S14B, S19B, S21B, S23, S24A, S24B, S24D, S25B, S27A, S29, L2, L9A, L9B, L10, L11, L13, L14, L15, L16, L7, L18, L21, L22A, L24, L26, L27, L30, L32, L33, L40, T2B, T2C/2, T2D, T4, T6A, T8B, T8D, T8F, T9, T10A, T11
Ruston & Proctor, Lincoln	S2, S5B, L9B, L36, L37
Tangye (Gas), Birmingham	L27
Vickers – Petter	M9A, M30, NM4, S9, S13, S19A, L28B
Worthington Simpson, London	M33B, S26C

CENTRIFUGAL PUMPS

Allen, Bedford	M1C, M3C, M3G, M4, M10, M12B, M27D, M32A, M45, NM3, N2B, S2, S10, S14A, S14C, S15C, S17A, S17C, S20, S22A, S22B, S23, S24C, S25B, S28B, L22B
Clayton & Shuttleworth, Gainsborough	S29
Dodmans, King's Lynn	M6B, M7B, M11, M14, M37A, NM3, S11, S12
Drysdale, Glasgow	L29, L31, L32, T8D
Easton & Amos, London	M1A, M33A, M40
Easton Amos & Sons	L22A
Easton Amos & Anderson	M6C, M13B, M24
Easton & Anderson	M5, M41, NM5, N2A, S17A, S22B, L27, T11
Edward Easton	S15A
Hathorn Davey, Leeds	S1A, S1B
Hetts, Brigg	T3, T5
Holmes, Norwich	L6

Mirrlees, Stockport	M26
Mirrlees - Watson	M2, S26A
Ruston & Hornsby, Grantham	L4
Ruston & Proctor, Lincoln	S5B, L30
Smithdale, Norwich and Acle	M3F, M13D, M13E, M29, M35A, M36, M37B, M38, L8, L9A, L12, T8F
Tuxford, Boston	L11, L14, L35, L37
Worthington Simpson, London	S26B, S26C

N.B. Gwynnes pumps are not listed as being so common that the vast majority of 20th century stations were equipped with these.

APPENDIX 3

PARTICULARS OF SOME ENGINE AND PUMP MAKERS

Allens

W.H. Allen (1844 – 1926) at first worked for Gwynne & Co. He formed his own company at York Street, Lambeth, in 1880. In 1894 this was moved to Queen's Engineering Works, Bedford. In 1900 the business was incorporated as W.H. Allen & Co. Ltd. In 1960 the company acquired William Foster & Co. Ltd. and Gwynnes. From 1962 it traded as Allen-Gwynnes. In 1968 it merged with Bellis & Morcom, owners of Crossley Premier engines, and formed Amalgamated Power Engineering Ltd. In 1989 this became part of Rolls Royce plc.

Armitage & Ruston

This firm was established c. 1870 in Chatteris by S.C. Armitage, who claimed ten years experience with Clayton & Shuttleworth, probably in succession to his father, John Armitage, iron founder (by then deceased). In about 1874 he was joined by C.R. Ruston, nephew of Joseph Ruston of Ruston & Proctor, to form Armitage & Ruston. By 1883 Ruston had left the firm to form his own business. In 1896 this became Chatteris Engineering Co. In 1943 it became Fairleade Engineering Co. Ltd. The business of Armitage & Co. was liquidated in 1884.

W.P. Baker

This business was established in 1839 at Union Place, Austin Street, King's Lynn. In 1854 it was moved to Blackfriars Road. It ceased trading before 1925.

Boulton & Watt

1796 Established at Soho Engine Works, Birmingham.
1848 Name changed to James Watt & Co.
1895 Liquidated

Dodmans

1851, established in King's Lynn. 1975 Liquidated

Drysdale

1768 Established at Bon Accord Engine Works, Glasgow

Eastons

1826 - 1829	Leahy & Easton of Grove Street, Guildford Street, Borough, London
1830	James Easton, hydraulic machine manufacturer, 160 Regent Street and Grove Street
1836 - 1859	Easton & Amos, Grove Street and Waterworks Chambers, Orange Street, Leicester Square
1860 - 1866	Easton Amos & Sons, Southwick Street
1867 - 1871	Easton Amos & Anderson, Southwick Street and Erith Ironworks
1872 - 1878	Easton & Anderson, Southwick Street and Erith Ironworks
1879	Easton Anderson & Co.
1880 - 1888	Easton & Anderson, Whitehall Pace and Erith
1889 - 1894	Easton & Anderson Ltd.
1895 - 1901	Easton Anderson & Goolden Ltd.
1903 - 1905	Pulsometer Engineering Co., Reading.
	This company took over Easton & Co. in 1908.

The pumps used by Eastons were designed by John George Appold (1800 - 1865). The son of a London fur-skin dyer, he took over his father's business in 1822. He was a considerable inventor in both chemistry and hydraulic engineering. His pump, exhibited at the Great Exhibition of 1851, was taken up by Eastons, but on what terms is not known. He also seems to have designed the air pumps for the Middle Level Syphon Sluice.

William Foster & Co. Ltd.

Established in Lincoln in 1856. Incorporated in 1877. Acquired by Allens in 1960.

Gwynnes

Founded in 1849 by John Gwynne (1800 – 1855) at Essex Street, Strand, London.

On his death, taken over by his eldest son, James Gwynne (1831 – 1915), who traded as Gwynne & Co.. In 1868 the two younger sons, John (1838 – 1912) and Henry (1840 – 1889), left the firm to create J. & H. Gwynne & Co. The two firms united in 1904. In 1927 the firm was acquired by William Foster of Lincoln and the works moved there, but Fosters retained the name of Gwynne. After acquisition by Allens in 1960, plant was marketed as Allen-Gwynnes. See Allens above for the later history of this firm.

Headly

The Eagle Foundry, Market Hill, Cambridge, was founded by James Ind Headly and Edward Ind Headly in 1843. They followed their father, Robert Headly, who had set up as an ironmonger and then ironfounder on Market Hill in the late eighteenth century. The foundry was moved to Mill Road following a fire in 1846.

The partnership was dissolved in 1852. James remained in Mill Road, at first in partnership with John Manning until 1858, the firm being known as Headly & Manning, the Eagle Foundry. Thereafter James traded as J.I. Headly, the Eagle Foundry, until his retirement in 1887. The site was then sold to the Great Eastern Railway Company and the machinery sold. This foundry must not be confused with the Eagle Foundry Co. of Downham Road, Ely, which existed in 1916 but had closed by 1925.

Meanwhile Edward had set up business as an ironmonger and ironfounder in Corn Exchange Street, Cambridge, trading as E.I. Headly, and later in various partnerships with his sons as E. Headly and Son, Headly and Son and Edward Headly and Son. Finally, just before his retirement, he set up The Exchange Ironworks in Newmarket Road with his younger son Laurence in 1885. The latter then went into partnership with Arthur Edwards and traded as Headly & Edwards until the death of Laurence in 1907. That firm continued to trade until 1932.

Hornsby

1815, established as Seaman & Hornsby at Grantham. 1828 Named Richard Hornsby. 1891 produced Hornsby-Ackroyd oil engines. 1918 Amalgamated with Ruston & Proctor & Co. Ltd. to form Ruston & Hornsby Ltd.

Ruston

1857 founded in Lincoln by Joseph Ruston, who had taken over Burton & Proctor. 1889 incorporated as Ruston Proctor & Co. Ltd. 1918 Amalgamated with Hornsby to form Ruston & Hornsby Ltd.

Thomas Smithdale & Sons

1847 Founded at St. Anne's Ironworks, King Street, Norwich. 1883 Moved to new works at Panxworth. 1897 Moved to Acle, Norfolk. 1900 Established a branch works at Ramsey St. Mary, Hunts. 1974 All assets sold.

William Tuxford & Sons

Founded in Boston, Lincs. In 1826. In 1887 the firm was sold to Collitt & Co., a firm which only survived for few years.

SOURCES

Allens

Lane, M.R. (1995): *The Story of Queen's Engineering Works, Bedford*

Armitage & Ruston

Clark, R.H. (1950): *Steam Engine Builders of Suffolk, Essx and Cambridgeshire*, 135, but his account is not wholly accurate
CIP, 3 October 1884
Kelly's *Directories of Cambridgeshire* 1875, 1879, 1883 and 1896
Census returns, Chatteris, 1851 and 1871

W.P. Baker

Clark, R.H. (1988): *Steam Engine Builders of Norfolk*, 7
Kelly's *Directory of Norfolk* 1925

Eastons

Eaton, D. (2001): *Easton & Amos*, Westonzoyland Engine Trust
Hillsdon, B.: Notes from the George Watkins's Collection, NMR
Kelly's *Post Office Directory of London*, 1846
Miles, I. (c. 1991): *Bogs and Inundations*, Westonzoyland Engine Trust
Piggott's *Directory of Cambridgeshire* 1838, 50
Porter, E. (1975) *Victorian Cambridge*, 52

Ruston and Hornsby

Newman, B. (N/D 1957): *One Hundred Years of good company – a history of Rustons 1857 – 1957*

Smithdale

Clark, R.H. (1988): *Steam Engine Builders of Norfolk, 203*

APPENDIX 4

EXAMPLES OF ENGINE RUNNING RECORDS

The following is a selection from surviving log books of annual hours of running, to illustrate the varying amount of work undertaken by plant from year to year and place to place. They are taken from those for Hundred Foot engine (S14B) and Stretham engine (S28A), both of which are in CRO, and Metheringham engine (L12), held by the author. Stretham discharged into the Old West River, which is locked off at Earith and has no tidal flow; thus it was rarely required to work as much as Hundred Foot, which discharged into the tidal New Bedford River. The extensive hours operated by the Metheringham engine may reflect greater rainfall or an engine underpowered for the size of district.

Year	100 Foot	Stretham
1879	2966	2615
1880	3184	1291
1881	1429	1360
1882	2088	1284
1883	2336	1702
1884	345	507
1885	867	468
1886	1674	703
1887	816	501
1888	342	135
1889	1309	833
1890	763	537
1891	1061	585
1892	1993	1190
1893	850	854
1894	1009	665
1895	931	630
1896	1395	878

Year	Metheringham	Stretham
1897	1503	903
1898	328	75
1899	936	261
1900	1879	991
1901	1335	143
1902	1247	49
1903	2217	1137
1904	1197	1044
1905	297	139
1906	1129	408
1907	1568	477
1908	877	339
1909	1336	548
1910	1864	1107

APPENDIX 5

BOILER LONGEVITY

Plant	Boiler installed	Replaced	Duration
Benwick First (White Fen)	1847	1869	22
	1869	1897	28
	1897	1937	40
Chatteris & Somersham - Chatteris Dock	1862	1899	37
	1899	1940	41
Ramsey, Bury Fifth - Nightlayers	1904	1920	16
Marshland	1849	1876	27
	1876	1901	25
	1901	1938	37
Ramsey, Doddington Fifth - Ranson Moor	1850	1891	41
Whittlesey Mere	1851	1877	26
Burnt Fen - Little Ouse	1829	1848	19
Littleport & Downham - Hundred Foot	1829	1869 (2)	40
	1843	1875 (1)	32
	1869	1911 (2)	42
	1875	1911 (1)	36
	1911	1951	40
Mildenhall	1844	1886	42
	1886	1930	44
Upper Padnal	1831	1873	42
Lower Padnal	1881	1925	44
Fordham	1847	1877	30
Swaffham & Bottisham - Upware	1821	1843	22
	1850	1887	37
	1887	1937	50
Waterbeach Level - Stretham	1831	1871	40
	1871	1941	70
Willingham (West Fen)	1847	1875	28
	1875	1901	26
Deeping Fen - Pode Hole	1827?	1883	56
Deeping Fen - Pinchbeck Marsh	1833	1895	62
	1895	1952	57
Witham First - Timberland	1839	1876	37
	1876	1910	34
	1910	1938	28
Witham Third - Dogdyke	1855	1909	54
	1909	1940	31

Average longevity: 37.22 years
Longest in use: Stretham – 70 years (16 being as stand-by)
Longest period used as sole prime-mover: Pinchbeck – 57 years.

APPENDIX 6

RUSTON DIESEL ENGINES – Types and Cylinder sizes

Horizontal

Notes:

Type HR was introduced in about 1932.

C indicates twin-cylinder

F indicates four-cylinder

X indicates a larger cylinder provided for the same class of engine

All operated on the four-stroke cycle

Only those cited in the text are listed below

Type	No. of cylinders	Rated bhp	Bore in ins.	Stroke in ins.
2YHR	1	15	65	12
3XHR	1	17	7.25	13.5
4YHR	1	20	7.5	14.5
10XHRC	2	156	13.25	22.5
5YHR	1	24	8	15.5
6HR	1	28	8.5	16.25
6XHR	1	34	9.25	17.5
7XHR	1	40	10	18.5
8HR	1	47	10.75	19.5
9HR	1	57	11.75	21
9XHR	1	66	12.5	22
7XHRC	2	80	10	18.5
8HRC	2	94	10.75	19.5
9HRC	2	114	11.75	21
9XHRC	2	132	12.5	22
8HRF	4	210	10.75	19.5
9XHRF	4	295	12.5	22
Vertical				
4VSH	4	45	4.5	4.5
3VCB	3	102	8	10.75
4VCB	4	136	8	10.75
5VCB	5	170	8	10.75
6VCB	6	204	8	10.75
5VEB	5	300	10.25	14.5
6VEBX	6	540	10.25	14.5
7VEBX	7	630	10.25	14.5

APPENDIX 7

SOME LONG SERVICE ENGINE DRIVERS

John Allen (1831 - ?)	Whittlesey Mere	1852 - 1893
Thomas Burrall	Waldersea	1832 - 1883
George Butler	Whittlesey Third	1891 - 1944
Joseph Flatt (1819 - 1900)	Mildenhall	1844 - 1900
Thomas Simpson Galley	Southery	1847 - 1898
Thomas Galley	Southery	1898 - 1913+
William Harrison (1794 - ?)	Burnt Fen	1831 - 1872
Isaac Housely (1850 - 1930)	Stretham	1884 – 1930
George Moule	Burwell	1881 - 1911
Charles Seymour	Pinchbeck Marsh	1908 - 1951
Richard Southwell (1839 - ?)	Ramsey Hollow	1867 - 1897
Edwin Stanley (1813 - 1880)	Stretham	1833 - 1880
James Stevens (1807 - 1873)	Hundred Foot	1829 - 1873
John Stevens (1851 - 1911)	Haddenham	1889 - 1911
Joseph Stevens (1836 - 1917)	Marshland	1861 - 1912
William Stevens Snr. (1813 - 1884)	Ten Mile Bank	1860 - 1884
Jonathan Stevens (1839 - 1913)	Ten Mile Bank	1884 - 1913
William Stevens Jnr. (1833 - 1908)	Swaffham & Bottisham	1881 - 1906
Arthur William Stevens (1860 - 1946)	Swaffham & Bottisham	1906 - 1931
William Underwood (1822 - ?)	Willingham	1847 - 1883
Tom Wheatley (? - 1926)	Ranson Moor	1890 - 1926

APPENDIX 8

BIBLIOGRAPHY

Besides the works cited in the Abbreviations and footnotes, the following publications are of general relevance to the subject.

Astbury, A.K. (1958) *The Black Fens*, GoldenHead Press, Cambridge

Beezeley, A. (1900) *The Reclamation of land from tidal waters*, Crosby Lockwood

Cook, H. & Williamson, T. (ed.) (1999) *Water Management in the English Landscape*, Edinburgh University Press

Darby, H.C. (ed.) (1938) *The Cambridge Region*, CUP

Darby, H.C. (1940) *The Medieval Fenland*, CUP

Dugdale, W. (1772) *History of Imbanking and Draining*, 2nd edition

Edginton, D. & Hudson, C. (1981) *Stationary Engines for the Enthusiast*, David & Charles

Godwin, Sir Harry (1978) *Fenland – its ancient past and uncertain future*, CUP

Hodge, C.A.H. & Searle, R.S. (1966) *The Soils of the District around Cambridge*, Agricultural Research Council, Harpenden

Miller, S.H. & Skertchley, S.B.J. (1878) *The Fenland Past and Present*, Longmans Green

Padley, J.S. (1882) *The Fens and Floods of mid-Lincolnshire*, C. Akrill, Lincoln

Robson, J.D. et al. (1974) *Soils in Lincolnshire – I*, Soil Survey, Harpenden

Salway, P. et al. (1970) *The Fenland in Roman Times*, Royal Geographic Society

Searle, R.S. (1975) *Soils of the Chatteris District in Cambridgeshire*, Soil Survey, Harpenden

Searle, R.S. (1975) *Soils of the Ely District*, Soil Survey, Harpenden

Skertchley, S.B.J. (1877) *The Geology of the Fenland*, Mem. Geol. Survey G.B.

Steers, J.A. (ed.) (1965) *The Cambridge Region 1965*, The British Association

Summers, D. (1976) *The Great Level*, David & Charles

Williams, D.S.D. (1939 – c. 1946) *The Oil Engine Manual*, Temple Press, 5 editions

Worssam, B.C. et al. (1969) *Geology of the Country around Cambridge*, HMSO

APPENDIX 9

INDEX OF NAMES OF PUMPING STATIONS

The detailed description of plant is arranged by areas and districts and estates within those areas. Pumping stations were often given a name or names unrelated to that of the district. In some cases, different stations bore the same or a similar name; and in others, the same station was known by more than one name at different times. This index is provided to enable easy identification of these. Plant which bore the same name as its district is marked with an asterisk. Subject to this, in all cases the names of pumping stations are given in lower case, and those of districts or estates in upper case.

Serial No.	Name of Station	District or Estate	Page
M19A	Acre Fen	RAMSEY BURY FIFTH	61
S15D	Ammonia Plant	METHWOLD & FELTWELL	133
T6A	Anderby	LINDSEY MARSH	196
L25	Anwick	ANWICK & NORTH KYME	178
L9	Barling's Lock	STAINFIELD	169
M32B	Bedlam Bridge	UPWELL SOUTH	72
M37A	Beeby's	WHITTLESEY FOURTH	77
M3H	Beezlings	BENWICK	46
T8E	Belton	SOUTH AXHOLME	201
M6A	Bensons	CURFF & NORMOOR	48
M2	Benwick	BENWICK WHITE FEN	42
M3F	Benwick Mere	BENWICK IDB	45
M3G	Betty's Nose	BENWICK IDB	46
M1D	Bevill's Leam	MIDDLE LEVEL	42
L35	Bicker Fen*		186
M23	Bill, The	RAMSEY MIDDLEMOOR THIRD	62
L16	Billinghay North*		172
M10	Binnimore Fen	MARCH FIRST	54
M7B	Bird's	FARCET – Frog Hall	50
M35A	Blackbush	WHITTLESEY SECOND	76
T8E	Black Dyke	SOUTH AXHOLME	201
M33B	Black Ham	WHITTLESEY MERE	74
L26	Black Sluice*		184
L3	Blue Gowt	PINCHBECK MARSH	164
M4	Bluntisham*		46
M45	Boot's Bridge	WIMBLINGTON FIRST	80
N1	Borough Fen	NORTH LEVEL FIRST	104
M12B	Botany Bay	MARCH THIRD	57
M26C	Bottisham Lode	ENVIRONMENT AGENCY	149
L5	Bourne South	BOURNE SOUTH & THURLBY	165
S1A	Brandon	BURNT FEN FIRST	108
L11	Branston Island*		170
M48B	Brick Mere	WOODWALTON	83
M3A	Broadalls	BENWICK IDB	45
T10A	Bull Hassocks	HATFIELD CHASE	202
M37B	Burnt House	WHITTLESEY FOURTH	77

Serial No.	Name of Station	District or Estate	Page
T4	Burringham	SCUNTHORPE	196
M12A	Burrowmoor	MARCH THIRD	56
S2	Burwell*		112
S28B	Cam	WATERBEACH LEVEL	152
M48C	Castlehill Farm	WOODWALTON	83
S15C	Catsholme Farm	METHWOLD & FELTWELL	132
S3	Cawdle Fen*		114
L15	Chapel Hill	BILLINGHAY SOUTH	172
M20	Chatteris Dock	RAMSEY BURY LOWER	61
S5A	Chear Fen	COTTENHAM	115
S4	Chettisham*		115
M8	Coldham Hall	LADDUS	50
M5	Conington*		48
M3D & E	Copalder	BENWICK	45
M14	Creek Farm	MARCH FIFTH	59
N3B	Cross Guns	NORTH LEVEL SECOND	105
S13	Cross Waters	LAKENHEATH	124
M6D	Curff	CURFF & NORMOOR	49
L36	Damford Grounds*		186
S15B	Decoy Bridge	METHWOLD & FELTWELL	132
S6	Denver Parts*		118
L24	Digby	WITHAM FIFTH	178
S28B	Dimmock's Cote	WATERBEACH LEVEL	152
T10B	Dirtness	HATFIELD CHASE	203
L21	Dogdyke	TATTERSHALL	175
N3A	Dog-in-a-Doublet	NORTH LEVEL SECOND	104
NM1	Downham West Fen*		94
L31	Dowsby	DOWSBY & ASLACKBY	185
M37A	Duncombes	WHITTLESEY FOURTH	77
S23	Dunn Gardner	SOHAM MERE	142
L29	Dunsby*		185
T3	East Butterwick	MESSINGHAM	195
S7	East of Ouse, Polver & Nar*		118
L39	Ewerby*		187
L23	Farroway	RUSKINGTON, DORRINGTON	178
M42	Feldale	WHITTLESEY	79
S1B	Fish and Duck	BURNT FEN FIRST	110
L17	Fiskerton	GREETWELL	172
L9A	Five Mile House	WASHINGBOROUGH	169
M13E	Flood's Ferry	MARCH FOURTH	58
M28A	Flood's Ferry	RANSONMOOR	67
S24A	Fordham	STOKE FERRY	143
M7B	Frog Hall	FARCET	50
M3B	Four Hundred	BENWICK IDB	45
N4	French Drove	NORTH LEVEL THIRD	105
S8B	Further Fen	FELTWELL NEW FEN	120
T6B	Gayton	LINDSEY MARSH	198

Serial No.	Name of Station	District or Estate	Page
M40	Glassmoor	WHITTLESEY	78
M13 F & G	Goosetree	MARCH FOURTH	58
M27D	Green Dyke Bank	RAMSEY UPWOOD etc.	65
T8B	Gringley Carr	SOUTH AXHOLME	200
L27	Gutheram Gowt	BOURNE NORTH FEN	184
L32	Hacconby*		185
S10A	Haddenham*		121
S15B	Harwins Bridge	METHWOLD & FELTWELL	132
T8C	Heckdyke	SOUTH AXHOLME	200
L33	Heckington*		186
M16	High Fen	RAMSEY BURY THIRD	60
M48A	Higney Mill	WOODWALTON	83
S11	Hilgay Great West Fen		123
M47	Hobbs Lot	WISBECH ST. PETER	81
L22B	Hobhole Sluice	WITHAM FOURTH	176
S9	Hockwold	FELTWELL NEW FEN	120
M45	Hook	WIMBLINGTON HOOK	80
S14B	Hundred Foot	LITTLEPORT & DOWNHAM	128
S15A	Hunt's Sluice	METHWOLD & FELTWELL	131
M3F	Ibbersons	BENWICK IDB	45
M13C	Infields Farm	MARCH FOURTH	58
M38	Ironsides	WHITTLESEY FIFTH	77
T2C	Jenny Hurn	GAINSBOROUGH	194
S12	Jones	HILGAY, WOOD HALL	124
T12	Keadby	ISLE OF AXHOLME	203
T8E	Kelfield	SOUTH AXHOLME	201
M34	King's Delph	WHITTLESEY FIRST	76
M41	Kingsland Coates	WHITTLESEY	78
T11	Kirk Bramwith	DUN	203
L20	Kirkstead*		174
L8	Kirton Marsh	WELLAND & DEEPING	166
M8	Laddus Fen*		50
L22A	Lade Bank	WITHAM FOURTH	175
S13	Lakenheath	LAKENHEATH & BRANDON	124
S1B	Lark	BURNT FEN FIRST	110
M46	Latches Fen	WIMBLINGTON – Stonea Grange	81
L28B	Leaves Lake	PINCHBECK NORTH	184
M3C	Lilly Holt	BENWICK	45
S1A	Little Ouse	BURNT FEN FIRST	108
M25	Lodesend	RAMSEY MIDDLEMOOR FIFTH	63
M39C	Lord's Farm	WHITTLESEY & FARCET	78
M27E	Lotting Fen	RAMSEY UPWOOD etc.	66
S22B	Lower Padnal	PADNAL & WATERDEN	141
NM2	Magdalen*		95
L38	Mallard Hurn	DONINGTON	187
M9A	Manea	MANEA & WELNEY	50
M13A	March West Fen	MARCH FOURTH	58

Serial No.	Name of Station	District or Estate	Page
L13	Martin	BLANKNEY LINWOOD & MARTIN	171
S14C	Martin's Farm	LITTLEPORT & DOWNHAM	130
T1C	Marton	NEWARK	193
NM3	Marshland	MARSHLAND SMEETH & FEN	96
M30	Mepal	SUTTON & MEPAL	68
M26	Mereside	RAMSEY MIDDLEMOOR SIXTH	63
L12	Metheringham	DUNSTON & METHERINGHAM	170
S16	Methwold Severals*		133
M35B	Micklewaite	WHITTLESEY SECOND	76
M24	Middlemoor	RAMSEY MIDDLEMOOR FOURTH	63
S18	Middleton	MIDDLETON TOWERS ESTATE	138
S19	Mildenhall*		138
T8A	Misterton	SOUTH AXHOLME	199
S14A	Modney Court	Ten Mile Bank	126
L30	Morton*		185
T2A	Morton Carr	GAINSBOROUGH	193
M6C	Mount Pleasant	CURFF & NORMOOR	49
N2B	Mouth Lane	WISBECH NORTHSIDE	104
M29	New Barn	STILTON	68
N1	Newborough	NORTH LEVEL FIRST	104
M27A	New Fen	RAMSEY UPWOOD & GT. RAVELEY	64
S8B	New Fen	FELTWELL NEW FEN	120
T8E	Newlands Farm	SOUTH AXHOLME	201
S17C	New Mills, Isleham	MIDDLE FEN	136
M19B	Nightlayers	RAMSEY BURY FIFTH	61
L10	Nocton	NOCTON POTTERHANWORTH etc.	169
M33	Nordelph	UPWELL NORTH	73
M6B	Normoor	CURFF & NORMOOR	48
L6	Northborough	MAXEY	166
L6	North Fen	MAXEY	166
L23	North Kyme	RUSKINGTON DORRINGTON etc.	178
S20	Northwold Severals*		139
M15	Norwood	MARCH SIXTH	59
M33	Outwell	UPWELL NORTH	73
S21	Over*		140
S17B	Overfall	MIDDLE FEN	136
S24D	Oxborough	STOKE FERRY	145
T8D	Owston Ferry	SOUTH AXHOLME	200
M18	Pidley	RAMSEY BURY FOURTH	60
L3	Pinchbeck	SPALDING & PINCHBECK	164
L28	Pinchbeck North*		184
L4	Pinchbeck South	PINCHBECK FOURTH	165
L2	Pode Hole	WELLAND & DEEPING	163
M7C	Pondersbridge	FARCET	50
M32A	Popham's Eau	UPWELL SOUTH	70
S17A	Prickwillow	MIDDLE FEN	133
N5	Protection Sluice	NORTH LEVEL	105

Serial No.	Name of Station	District or Estate	Page
M16	Puddock Bridge	RAMSEY BURY FIRST & THIRD	60
M9B	Purl's Bridge	MANEA & WELNEY	54
L40	Pyewype	UPPER WITHAM	190
L34	Quadring*		186
M27D	Ramsey Heights	RAMSEY UPWOOD etc.	65
M21	Ramsey Hollow	RAMSEY MIDDLEMOOR FIRST	62
M28B	Ranson Moor*		68
T2B	Ravensfleet	GAINSBOROUGH	193
S26A	Reach Lode	ENVIRONMENT AGENCY	147
T5	Redbourne	ALTHORPE	196
S4	Redmoor Farm	CHETTISHAM	115
NM6	Redmoor	WISBECH	101
S1C	Redmore	BURNT FEN FIRST	112
M11	Reed Fen	MARCH SECOND	54
N2A	Rummers	WISBECH NORTHSIDE	104
T9	Rush Carr	WEST AXHOLME	202
M1A	St. Germans Syphon Sluice	MIDDLE LEVEL	38
M1B	St. Germans P.S.	MIDDLE LEVEL	40
L9B	Sandhill Beck	WASHINGBOROUGH etc	169
L37	Sandilands Farm	SOUTH KYME	187
L17	Short's Ferry	GREETWELL	172
M27B	School Farm	RAMSEY UPWOOD etc.	65
S5B	Smithey Fen	COTTENHAM	117
S23	Soham Mere*		142
M18	Somersham	RAMSEY BURY FOURTH	60
S8A	Southery	FELTWELL NEW FEN	119
L8	Southrey	BARDNEY STIXWOULD	166
M13B	Stafforths Bridge	MARCH FOURTH	58
L19	Stainfield*		174
M29	Stilton*		68
M43	Stitches Farm	WIMBLINGTON (Hook)	79
L18	Stixwould	BARDNEY STIXWOULD	173
M22	Stocking Fen	RAMSEY MIDDLEMOOR SECOND	62
S12	Stocks	HILGAY WOOD HALL	124
M44	Stonea Grange	WIMBLINGTON	79
NM4	Stow Bardolph*		98
S28A	Stretham	WATERBEACH LEVEL	150
S27B	Stretham Common	THETFORD	150
T7	Sturton	LANEHAM	199
L7	Surfleet	WELLAND & DEEPING	166
T2D	Susworth	GAINSBOROUGH	195
L1	Sutton St. Edmund	SOUTH HOLLAND	162
S10B	Sutton Gault	HADDENHAM LEVEL	122
S26B	Swaffham Lode	ENVIRONMENT AGENCY	149
M7A, M39B	Tebbitts Bridge	WHITTLESEY & FARCET (FARCET)	50
S14A	Ten Mile Bank	LITTLEPORT & DOWNHAM	126

Serial No.	Name of Station	District or Estate	Page
S27A	Thetford*		150
M16	Tick Fen	RAMSEY BURY FIRST	60
L14	Timberland	TIMBERLAND & THORPE	171
M13D	Top Hakes	MARCH FOURTH	58
T1A	Torksey	NEWARK	192
T1B	Torksey LNER	NEWARK	192
M37	Turves, The	WHITTLESEY FOURTH	77
N5	Tydd	NORTH LEVEL	105
M27C	Ugg Mere	RAMSEY UPWOOD etc.	65
M39A	Underwoods	WHITTLESEY & FARCET	78
S22A	Upper Padnal	PADNAL & WATERDEN	141
S25	Upware	SWAFFHAM & BOTTISHAM	145
M36	Upwell North*		70
M32	Upwell South*		70
M27F	Upwood Common	RAMSEY UPWOOD & GT. RAVELEY	66
M13E/F	Wakelin Estate	MARCH FOURTH	58
NM5	Waldersea*		99
M1C	Welches Dam	MIDDLE LEVEL	42
M11	Well Fen	MARCH SECOND	54
T8F	West Butterwick	SOUTH AXHOLME	201
S24B	West Dereham	STOKE FERRY	143
M17 & M3H	Westmoor	RAMSEY BURY SECOND	60
M2	White Fen	BENWICK WHITE FEN	42
M15	Whitemoor	MARCH SIXTH	59
M33A	Whittlesey Mere	HOLMEWOOD & STILTON	73
S29	Willingham	WILLINGHAM (WEST FEN)	152
S24C	Wretton	STOKE FERRY	145
M36	Wype	WHITTLESEY THIRD	76

IILLUSTRATIONS

1. St. German's syphon sluice (M1A) under construction 39 in 1862 (*Illustrated London News*, 25 October 1862

2. St. German's syphon sluice (M1A) – plan (Dempsey) 39

3. St. German's sluices (M1) – plan (Clark, R.G., Ch. 4, note 5) 40

4. St. German's pumping station (M1B) – exterior in 2004 41

5. St. German's pumping station (M1B) – interior in 2004 41

6. Benwick White Fen (M2) – scoop wheel (COC) 43

7. Benwick White Fen (M2) – beam engine cylinder 43 (COC)

8. Benwick White Fen (M2) – beam engine parallel 43 motion (COC)

9. Benwick White Fen 1937 (M2) – Blackstone engine 44 (MLO)

10. Benwick IDB – Beezlings (M3H) engine house 46 in 1990

11. Bluntisham (M4) engine house in 1992 47

12. Conington (M5) engine house in 1990 47

13. Mount Pleasant (M6C) engine house in 1996 49

14. Mount Pleasant (M6C) – Easton, Amos & Anderson 49 pump in 1996

15. Laddus Fen (M8) engine house in 2002 51

16. Laddus Fen (M8) - Ruston engine in 2002 51

17. Manea & Welney (M9A) Ruston engine house in 52 2002

18. Manea & Welney (M9A) – Ruston engines 52

19. Manea & Welney (M9A)Vickers Petter engine house 53 in 1995

20. Manea & Welney – Purl's Bridge (M9B) 53 engine house

21. March First (M10) engine houses in 1972 55

22. March First (M10) – empty beam loft in 1972 55

23. March Third (M12A) engine house in 1972 56

24. March Third (M12A) – Blackstone engine (MLO) 56

25. March Fourth (M13) engine house in 1972 57

26. March Fourth (M13) after conversion into a 57 dwellinghouse in 1992

27. Ramsey Middlemoor Sixth (M26) engine house 64

28. Ramsey – New Fen (M27A) engine house in 2004 65

29. Ramsey – Green Dyke Bank (M27D) engine house 66 in 1993

30. Ramsey – Green Dyke Bank (M27D) - Allen engine 67

31. Ranson Moor (M28A) engine house in 1972 68

32. Sutton & Mepal (M30) engine houses in 1972 69

33. Sutton & Mepal (M30) – Ruston engine 69

34. Sutton & Mepal (M30) – Brush engine 69

35. Upwell South (M32A) – diagram of scoop wheel 71 (Wheeler 1868)

36. Upwell South (M32A) engine house in 2002 71

37. Upwell South (M32A) – 1932 Allen plant (MLO) 71

38. Upwell IDB, Bedlam Bridge (M32B) engine house 72 in 1992

39. Upwell IDB, north of Bedlam Bridge (M32C) engine 72 house in 1992

40. Whittlesey Mere (M33A) engine houses in 1972 74

41. Whittlesey Mere (M33A) – Allen diesel plant (MLO) 74

42. Holmewood & Stilton, Black Ham (M33B) remains 75 of engine house in 2002

43. Whittlesey Second, Blackbush (M35A) engine house 75 in 1993

44. Whittlesey, Glassmoor (M40) engine house 78

45. Wimblington Combined, Boot's Bridge (M45) 80 engine house in 1993

46. Wisbech St. Peter, Hobbs Lot (M47) scoop wheel 81 race in 2000

47. Woodwalton, Higney Mill (M48A) - Dodmans pump 82 in 2002

48. Woodwalton, Higney Mill (M48A) - Ruston engine 82 in 2002

49. Downham West Fen (NM1) engine house in 1900 95 (J. & H. Gwynnes 1901)

50. Downham West Fen (NM1) - Gwynnes steam engine 95 and pump (Gwynnes 1901)

51. Magdalen (NM2B) engine house in 1994 96

52. Magdalen (NM2B) - Ruston engines in 1994 96

53. Marshland (NM3) engine house in 2003 97

54. Marshland (NM3) – Crossley engine in 2003 98

55. Marshland (NM3) – Dodmans pump in 2003 98

56. Stow Bardolph (NM4) beam engine house in 1972 98

57. Waldersea (NM5) engine houses in 1992 99

58. Waldersea (NM5) – diagram of 1900 Allen plant 100 (Allen)

59. Waldersea (NM5) – 1900 Allen steam engine 101

60. Wisbech North Side, Mouth Lane (N2B) engine 105 house in 1992

61. Burnt Fen, Little Ouse (S1A) engine house in 1972 109

62. Burnt Fen, Lark (S1B) engine house in 1972 111

63. Burnt Fen, Lark (S1B) – diagram of 1883 Hathorn 111 Davey engine (Davey)

64. Burwell (S2) engine house in 1969 113

65. Burwell (S2) engine house being converted into a 113 dwellinghouse in 2000

66. Hornsby-Ackroyd oil engine as installed at Burwell 113 (S2) (*Engineering, 30 April 1897*)

67. Cawdle Fen (S3) – diagram of remains in 1972 114 (M. Salzer et al.)

68. Chettisham (S4) – diagram of remains in 1972 115 (M. Salzer et al.)

69. Cottenham, Chear Fen (S5A) – Ruston engines 116

70. Cottenham, Chear Fen (S5A) – Blackstone engine 116

71. Cottenham, Smithey Fen (S5B) engine house 117

72. East of Ouse, Polver & Nar (S7) engine house 118 in 1989

73. East of Ouse, Polver & Nar (S7) - Ruston engines 118 in 1989

74. Southery (S8A) steam engine house c. 1990 119

75. Southery (S8A) - Crossley engine house in 1993 119

76. Southery (S8A) – Crossley engine in 1993 119

77. Feltwell Second (S9) engine house in 1996 121

78. Haddenham (S10A) steam engine house in 1949   121
(Cambs. Coll. – KH)

79. Haddenham (S10A) - Allen steam engine in 1949   122
(Cambs. Coll. – KH)

80. Haddenham, Sutton Gault (S10B) engine house   123
c. 1930 (CC)

81. Haddenham, Sutton Gault (S10B) -   123
1924 Petter engine (Cambs. Coll.)

82. Hilgay Great West Fen (S11) engine house in 1972   124

83. Hilgay Great West Fen (S11) - Dodmans pump   124
after removal

84. Hilgay, Wood Hall Estate (S12) engine house   125
in 1990

85. Lakenheath (S13) engine houses c. 1920   125
(Cambs. Coll.)

86. Lakenheath (S13) - diesel engine house in 1993   125

87. Ten Mile Bank (S14A) beam engine house c. 1900   127
(Cambs. Coll.)

88. Ten Mile Bank (S14A) beam engine in 1912 (Allen)   127

89. Ten Mile Bank (S14A) beam lift in 1912 (Allen)   127

90. Ten Mile Bank (S14A) engine house in 1972   127

91. Hundred Foot (S14B) beam engine c. 1913   128
(Cambs. Coll.)

92. Hundred Foot (S14B) engine house c. 1927 (COC)   128

93. Hundred Foot (S14B) Gwynnes steam engine   129
in 1949 (Cambs. Coll. – KH)

94. Hundred Foot (S14B) Mirrlees engine house   129
c. 1927 (COC)

95. Martin's Farm (S14C) engine house c. 1912 (Allen)   130

96. Martin's Farm (S14C) – Allen plant (Allen)   130

97. Hunt's Sluice (S15A) – engine foundations in 2004   131

98. Decoy Bridge (S15B) – Campbell engine in 1913   132
(Crocker)

99. Catsholme Farm (S15C) engine house in 1990   132

100. Middle Fen, Prickwillow (S17A) – 1832 and 1880   134
engine houses c. 1900 (CC)

101. Middle Fen, Prickwillow (S17A) –   135
diagram of Easton & Anderson plant (Gibbs)

102. Middle Fen, Prickwillow (S17A) –   135
Easton & Anderson engine (CC)

103. Middle Fen, Overfall (S17B) engine house c. 1930   137
(Cambs. Coll.)

104. Middle Fen, Overfall (S17B) engine house in 1993   137

105. Middle Fen, Overfall (S17B)Mirrlees engine   137
(Cambs. Coll.)

106. Middleton (S18) chimney in 1992   138

107. Mildenhall (S19A) engine house in 1992

108. Northwold Severals (S20) –   139
remains of engine house in 1996

109. Upper Padnal (S22A) engine house in 1973   141

110. Lower Padnal (S22B) engine house in 1973   142

111. Fordham (S24A) engine house in 1973   143

112. West Dereham (S24B) engine house in 2003   144

113. West Dereham (S24B) – Ruston engine in 1990   144

114. West Dereham (S24B) – remains of boiler in 1990   144

115. Swaffham & Bottisham (S25B) engine house   146
from drain side in 1927

116. Swaffham & Bottisham (S25B) –   146
drop valves of beam engine (COC)

117. Swaffham & Bottisham (S24B)–   146
first diesel engine house under construction, 1927

118. Reach Lode engine (S26A) being dismantled   148
in 1989

119. Swaffham Lode (S26B) engine house in 2000   148

120. Bottisham Lode (S26C) engine house in 1955   149

121. Bottisham Lode (S26C) – Worthington engine   149
in 1995

122. Thetford (S27) engine house with River Ouse   150
in flood (Cambs. Coll.)

123. Stretham (S28) beam engine c. 1930 (COC)   151

124. Stretham (S28) boiler house c. 1960   151
(Stretham Engine Trust)

125. Willingham (S29) – engine house plan 1846   153
(Willingham Pumping Station Trust)

126. Willingham (S 29) engine house in 1936 with   153
traction engine in operation (Willingham Pumping
Station Trust)

127. Willingham (S29) – Clayton & Shuttleworth pump   153

128. Pode Hole (L2) – engine houses in 1920   163
(Miles, Ch. 8, note 9)

129. Pode Hole (L2) old engine house in 1994   164

130. Pinchbeck Marsh (L3) engine house in 1994   164

131. Pinchbeck South (L4) - diagram of 1919   165
Ruston engine and pump (RH)

132. Northborough (L6) Holmes pump at   166
Pinchbeck (L3) in 1994

133. Branston Island (L11) engine house in 1993   170

134. Metheringham (L12) engine house in 1992   170

135. Timberland (L14) engine house in 2003   171

136. Fiskerton (L17) engine house in 2003   173

137. Stixwould (L18) engine house in 2003   173

138. Dogdyke (L21) engine house in 2003   174

139. Lade Bank (L22A) engine house in 1994   176

140. Lade Bank (L22A) - Ruston engine in 1994   176

141. Hobhole (L22B) engine house in 2003   177

142. Hobhole (L22B) - Allen engine in 2003   177

143. North Kyme (Farroway) (L23) engine houses   178
in 2003

144. Black Sluice (L26) engine house in 2003   182

145. Black Sluice (L26) - Ruston engines in 2003   183

146. Pyewype (L40) engine house in 1935 (RH)   190

147. Pyewype (L40) engine house in 1988 (RH)   190

148. Torksey (T1A) engine house in 2000   192

149. Morton Carr (T2A) engine house in 2000   192

150. Ravensfleet (T2B) engine house in 2000   193

151. Jenny Hurn (T2C) engine house in 2000   194

152. Jenny Hurn (T2C) - Ruston engine in 2000   194

153. Jenny Hurn (T2C) - Gwynnes plant in 1897   195
(J. & H. Gwynnes 1899)

154. Anderby (T6A) engine house in 2003   197

155. Anderby (T6A) - Ruston engine in 2003   197

156. Gayton Marsh (T6B) engine house in 2003   198

157. Gayton Marsh (T6B) – Petter engine in 2003   198

158. Misterton (T8A) engine houses in 1899   199
(J. & H. Gwynnes 1899)

159. Misterton (T8A) – Gwynnes plant in 1899   199
(J. & H. Gwynnes 1899)

160. Heckdyke (T8C) engine house in 2000   200

161. Owston Ferry (T8D) engine house in 2000   200

162. West Butterwick (T8F) steam engine house (RH)   201

163. West Butterwick (T8F) - Easton & Amos engine (RH) 201

164. Bull Hassocks (T10A) engine house c. 1925   202
(Korthals-Altes)

165. Bull Hassocks (T10A) engine house in 2000   203